G000096582

Planning with Multiple Criteria

Planning with Multiple Criteria

Investigation, Communication and Choice

Peter Bogetoft and Peter Pruzan

HANDELSHØJSKOLENS FORLAG
Copenhagen Business School Press

Printed by Reproset, Copenhagen, 1997
Cover designed by Kontrapunkt
ISBN 87-16-13386-2

2. edition
The first edition was published by Elsevier Science, 1991

Series A
COPENHAGEN STUDIES IN ECONOMICS AND MANAGEMENT, NO. 13

Distribution

Scandinavia:
Munksgaard/DBK, Siljangade 2-8, P.O. Box 1731,
DK-2300 Copenhagen S, Denmark,
phone: +45 3269 7788, fax: +45 3269 7789

North America:
Global Management, LLC, Book Service, 2564 Branch Street, B2,
Middleton, WI 53562, USA
phone: +1 608 836 0088, fax: +1 608 836 0087
E-mail: 102135.2151 @compuserve.com

Rest of the World:
Marston Book Services, P.O. Box 269,
Abingdon, Oxfordshire, OX14 4YN, UK
phone: +44 (0) 1235 465500, fax: +44 (0) 1235 465555
E-mail Direct Customers: direct.order@marston.co.uk
E-mail Booksellers: trade.order@marston.co.uk

Dedicated to
Nete and Stina
Rebecca and Julie

PREFACE

Eight postulates which provide the leitmotif for this book are presented in the introductory chapter. Several of these postulates are descriptive and deal with basic notions of how and why we plan within the context of an organization. Several others are normative and assert that we can improve our ability to make decisions which are in harmony with our fundamental values. Based on these postulates, the book develops an operational *framework for planning which integrates the concepts of values, objectives, criteria, preferences, decisions, and conflicts* – and therefore improves our ability to establish harmony between our thoughts, words and deeds. In particular, it provides guidelines for how to choose between alternative actions so as to obtain the best balance between the multiple criteria we choose to represent our objectives and underlying values.

It is our conviction that there is a need for developing a perspective and methods which enhance our ability to behave in accordance with our preferences and thereby to integrate our personal and our organizational values. It follows that the book is methodologically rather than technique oriented. The stimulation of ideas, insight and creativity with respect to planning with multiple criteria are its goals rather than the production of specific, context-dependent knowledge. In particular new inroads are made into some rather virgin territory. These include the choice of which multiple criteria approach is most appropriate in a given context and the relationship between ethics and multiple criteria planning.

The book is intended for all who are interested in the theory and practice of planning, no matter whether the field is economic planning, town planning, ecological planning, energy planning – or just planning itself as a purposeful activity in social systems. A major, perhaps the major, target group consists of those researchers and practitioners who are attempting to integrate "soft" and "hard" systems' approaches to planning and in particular, those interested in relating multiple criteria perspectives to strategic planning and ethics. We note for example that since the first edition of this book in 1991, a whole new field of "social and ethical accountability" has developed and that this field represents a "soft" application of a multiple criteria perspective within a multiple stakeholder context. Similar comments hold true for the fields of environmental and ecological accountability. Those who have a background in management, economics or operations research will also be relevant target audiences; they will find their world-views strongly challenged.

Although not specifically developed as a textbook, the book should also be useful at the undergraduate level for students of operations research, engineering and economics as well as for students in "softer", less technical disciplines such as business administration and sociology. However, as it presupposes a rather mature, conceptual approach to planning, it should be used towards the end of the undergraduate program. The book will be also be useful at the graduate level as a thought-expanding, critical synthesis of multiple criteria decision making (MCDM) and planning. Although no prior knowledge of MCDM is presumed, readers with some familiarity with concrete MCDM techniques will in particular be able to find considerable food for thought in the emphasis on methodology and on the relationship between choice of technique, planning approach and context.

Only a minimum of familiarity with mathematical notation is required to read the text proper, while two appendices formalize those aspects of the text which gain in precision from a mathematical presentation. In addition, to provide some support to readers who are not familiar with the notation and the elementary set-theoretical concepts employed on occasion, care is taken to introduce and explain the basic symbols and terminology in chapter 2, and a brief list of symbols and terminology is provided in appendix 3.

The book is organized in three major parts and a series of appendices. Part one, chapters 1-4, commences with a brief introductory chapter which motivates the sequel and leads up to three chapters which describe the multiple criteria setting in terms of rationality, conflict and compromise. Part two, chapters 5-9, commences with a classification scheme for multiple criteria planning methods. This taxonomy provides the starting point for operationally oriented treatments of the four major approaches to multiple criteria planning, viz. a) the prior articulation of alternatives, b) the prior articulation of preferences, c) the progressive articulation of alternatives, and d) the progressive articulation of preferences. These approaches are continually illustrated and interpreted within familiar economic and managerial contexts. Part three, chapters 10-11, provides two new perspectives on multiple criteria planning: how to choose between alternative planning methods – including when and when not to apply multiple criteria planning methods – and how to integrate the traditional perspectives of decision-making with an ethical perspective. This latter perspective may be appreciated without having read part two on approaches to multiple criteria planning. Finally, three appendices present an overview of the mathematical notation employed as well as concise mathematical treatments of several major themes developed in the text.

Two groups of students in the one year course on "Planning Theory" at the Copenhagen Business School have been the guinea pigs used to test the conceptual, practical and pedagogical qualities of the book. The course is offered during the last year of an analytically oriented bachelor's program on management science and business administration. It is based on two hours of teaching and two hours of exercises a week for 28 weeks spread out over two semesters. The material presented in the present book covered approximately one third of the course load, i.e. 9-10 weeks.

In addition, and as will be seen from chapter 11, several Scandinavian enterprises have participated in the development of the multiple stakeholder, multiple criteria approach to systemic conflict and to the establishment of management by values.

We express our sincere appreciation to the students, colleagues and enterprises who have contributed to the development of the manuscript; of course, we are solely responsible for the contents and opinions presented.

Peter Bogetoft Peter Pruzan

Contents

Chapter 1

INTRODUCTION

In this introductory chapter we introduce the conceptual framework for the study of planning with multiple criteria. We provide brief statements of our fundamental motivations as well as preliminary definitions of key concepts such as values, objectives, criteria, preferences, decision making and planning.

1.1. Postulates and Motivations

The following eight postulates are concise assertions which motivate the study of planning with multiple criteria and provide the leitmotif which premiates the content and structure of the book. The validity of these statements cannot be established by logical proof. Neither do we attempt to justify them by referring to extensive empirical evidence. Rather, the reader must judge whether these postulates are reasonable and are substantiated by his or her experience.[1]

Postulate 1. An individual's ability to make choices which are internally consistent and in accordance with his preferences will be enhanced if attempts are made to model his perception of the choice situation.[2]

---

[1] To avoid employing the awkward phrase "his or her" each time we refer to a person, we will for ease of exposition use the possesive pronoun "his" throughout. This term is employed completely free of sexual conotation and it is by no means intended to indicate that decision makers should be masculine. In fact, by advocating and facilitating the integration of personal and organizational values and of "soft" and "hard" criteria we may be said to introduce a "feminine" perspective.

[2] By "individual" we generally mean a single person. However, as briefly introduced in section 1.3 and discussed more fully in chapter 11, the term may also cover a group of people or an organization which, via a process of self-organization, identifies itself and in so doing develops preferential competence.

This postulate underlines all that follows. It is also the (implicit) assumption underlying the literature on "rational choice", e.g. as developed in economics and operations research. Although considerable empirical data exists as to simple choice situations, there is essentially only case study evidence as to the reasonableness of the postulate. It is therefore axiomatic in nature - if it is denied, then the edifice we build upon this foundation topples to the ground.

Postulate 2. If an individual is to make choices which are consistent with his preferences, it is inappropriate to model decision problems as if there is only one measure of performance.

This postulate is not new. It provides the basis for most of the literature on the discipline "multiple criteria decision making", usually referred to by the abbreviation MCDM. By denying the ability of a single measure of performance to capture the depth and complexity of our values, objectives and preferences, this postulate implicitly challenges the relevance of traditional economic rationality and its orientation towards the **means** rather than the **ends** underlying our preferences. This leads to our next postulate.

Postulate 3. In realistic planning contexts, the concept of optimal choice is not only misleading, it may be harmful as well.

Optimality presumes that some single measure of performance is maximized, e.g. profits, or minimized, e.g. costs. If we are not willing to accept that all our objectives can be translated into a single measure of performance, but must be considered in their own right and expressed in their own criteria, then we must also reject formulating decision problems in terms of a search for an "optimal solution". Such formulations may lead to solutions which are far removed from the solution the decision maker actually would have preferred. However, it is not enough to simply criticize traditional uni-criterion approaches to planning, also MCDM has significant shortcomings. This leads to our next postulate.

Postulate 4. MCDM has not provided adequate support to planning in complex contexts.

It has been characterized by sundry mathematical approaches and ad hoc computer packages which purport to recognize the multiple criteria aspect of decision making. The resultant focus upon technical details rather than planning methodology has suppressed the potential contribution to practical planning that was hearalded with the development of MCDM as a discipline in the 1970's and 1980's.

Postulate 5. Managers spend far too little time and effort on questions as to which values are central for their decisions and which alternative courses of action best may contribute to their preferences.

Values are the foundations of our objectives and underly the criteria we choose to measure how well our decisions and actions meet our objectives. Decision makers often have rather imprecise insights as to their values, objectives, criteria and preferences, as well as to how their planning behavior may promote their values. Nevertheless, the effort which is made to gain insight as to these fundamental aspects of planning is insignificant compared to the resources spent on traditional technical and economic analyses as well as the investments and operating costs which result from the decisions made. Far greater managerial participation in the planning process is required if preferences and actions are to be in harmony. This leads to the next postulate.

Postulate 6. The choice of planning technology should not be a matter for analysts alone to decide.

The analytical and the political or decision making aspects of planning cannot in general be separated. The choice of planning technology influences the way problems are formulated, alternatives are investigated, the results presented - and therefore the decisions made. While this postulate may be appealing, the logic which supports it leads to the following more controversial postulate.

Postulate 7. Decision making should not be left to "decision makers" alone even though they are responsible for their choices.

The analyses a decision maker receives are the "products" of the analyst's decisions. They are therefore subject to interpretation and may require considerable reworking due to the analyst's assumptions, the decision maker's own doubts, etc. Postulates 6 and 7 lead to an explicit recognition of the desirability of integrating analysis and decision making. The picture becomes even more complex if the focus is not only on those who develop analyses and make decisions, but also on those who are the recipients of the decisions, the "decision receivers". This leads to the final postulate.

Postulate 8. Almost all significant planning situations are characterized by a multiple of decision makers and decision "receivers", each having his own values, objectives, criteria and preferences.

The literature on MCDM by and large considers decision making as a process where an individual resolves his "intra-personal" conflicts, i.e. how he should chose between alternatives so as to obtain his best balance between a number of conflicting criteria. If this frame of reference must be expanded to include the preferences of multiple decision makers and receivers, then multiple criteria planning cannot only focus on intra-personal conflict. It must be extended to consider cases characterized by a) "inter-personal" conflict where a multiple of decision makers, each with his own values, objectives, criteria, preferences and language, jointly are to make a decision, and b) "systemic-conflict" where not only the decision makers but also the decision receivers affect and are affected by the decision.

These postulates point towards the need for an extended methodological approach to planning with multiple criteria. We elaborate first on what we mean by the notion of multiple criteria and commence by introducing some basic definitions.

1.2. Values, Objectives, Criteria and Preferences

Most - if not all - real-world planning contexts are characterized by multiple, noncommensurate, and often conflicting goals or **objectives**. We intend to accomplish many different things when we plan. These different things may be of a qualitatively distinct nature. For example, when considering moving to a new house, a person might very likely desire a good location, a reasonable and affordable price, a house which is large enough and has an adequate number of rooms without being too large or too small, a house which is convenient as to upkeep, has attractive grounds which do not require too much care and has low real estate taxes. Similarly, within the context of an enterprise, a manager may seek to improve profitability, enter new markets and increase market share in existing markets, improve product quality and competitive position, develop a talented and dedicated group of employees and derive pleasure, pride, high remuneration and the respect of his family, friends and peers.

In general, we will not distinguish between two possible types of objectives. The first is of the form: get as close as possible to a predetermined, desirable state. An example could be a runner who has as his goal running a mile in 4 minutes. Another example could be a marketing manager who has the objective of achieving a market share of 15% in a given market within the next year. A second type of objective is met in the concept of optimization. An example might be to minimize the cost of carrying inventories or to design a portfolio of stocks which maximizes the return on investment.

No matter how we consider our objectives, each of them can be derived from certain more fundamental **values**. For example, when considering acquiring a new house, a young couple with small children might be motivated by the value: being able to raise healthy, happy and secure children. Such a value could underly such objectives as: the house should have a cozy garden in a friendly neighborhood with lots of children, easy access to good schools and close to nature. In addition, the house should not be so expensive that the work required to cover the costs would not leave sufficient time and energy for being with the children. And so on. In other words, when we use the word "value" we are referring to a more fundamental concept than "objective" One way to distinguish between these concepts is to consider values to be ends and objectives to be means to achieving the more fundamental values. When a question as to "why do you want to achieve that objective" cannot be answered, by referring to a new objective, but simply by the reply "because", we are dealing with a value. And when such a question can be answered by referring to some other, more fundamental objective, we are dealing with an objective and not a value.

These distinctions between values and objectives may be rather subtle, and we have no intention of hair-fine precision. In fact, it is not seldom that means may also be considered as ends in themselves. For example, a politician may consider improving educational standards to be instrumental as a means of improving the society's productive capacity. But he may also consider improving educational standards to be an end itself which does not have to be justified by referral to, e.g. economic arguments. Similarly, at the level of the enterprise, profits should logically be considered to be means and not ends. Nevertheless, in a society which myopically has focused on "the bottom line", profits begin to become ends in themselves.[3]

Common to both objectives and values is their non-stationarity. Our values and goals change with time and place when we learn, and when we and the world around us change. As we shall see, recognition of this fact is one of the major reasons for distinguishing between decision making and planning as well as one of the greatest challenges to combining more substantive considerations with more procedurally oriented considerations.

Another term which plays a central role throughout the presentation is **criteria.** We characterize our objectives by measures of performance which we refer to as criteria. For example, when referring to the location of a new house, we may operationalize the objective of "a good location" by considering the criteria: distance to work, shopping, recreational, educational and cultural facilities, the attractiveness of the surrounding area, the level of noise, etc. Clearly, each objectives may be characterized by a multiple of criteria - just as each value may lead to a multiple of objectives.

Note that several of these criteria can be rather easily quantified; e.g. distance to place of work. Other criteria could be quantified but are in practice better treated by a ranking. For example, to characterize a location's noise level, the noise could be measured on a decibel scale several times a day over the course of a week and averaged. But a subjective evaluation such as "low", "moderate" or "high" might be quite adequate. And yet other criteria could be very personal, subjective, and qualitative and in practice could only be evaluated by a subjective ranking. An example is the assessment of how aesthetically appealing the location is.

---

[3] This observation has historical antecendents. According to the philosopher John Stuart Mills ("Utilitarianism", 1861): "There is nothing originally more desirable about money than about any heap of glittering pebbles. Its worth is solely that of the things which it will buy; the desires for other things than itself, which it is a means of gratifying. Yet the love of money is not only one of the strongest moving forces of human life, but money is, in many cases, desired in and for itself; the desire to possess it is often stronger than the desire to use it, and goes on increasing when all the desires which point to ends beyond it, to be compassed by it, are falling off. It may, then, be said truly, that money is desired not for the sake of an end, but as part of the end. From being a means to happiness, it has come to be itself a principal ingredient of the individual's conception of happiness."

Closely related to the notions of value, objectives and criteria is that of **preferences**. Loosely speaking, when a reflective decision maker says "I prefer A to B", he gives vocal expression to a cognitive synthesis of his multiple values, objectives and criteria. We do not argue that this synthesis is simply the rational result of a consistent application of some hidden formula. Still, as a conceptual support it is often convenient to think of preference in this way. Specifically, in much of the book we choose to let preferences be closely related to criteria. This is achieved via the abstract notion of a **preference function**. If a decision maker is to choose between alternative actions each of which is characterized by the values of the criteria chosen to represent his objectives, then such a function enables him to rank the alternatives according to his underlying preferences. It follows from this perspective that his decision corresponds to the most preferred alternative.

We have already used the terms **alternatives** and **decisions**. A closely related notion is that of **actions**. In principle, the alternatives are the set of possibilities available to a decision maker, a decision is a choice of alternative, and the action is what is actually executed. In practice, we shall however not keep a clear distinction between these terms. We shall for example talk about the set of possibilities as the set of possible alternatives, the set of feasible decisions or the set of available actions. It will in general be clear from the context which interpretation is appropriate. Indeed, much of the literature dealing with decision making and planning does not distinguish between decisions and actions; it is implicitly assumed that what has been decided upon will be executed. It is worth noting, however, that there are at least two good reasons why one could maintain such a distinction. The first of these is that the "decider" seldom is the "doer". This means that communication, interpretation and control all play a role before a decision is transformed into action. The second reason for maintaining the distinction is that there is a time gap between decision and action, a gap which is often proportional to the significance and complexity of the decision. With the passing of time, new information may be obtained which leads to adaptive behavior and to action which deviates from the original, formal decision.

A final term to be introduced here is the notion of **conflict**, with particular emphasis upon the notion of **intra-personal** comflict. In most cases we must accept poorer results for some criteria in order to achieve better results for others. It would be too good to be true to find a house which is the most beautiful, has the loveliest and quietest surroundings, is the most inexpensive and is closest to work, the city-center and the children's school. We will say that a decision maker has an intra-personal conflict when none of the possible alternatives available to him is best on all counts, i.e. when no single alternative is characterized by the optimal values of all the criteria chosen to represent his objectives. Such a concept of conflict is central to multiple criteria planning.

We will however in chapter 11 extend this concept of intra-personal conflict to include both **inter-personal** conflict between members of a group who are to make a decision, as well as **systemic** conflict which can arise between decision makers and those who are on the receiving end of the decisions, the "decision receivers"; as will be seen, this final concept of systemic conflict will lead us to extend the notion of planning to include ethical considerations.

1.3. Incomplete Descriptions of Wishes and Possibilities

In much of the literature on "rational choice", planning and economics, it is assumed that a decision maker attempts to maximize a single overall measure of performance such as his overall "well-being". Furthermore it is assumed that the set of alternatives is given. As the brief discussion above indicates however, in real world planning contexts, these may not be either realistic or useful assumptions.

First of all, this overall objective must be operationalized if we are to use it to plan. In general, as the example above indicates, this may require several criteria; a single proxy, e.g. the price of the house, will clearly not do justice to the complex nature of "well-being". In this case, the concept of a single overall objective is of little use for we must nevertheless deal with its expression by introducing multiple criteria.

Secondly, even if a single objective expressed via a single criterion were given, the approximate and partial nature of any model and analysis would make the pursuing of the single objective hazardous. For example, optimizing a single criterion in a specific period may lead to a miserable future. Therefore, if we are only able to analyze single period models, we should at least include an additional objective representing the potential for doing well in the future implied by our present decision. And we once again face multiple criteria.

Finally, even if it were possible to construct a single overall objective which somehow contained all an individual's many intentions and which could be evaluated using a single criterion, it might not be worthwhile. The improvement in the plan might not justify the effort needed to develop such an all-inclusive measure of performance, i.e. it would not be an appropriate strategy from a metaplanning perspective.

Similar reservations hold as to the assumption of a complete description of the set of alternatives.

Let us illustrate the reservations as to the possibility of capturing the richness of a planning situation via the construction of a single, aggregate measure of performance to evaluate a given set of alternatives.

Consider first the rather trivial problem of buying a car. Presumably we have objectives with respect to attributes like price, safety, prestige, comfort, bagagespace, size, operating costs, driving characteristics and motor-power. So, if we decide to explicitly formulate such a problem, it immediately presents itself as one of multiple criteria. These are of a very distinct nature involving for example measures such as dollars, volume, "safety" and "snob units"; and they are certainly conflicting since for example cheap cars are seldom prestigious. Also, we see the limits of theoretical "rational choice" prescriptions. It is clearly not very useful to know that you are intrinsically trying to optimize your "well-being". Furthermore, we cannot hope to have a complete description of the available choices. You may look for cars at other dealers, consider used as well as new cars, and consider replacing a purchased car by taxis, public transportation, a bicycle or a rented car. You might also consider changing your housing location and family planning. Finally, there are limits to the time and effort you would use. The car market may change before you could set up a complete car-housing-family-work model, watching car commercials may effect your well-being adversely; and after all, a car is just a car.

As another, far more complex example, consider the problem of planning an airport. This is obviously a problem involving multiple objectives and criteria such as minimize costs (investment, operational), maximize user convenience (capacity, access time from major metropolitan areas), maximize safety (accident severity, probabilities) and minimize environmental damages (noxious emissions, noise levels). An overall social welfare objective is not available to begin with. Hard work is needed just to identify and approximately state and operationalize our objectives. Also it is not immediately clear what degrees of freedom we have in determining the possible alternatives. Different runway constructions may affect costs, convenience, safety and environmental damage in many different ways. Other relevant design variables may include the location, the communications and control technology employed, the alternative means of local transportation etc., all of which may certainly affect the different objectives in diverse ways. And we have not yet considered the span of operational opportunities within a given design - nor taken into account the considerable time lags between decisions and their executions as actions, which may lead to the generation of new alternatives and objectives. So, neither the objectives, their measurement via appropriate criteria nor the set of alternatives are clear to begin with.

As a final, more curious example, consider the very problem of planning. Meta-planning - the planning of planning - is itself a planning problem which involves a multiplicity of objectives. We want to design planning approaches and procedures which will lead to good decisions as evaluated via the criteria chosen as well as by our intuition, will ease implementation, and will receive the backing of the various interest groups affected by the planning. We want to live up to our responsibilities to those within our own organization as well as to the society at large. And, in general, we want to learn about the system being planned for. Also, we would like to avoid too much effort, too many foregone options, too many confidential matters being revealed, too many risks, etc. Finally, the set of alternatives - here, planning approaches and procedures - is certainly not well defined as the planning literature reflects.

We conclude these reflections on the multiplicity of goals and criteria by referring to literature outside of the framework of "rational choice". In a massive study of "power", the organizational theorist Mintzberg introduces his subject by reflecting on the management literature and its shift of focus "from goals to power". He concludes that four fundamental questions emerge from his review, and his book on power has been written to address them:

> "First, how does the organization deal with multiple goals or conflicting measures? ..."
>
> "Second, are goals independent variables? ..."
>
> "Third, can organizations be said to have goals at all, or only their participants? ..."
>
> "Fourth, and the concluding question, how do all of the personal goals, values, intentions, needs, and expectations of the individual actors get translated into organizational decision and action? ..."

It appears that our concern with multiple goals and criteria within a framework of planning is shared by researchers with a quite different perspective, that of "power in and around organizations", the title of Mintzberg's book, referred to in the bibliographic notes, section 1.7. While we speak of decisions "in accordance with our preferences (which) integrate our personal and organizational values", Mintzberg asks "What takes us from individual need to organizational action?" The focus in both cases is the multiplicity of goals and criteria.

1.4. Multiple Criteria Decision Making

Multiple Criteria Decision Making (MCDM) is both an approach and a body of techniques designed to help people make choices which are in accord with their values in cases characterized by multiple, noncommensurate and conflicting criteria. It is considered by many to be a sub-discipline within Operations Research (OR). From this vantage point, it has probably been the single most expanding branch of OR in the past decade. Interestingly enough, it represents at the same time a renewal and revitalization of Operations Research by recalling its original character as an approach to problem solving based on systems thinking, multidisciplinarity and a scientific approach. In particular, the emphasis is again seen as one of helping a decision maker to structure his problems and to make good choices. The optimization of given, well-structured problems using more and more computationally efficient algorithms is **not** in focus, particularly in the case of more significant or strategic decisions.

Still, MCDM does not yet present itself as a mature, comprehensive theory. Its youth and very nature as a multidisciplinary subject probably provide some explanation. However, this implies that a lot of research is still needed and the present book should be read with this in mind.

In particular, research on the relationship between contextual factors and the methods applied is needed. The rationale for MCDM is basically contextual due to such factors as the multiplicity of values, objectives and criteria in the real world and the bounded rationality of real decision makers, i.e. their limited capacities to collect and process information. Nevertheless, the contextual setting is seldom considered in any depth. A typical article on MCDM in a scientific journal only devotes a few lines to the contextual characteristics that are supposed to motivate its technical developments. This lack of explicit contextual consideration, motivation and precision has serious implications. No sound foundation has been developed which permits synthesizing, comparing and evaluating different MCDM procedures. The result is an overwhelming number of ad hoc procedures. Therefore, although often rather technically advanced, the procedures cannot claim to be scientifically based or generally applicable. Nor do there exist broadly accepted criteria for the evaluation of such approaches; we will return to this matter in some detail in chapter 10.

In addition, the literature on MCDM seldom pays attention to such vital matters as the choice of criteria, the identification of alternative actions, and the symbiotic relationship between these two activities. Ignoring these behavioral and cognitive aspects leads once again to a fixation on algorithmic procedures and their characteristics based upon the presupposition that the means and ends have already been operationally identified. Rather than to consideration of how multiple criteria procedures can contribute to structuring choice situations and to decisions which are in harmony with our preferences.

The study of MCDM is nevertheless fascinating. It can stimulate critical thinking, inspire new developments and provide bricks which can be used to build an intellectual framework for structuring and solving real-world planning problems. These are our own overall motivations for developing the present book.

1.5. Planning

We refer repeatedly to planning. It seems natural therefore to clarify the relationship between planning and decision making within our major contextual background, multiple criteria. Unfortunately, there is no generally accepted way to delineate planning. Rather, there exists a multiplicity of more or less vague definitions. It is often thought of quite broadly as a process of cognition and compromise, that is, as a search and learning process successively increasing our awareness of our objectives, the alternatives which can be considered, and the relationships between alternatives and objectives. It is also referred to as the process of considering how to describe and improve the performance of a system, i.e. how, given our present state of affairs, we can create desirable future states.

At this point a rather subtle, but nevertheless significant, proviso must be made. While a decision can in principle be localized in time and space and identified as a choice of a particular alternative, planning is an ongoing process. The world around us changes and we change too. Our ideals, values, communicative abilities and the possibilities we consider as feasible all undergo changes with time. Therefore, when we plan and attempt to design attractive future states, we must be aware of the fact that what we consider to be very attractive now, may appear to be less attractive when the future becomes the present. This correponds to the simple statement of regret: "If only I knew then, what I know now". The moral is, that we must learn to balance our current substantive desires with the desire to maintain our degrees of freedom.

We might also think of **planning** as the **process of decision making**. From this perspective, planning involves the following activities which, though they may be identified at any given time, in fact are continually being modified as we learn about our wishes and possibilities: introspection necessary to identify and operationalize our values and objectives; the collection and processing of information about a decision to be made including the identification of the criteria to be employed, the alternative actions we wish to consider, and how we will evaluate our preferences; possible model building and the subsequent analysis of the problem formulated; the choice of a decision; and finally all the organizational and other considerations surrounding the implementation and control of the choice and its effectuation as action.

In other words, while the "output" of decision making is a choice of a specific alternative the "output" of planning is a plan - and this includes consideration of what is to be done, when, by whom, and what to do if unexpected stimuli occur. As well as of the more fundamental assumptions and analyses as to values, objectives, criteria, and preferences. These latter are an integral part of planning, since we modify our decisions as we learn about our wishes and possibilities.

To emphasize the wider, more inclusive scope of planning, let us observe that planning has multiple effects. The potential **benefits** to be gained from planning include:

> * **Compensation for "bounded rationality"** by increasing the chances of identifying opportunities and potential problems and of allocating resources in a manner which is consistent with our preferences,
>
> * **Facilitation of the implementation of decisions** by focusing upon communication and coordination and by inducing commitment of the members of the organization,
>
> * **Insight as to the system** by participating in discussions with a broader scope and context then the actual decision problem, and
>
> * **Insight as to one's self** by the ongoing reflexive investigation of values, objectives, criteria, preferences and choices.

On the other hand, the **costs** accompanying planning include:

> * **Direct costs** by requiring managerial time and effort, participation in public hearings, computer usage etc.
>
> * **Indirect costs**, for example due to confidential matters being exposed during the planning process, and opportunity costs which result from opportunities which are foregone due to inadequate planning.

These costs and benefits will be considered in greater detail in chapter 10.

Now, having introduced the broader notion of planning, let us emphasize that although the multiple criteria perspective has been primarily related to the **choice** moment in a planning process, it can contribute significantly to the **investigation** and **communication** aspects of planning as well. Its intelligent use can also inspire creativity, commitment and **ethical** behavior. Ideally, this perspective provides a way of thinking that may help us select actions when - to begin with - we do not really know what we want or what opportunities we have. Ideally again, it describes how we might search for appropriate actions when, as typically is the case in planning situations, the means and ends are not "givens". These themes will permeate the text.

1.6. Purpose and Outline

As indicated in the preface, the major goal of the book is to develop a multiple criteria approach to planning based upon the fundamental assumption that we aspire to make decisions which are in harmony with our underlying values. In the case of trivial, daily decisions having insignificant consequences, we perform such balancing acts more or less spontaneously and without turning to more formal, explicit problem formulations. It is extremely unlikely that we will go through detailed analyses in order to determine whether or not to take an umbrella to work on a morning where it appears as though it might rain. On the other hand, when our decisions are of some significance and when it is difficult to decide which choice is best due to the fact that no available choice appears to be best with respect to all of our values, we may seek support via more formalized approaches to planning. We refer to such approaches which emphasize the relationships between our values, the criteria we choose to represent them, and the evaluation procedures we employ in our decision processes as **"multiple criteria planning"**. The book develops guidelines for such planning and emphasises how to generate and choose between alternative plans so as to obtain the best balance between the multiple criteria we select to represent our underlying values.

Hence, the emphasis is upon methodology which stresses the inherent multiple crtieria nature of planning rather than on providing a comprehensive and technical review of existing techniques. We attempt to develop the exposition with a minimum of mathematical and technical details. Aside from two appendices, mathematics as such is banned from the book. On the other hand, we will frequently employ some elementary mathematical notation in order to shorten the presentation and make it more precise; to assist readers who lack familiarity with such notation, rather detailed explanations are given in chapter 2 and a list of notation is provided in appendix 3.

The outline of the book is as follows. In chapters 2-4 we delineate more precisely the multiple criteria planning context. Then in part 2, chapters 5-9, we develop a taxonomy and based upon this we provide an analytically oriented treatment of different multiple criteria planning modes. Part 3, chapters 10-11, offers two new perspectives on multiple criteria planning: how to choose between the different modes and how to integrate the traditional perspective of decision making with an ethical perspective of decision receiving. A more formal, mathematical treatment is given in appendices 1 and 2, and an overview of mathematical symbols and terminology is offered in appendix 3.

1.7. Bibliographic Notes

Most of the literature on MCDM consists either of articles in OR-journals such as The European Journal of Operational Research, Journal of The Operational Research Society, Operations Research, Mathematical Programming, and Management Science, or in conference proceedings etc. such as Cochrane & Zeleny(eds)(1973), Fandel & Gal(eds)(1980), Fandel & Spronk(eds)(1985), Grauer & Wierzbiki(eds) (1984), Haimes & Chankong(eds)(1985), Hansen(ed) (1983), Morse (ed)(1981), Serafini(ed)(1985), Starr & Zeleny(eds)(1977), Zeleny(ed)(1976a) and Zionts(ed)(1978). A seminal work is Johnsen(1968). A few textbooks - often favoring special approaches - are also available by now, c.f. for example Chankong & Haimes(1983a), Hwang & Masud(1979), Keeney & Raiffa(1976), Roy(1985), Steuer(1986), and Zeleny-(1974,82). An interesting study of power from a perspective of multiple goals is Mintzberg(1983). A short overview of different costs and benefits of planning and of several planning theories are provided in Matsuda & Hirano(1982,83), and an attempt to evaluate different MCDM approaches from the point of view of such costs and benefits is given in Bogetoft(1990) and Bogetoft & Pruzan(1990). Pruzan(1984) provides a systemic framework for planning theory. An early discussion of the relationship between planning and MCDM is given in Rietveld(1980). A comprehensive treatment of planning from the point of view of decision making is Johansen(1977,78).

Chapter 2

THE RATIONAL IDEAL

In this chapter we review what we call the **rational ideal model** which tacitly underlies economics, operations research, systems analysis and other quantitatively oriented planning disciplines. This is the model which multiple criteria planning both challenges and complements.

Although the presentation presumes familiarity with elementary mathematical notation, it is emphasized that mathematics as such is not employed at all, i.e. there are no formal proofs or analytical manipulations. Rather, the symbols are employed solely to provide a concise notation as well as a precision and consistency which otherwise would be difficult to obtain employing everyday language. Those readers who at first glance find it difficult to cope with the notation employed should not lose heart; the extensive explanation offered in this chapter and the list of symbols and terminology in appendix 3 should enable you to follow the presentation.

2.1. The Rational Ideal Model

The rational ideal model of an individual's choice behavior basically runs as follows.

A decision maker is to make a choice from amongst a given set X of some number, n, of **alternatives**, feasible choices or plans, say

$$X = \{x^1, x^2, \ldots, x^n\}$$

where $x^1, x^2, \ldots, x^n$ symbolize the n distinct alternatives. We will often refer to an arbitrary alternative, say the i'th, by writing x^i or simply x. The decision maker's evaluation of these different alternatives can be represented, that is, modelled, by a so-called **preference ordering,** $\geq^*$. This is a convenient, symbolic way of expressing his attitudes towards the different alternatives. An alternative, say x^1, is said to be weakly preferred to (at least as good as) another alternative, say x^2, if and only if the decision maker considers the first alternative to be either better than or equally desirable as the second alternative. The interpretation of $\geq^*$ is thus

$$x^1 \geq^* x^2 \Leftrightarrow \text{" } x^1 \text{ is at least as good as } x^2 \text{ "}$$

where $\Leftrightarrow$ is a mathematical short-hand for "if and only if".

It is often assumed that for any alternative, x, a real number, v(x), can be determined which is a measure of how attractive the alternative is. In a more precise, analytical sense we say that there exists a function

$$v : X \rightarrow \Re$$

which represents $\geq^*$ in the sense that more preferred alternatives get values[1] which are at least as high as the values attached to less preferred alternatives, i.e.

$$x^1 \geq^* x^2 \Leftrightarrow v(x^1) \geq v(x^2)$$

The function v, depending on one's tradition, is termed a utility, value, or preference function. The rationale underlying the different adjectives preceding the term "function" is as follows: a) **utility** in the sense that more useful alternatives get higher numbers, b) **value** in the sense that more valuable alternatives or alternatives which better correspond to one's underlying values, get higher numbers, and c) **preference** since more preferred alternatives get higher numbers. We will mainly employ the term **preference function** as it comes closest to the notion of choice emphasized throughout. In summary, then, the preference function v(.) attaches a number v(x) to each alternative x in X and we interpret the number v(x) as a measure of the decision maker's well-being, if he chooses the alternative x.

---

[1] Note that the term "value" as employed here corresponds to the ordinary, daily usage as "measurement", e.g. as in the term "evaluate". This is in contrast to the more fundamental meaning introduced in chapter 1 where we considered values to be "the foundations of our preferences, the ends we seek and not the means of achieving them, while criteria are the measures we choose to operationally express our values." It will be clear from the context which of the two meanings, "measurements" or "ends", are referred to.

Usually, it is only the so-called "ordinal" properties of v which matter. By this we mean that "more is better than less" so that we can rank the alternatives according to the number associated with them by the preference function. It should be noted that value differences, e.g. $v(x^2)$-$v(x^5)$, or any other algebraic manipulations, e.g. $v(x^1)/v(x^2)$, are meaningless here unless very strong assumptions are made as to the function.

Now, given the set of alternatives X and the preference function v, we may define an **optimal alternative** x^* as an alternative in X with the highest value of all the alternatives in X, i.e. x^* is a solution to

$$\begin{array}{ll} \max & v(x) \\ \text{s.t.} & x \in X \end{array}$$

where max means "maximize", s.t. stands for "subject to", and $x \in X$ means that "x is an element in X". Hence, to find an optimal alternative, we search through X, attach the value v(x) to each x and pick an alternative with the highest possible or maximal value. In the case of ties, any of the alternatives having this highest value can be chosen since, according to the preference function v, they are equally attractive.

In the world of the rational ideal model, the optimal alternative x^* is the one the decision maker **should** choose and the one the analyst assisting the decision maker **should** help him locate during the search. In this world, individuals described as above are defined to be **rational.** Thus, by definition, rational decision makers are characterized by their systematical search (max) for the best means ($x \in X$) to accomplish their ends (v(x)).

Note, however, that there is no deep description of humankind involved here. Such rationality is not to be interpreted as an expression of admirable behavior as the every day use of the term may suggest. It is simply a definition of a specific behavior in the specific abstract world of the rational ideal model where preference functions are employed to measure the attractiveness of alternatives. To distinguish it from other types of rationality, to be introduced later, let us term it classical or **substantive rationality**. As we will see subsequently, assuming that decision makers should attempt to behave substantively rational is not necessarily consistent with normative or descriptive theories which employ broader concepts of rationality.

For now, let us explain the term **ideal** in "Rational Ideal Model". We employ it to indicate that we have, or can generate, a "true" description of the decision maker's set of alternatives (X) and preferences (v). Often, the term **comprehensive** is used instead. Thus, it is supposed that we have a complete description of all that matters to the decision maker and how it matters. No instances of approximate descriptions of his wishes or incomplete, partial models of his possibilities are allowed here. Clearly, this is an ideal in the sense that it is unattainable in real-world planning.

However, it may not be a very useful ideal in the sense of being something we should aim for. The following are three arguments against striving for such an ideal:

* If all alternatives are delineated and all preference information is subsummed in a preference function, then planning is reduced to a computational task. Seeking to replace doubt, curiosity and creativity by certainty, consistency, and computation is equivalent to attempting to replace human subjectiveness, personal involvement and responsibility by a formula. Where in this "ideal" world would there be room for emotions, aesthetics, and ethics?

* Even if one disregards the above argument, it is questionable whether the "benefits" which could be obtained by slavishly following the rational ideal model could outway the "costs" involved in obtaining the comprehensive descriptions of the alternatives and the preferences.

* Even if one disregards both the above arguments, there would be no room for compromise, negotiation and teamwork since each individual would be tied down by his own choice of "optimal solution".

We will return to these three arguments many times in the course of the exposition. For the moment, it suffices to note that since this ideal is far from attainable, it becomes of paramount importance to determine whether and how to strive for it. Clearly, the ideal itself does not provide guidance here.

2.2. An Example

At this point, let us illustrate how managerial economics and operations research implicitly attempt to implant the rational ideal model into the context of planning.

The president of a small company wonders if the company is producing and selling the best mix of its two products. So he decides to undertake some production planning. From the production and sales managers he learns that the set of feasible production combinations, taking into account technical constraints and sales commitments, consists of the following six alternatives:

$$X^{\#} = \{(0,10),(3,8),(4,9),(6,5),(7,3),(8,0)\}$$

where an alternative $x^i=(x^i_1,x^i_2)$ for $i=1,2,\ldots,6$ defines how many million units of product 1 to produce, x^i_1, and how many million units of product 2 to produce, x^i_2. Also, remembering perhaps his micro-economic studies, he decides that the objective should be to maximize contribution to profit, i.e. profit becomes the criterion for how attractive an alternative is. Using cost and sales data he estimates that the products' contributions to profit are $2.5 and $1 per unit respectively. Therefore, he delineates his preference function as

$$v^{\#}(x^i_1,x^i_2)=2.5x^i_1+1x^i_2$$

Now it is straightforward to determine the optimal alternative. Evaluating the different production plans results in the following table of preference function values:

Plan no. i	1	2	3	4	5	6
Prod.levels (x^i_1,x^i_2) Mill. units	(0,10)	(3,8)	(4,9)	(6,5)	(7,3)	(8,0)
Value $v^{\#}(x^i_1,x^i_2)$ Mill. $	10	15.5	19	20	20.5	20

We see that the maximum profit which can be obtained is $20.5 million and that the corresponding optimal production plan is $x^*=x^5=(7,3)$. This is illustrated in figure 2.1

below, where the straight lines are so-called "iso-profit curves". Two product-mixes like (6,5) and (8,0) on the same iso-profit curve give the same overall profit, here $20 million, and higher profit levels correspond to movements towards the north-east of the coordinate system.

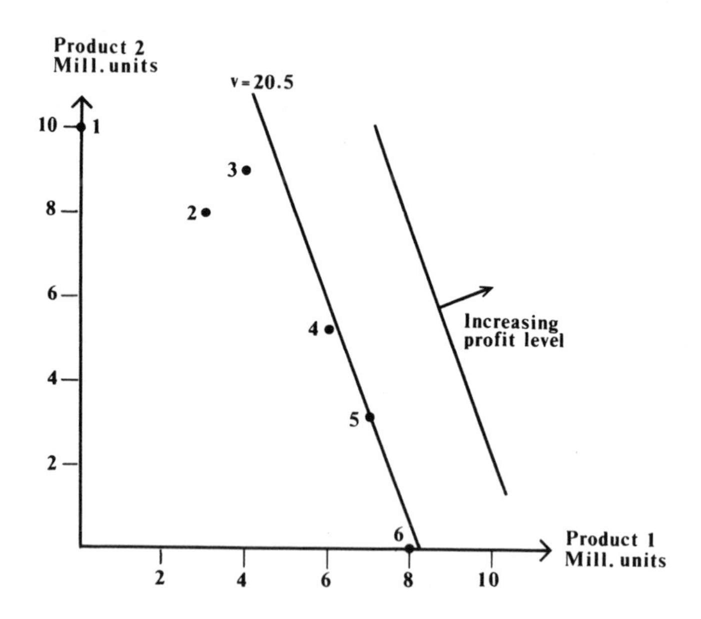

Figure 2.1 One Criterion Production Planning

2.3. Optimizing Planning

The example above, although technically simplified to ease the exposition, is in fact conceptually representative of the "rational" approach to planning often presented in operations research (OR), micro-economics and related disciplines - but not very often met in the "real world". We might call it the typical **rational OR approach, optimizing planning,** or **rational-comprehensive planning.** We see that it simply applies the Rational Ideal Model by specifying a given set of alternatives X*, a preference function v* and a search procedure (maximize profit).

But of course, as already noted, we are not in the ideal world of the Rational Ideal Model when we have to plan.

To begin with, we do not ordinarily possess a complete, comprehensive description of the set of alternatives. Consider the example above. First, it presumably required considerable effort and deliberation to delineate the 6 alternatives. Secondly, even then the set of alternatives is hardly exhaustive. For example, what about expanding the set by changing sales and procurement contracts, or undertaking human and physical capital investments? And what about future alternatives? How does the product-mix affect the market-share and competitors' behavior? And how is the set of alternatives affected by competitors' behavior? What about improved or alternative product designs with different costs and prices? Thus, a major consideration in real world planning problems is how much effort to put into the descriptions of the alternatives. In other words, how precisely should we try to approximate the "ideal" set X? Clearly, the Rational Ideal Model does not provide any guidance here. It simply assumes that these strategic questions have been answered in advance and that the set of alternatives is well defined and available.

Also, we seldomly have a complete, comprehensive description of the decision maker's fundamental values or of the criteria which he selects to operationalize these values. In the example, it presumably required some effort to decide on profit as the overall objective and to describe, i.e. to estimate, the profit function. Even then we can hardly expect that myopic profit maximization is all that matters to the president. He may have many desires both as to his own person and regarding the enterprise. Just to suggest a few of these, he would probably like not only to make a high profit in the present period, but also to go into the future with an effective, well-educated, proud labor force, up-to-date capital equipment, a large market-share and good relations to the firm's financial supporters and the local community. So, we note once again that real-world planning problems inherently are multicriteria problems, even though in our attempts to reduce the complexities introduced by multiple values and criteria, we tend to seek uni-criterion formulations, e.g. maximize profit. Also, at the more abstract level, we see that a major issue becomes that of deciding how much effort to put into the study of our underlying values as well as how these values will be affected by the choice of problem formulation. Once again, the Rational Ideal Model does not provide any guidance here.

2.4. Bounded Rationality

Our critique of the rational OR approach is somewhat ad hoc. We could be more precise by introducing alternative models of human decision making.

The basic observations above: 1) that real planning problems do not simply exist as objective realities, but are subjective products of our cognition, 2) that they therefore do not present themselves with clearcut descriptions of wishes and possibilities, and 3) that humans have limited capacities for information production, processing, and analysis, are in no way new. Earlier, similar observations lead psychologists and economists to suggest alternative models of rationality. Notable here is the Nobel prize laureate H.A. Simon who used the term **bounded rationality** quite broadly about theories that incorporate an individual's limited information-processing capacities. More specifically, the above problems have lead to models of human decision making in terms of satisficing rather than optimizing behavior and to considerations of so-called procedural rationality to supplement the substantive rationality considered so far.

In **satisficing** models, the distinction between possibilities and wishes is not that clearcut. People are depicted as thinking in terms of aspiration levels which function as a sort of mediator between the ideal and the realizable outcomes, and which may be dynamically modified throughout the decision making process. The search for appropriate actions is terminated whenever the aspiration level is - perhaps only nearly - satisfied.

The idea of **procedural rationality** is to focus attention on the effectiveness of different decision making procedures rather than the effectiveness of a given decision as emphasized by substantive rationality. Hence, procedural rationality is "process-oriented" while substantive rationality is "outcome-oriented". Procedural rationality should guide the choice of whole investigation - choice - implementation procedures in much the same way as substantive rationality may guide the choice of action in a **given** decision problem.

In practice - without even contemplating expressions such as optimization, satisficing and procedural rationality - planners responsible for recommending a solution to a problem attempt to integrate such notions. They intuitively decide, for example, how best to balance the effort required to generate and analyze alternatives with the possible improvements in the resulting solutions. I.e., they integrate optimizing and satisficing behavior as well as substantive and procedural rationality.

It would be interesting to take a closer look at multiple criteria planning from the point of view of broader concepts of rationality. However, little help is available in the existing literature. Although the MCDM community has largely discarded the classical ideal of substantive rationality, it has not explicitly introduced a conceptual and operational framework for a new ideal based on the above considerations. Many of the observations used to motivate MCDM contributions have a definite flavor of bounded rationality, but they remain ad hoc as no serious, comprehensive and detailed modelling of the decision context along such lines exists. We will attempt to make a modest contribution here. We refer in particular to chapter 10 for a discussion of the relationship between problem context and choice of multiple criteria planning approach and to chapter 11 for a discussion of problem solving and conflict dissolution within a context of collective rationality and of ethics.

2.5. Summary

We introduced the notion of the Rational Ideal Model. In this model, a set of alternatives and a preference ordering are given, and decision making is reduced to a computational task of finding the most preferred alternative, i.e. of determining an optimal solution by maximizing the preference function. We then illustrated the typical OR or rational-comprehensive approach to planning which is a direct application of the Rational Ideal Model in a less-than-ideal world. We criticized this approach by observing that: 1) in real-world planning contexts we do not have comprehensive descriptions of the set of alternatives and of the decision maker's preferences, and 2) real-world preference structures seem to be characterized by multiple objectives. We can illustrate some of the above ideas as in figure 2.2.

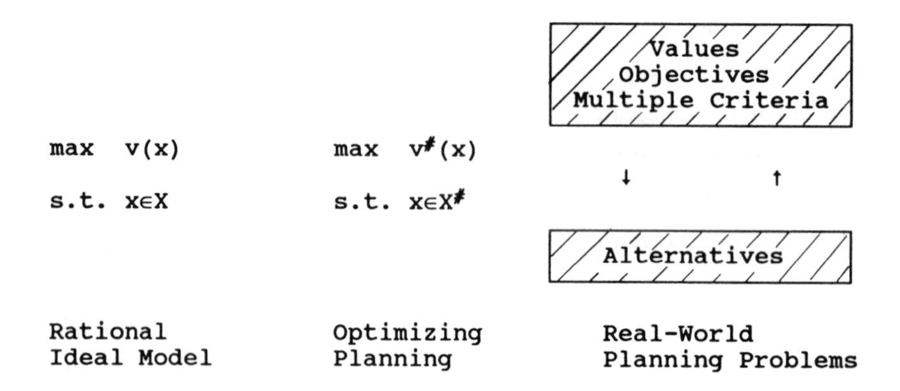

Figure 2.2 Ideal vs. Real-World Planning

The superscripts (#) indicate approximations, shaded boxes symbolize how the preference function and alternatives initially appear as black - or at least grey - boxes to the planner, and the arrows indicate that in the process of contemplating which alternatives exist - or may be created! - insight is gained as to how these alternatives may be evaluated. And vice versa.

Also, having observed that we do not have a well-defined preference function and set of alternatives to begin with - if ever - we identified a major (meta)planning problem. Namely, how much effort should we put into the delineation of means and ends, and how much effort should we put into the search for an optimal or a satisficing solution? We noted that the rational ideal model does not provide any guidance here.

Finally, we underlined that all these considerations are oriented towards an individual who is to make a choice and balance his multiple intentions with his possibilities; the situation becomes quite a bit more complex when multiple decision makers and/or decision receivers are involved.

2.6. Bibliographic Notes

In most of the literature on OR, systems analysis and economics, the rational ideal model is the basic conceptual structure underlying both normative and descriptive models of decision making. And little more than lip service is given to the problems of implementing this ideal - or of replacing it. Although there is an awareness of the quicksand foundation, there is an even greater fear of having to relinquish traditional notions of rationality and mathematical precision and consistency. A discussion of the nature and limitations of the rational approach to planning is provided in the books by Ackoff(1970), who talks about "optimizing planning", Faludi(1973), who talks about "rational comprehensive planning" and the seminal work by Rietveld(1980) who specifically introduces the limitations of traditional rationality within a context of MCDM. There is a large literature on bounded rationality, satisficing behaviour, and procedural rationality, c.f. for example Kickert(1980), March(1978), Pruzan(1988), Radner(1975), and Simon (1959,72,76,78). Cases where effective search procedures may be decribed in terms of aspiration levels are given by for example MacQueen(1964) and Rothschild(1974). Introductions to optimal search theory can be found in DeGroot(1970), Kohn & Shavell(1974) and for a more recent contribution Morgan & Manning(1985).

Chapter 3

CONFLICTS AND COMPROMISES

The single most significant contribution of MCDM to the theory and practice of planning has been its explicit recognition of multiple criteria. This is an important contribution since planning is usually undertaken to improve a system's performance in several, i.e. multiple, respects. This was illustrated earlier using examples of buying a house or a car, airport development, production planning and planning of planning. Before we consider additional contributions and start exploring different approaches to multiple criteria planning, it seems useful at this point to focus attention on this primary contribution. Therefore, in this chapter we go into more detail as to how basic values and their expression via multiple objectives and criteria can lead to operational definitions of conflict and of compromise solutions.

3.1. Objectives and Criteria

Initially, let us note that the existence of a multiplicity of objectives may be interpreted as either an **intrinsic** or an **induced** (extrinsic) property of problem formulations, or as both. The president of the small company in example 2.2 may be deeply concerned about the well-being of the workers as well as about profits, which was previously assumed to be the only objective of interest. In this case, both objectives might be considered to be expressions of values and the existence of multiple - here two - objectives is an intrinsic property of the planning situation.[1] Alternatively, he may cynically consider employee well-being to only be of instrumen-

[1] As touched on previously, logically speaking profits can only be considered as means to more fundamental values; on the other hand, profits and wealth have become such significant and pervasive symbols in our society, that they have taken on intrinsic properties and are considered by many as basic values.

tal importance insofar as it contributes to long-run profits and wealth accumulation. Then, due to the one period modelling, he may choose to trade off some short run profits to improve the satisfaction of the workers, since this may pave the way for even better profit performance in the future. In this case the existence of multiple objectives is an induced property since there is in fact only one underlying value.

Thus, no matter whether he considers worker satisfaction to be an intrinsic value, i.e. an end in its own right, or as an ice-cold tool for improving future profit performance, i.e. an extrinsic means, a more holistic vision of the company can induce a desire for satisfied workers in the partial model applied. And in either case, a multiple of objectives characterizes the planning situation.

A related distinction is between **true** and **proxy** or **surrogate** objectives, i.e. where one objective is used in place of one or more other objectives which are more expressive of the decision maker's underlying values but which are more difficult to measure and express. Typical examples are to be found in macro-economic planning where measures such as gross national product and inflation are employed instead of richer and more detailed measures of a population's economic well-being. The same applies to profit at the micro-economic level. Profit, an ill-defined concept to begin with, says very little about the qualities characterizing an enterprise's performance; it is simply one - of many possible - means to following diffuse and complex ends. Such ends, in addition to the more traditional economic measures, might include notions of customer satisfaction, product quality, employees' pride in their work, contributions to the local society and the environment, and secure relationships with suppliers and financers. It is our contention that most students of economics, due to their training, and most business leaders, due to the continual pressure on them to produce a big black bottom line, have a reflex action which leads them like Pavlov's dog to respond with "profit" when asked about the goals of the firm. In this way, profits have usurped the status of values while logically speaking, they are means. Or, using the terminology introduced here, profits logically speaking are not true but surrogate objectives. We will return to this discussion in chapter 11 where we introduce the notion of the ethical - or multiple criteria - accounting statement.

Theoretically, these distinctions may rightfully be questioned since we can never imagine a complete model of the decision maker's possibilities and wishes, and thus we lack a firm basis for distinguishing between intrinsic and induced objectives, i.e. between values and means, and between true and surrogate objectives. Still, from an applied point of view, these distinctions are useful. They emphasize that a multiplicity of objectives must indeed be expected and can be considered as inherent to planning problems in social systems. Also, they emphasize the role of multiple objectives as a protection against oversimplicity in the modelling of possibilities and wishes - a point which is often missing in presentations of MCDM. Finally, and in connection with strategic planning, they emphasize the need for extensive analyses **prior** to explicit problem formulations, as to which objectives and criteria best express a decision maker's values. It is our observation that the time and effort which is expended on such analyses is often trivial compared to the consequences of the decisions made.

Now, let us assume that a decision maker has reflected upon his basic values and given them verbal expression as objectives. Assume too, that he has operationalized these objectives by a choice of n criteria, i.e. n different properties of the alternatives. Hence, our starting point here is not one overall preference function v, but rather n different criteria functions:

$$
\begin{aligned}
f_1&: X \rightarrow \Re \\
f_2&: X \rightarrow \Re \\
&\;\;\vdots \\
f_n&: X \rightarrow \Re
\end{aligned}
$$

where, for each $i=1,2,\ldots,n$, f_i is the i'th **criterion function** and the interpretation is that $f_i(x)$ is a measure of how desirable the alternative x is with respect to the i'th attribute or criterion, higher values assumed here to be better than lower values.

This formulation is rather general. For one thing, the assumption about an attribute being measured in numbers does not exclude ordinal properties. Some criteria may for example simply take the values -1, 0, and +1 with the interpretation bad, medium and good performance with respect to the property in question.

Also, the assumption about higher values being better than lower values is quite general. Suppose for example that an attribute affecting your overall satisfaction with your job is the amount of time you spend traveling to and from your place of work. In this case you would like to minimize rather than maximize the objective "transportation time". Then a criterion like "24 minus the number of hours spent on transportation" could be employed, i.e. the time left over for other activities is what you would like to maximize.

The case where a particular value of a criterion is sought while all other (higher og lower) values are less attractive can be treated in a similar way. An example could be a person's own weight: if for some reason your objective is to weigh say precisely 70 kilograms, we can use the criterion -¦70-weight¦, i.e. minus the absolute deviation of your weight from your target 70. This measure has as its maximal value 0 when your weight is exactly 70 and is negative for any other weight.

Before leaving this rather introductory discussion of criteria, let us note that a rather subtle, but nevertheless restrictive assumption is implicit in the above remarks. When we assume that "more is better than less" for each criterion, we implicitly assume that we can talk about the improvement of one criterion independently of the other criteria. This "independence" assumption may be rather restrictive. To illustrate, consider the following situation. A modern day mad macho scientist, inspired both by Frankenstein films and the possibilities arising from genetic manipulation, decides to create the perfect woman. To do so, he gathers detailed information on the physical, mental and spiritual attributes of famous females and "creates" a woman having for example the will-power of a Golda Meir, the chest of a Marilyn Monroe, the strength of an amazon, the voice of a Birgit Nilsson and the empathy of a Mother Theresa. When she is materialized it turns out that she is far from the marvelous person the scientist expected; he made the mistake of focusing on the individual objectives without considering the "whole". For example, she may be so beautiful, strong and intelligent that he feels insecure and inferior in comparison. In addition the sexual charisma of a Marilyn Monroe is probably poorly matched with the operatic voice of a Birgit Nilsson, the "masculine" political punch of a Golda Meir and the biceps of an amazon.

A more poetic expression of this idea is provided in the first novel written by Simone de Beauvoir, "Tous les hommes sont mortels", edition Gallimard, 1946. A beautiful actress at the height of her career seeks eternal life in order not to grow old and lose her beauty and her position; she longs for a continual repetition of her present experiences. Her counterpart, who for a short period of time becomes her lover, has as a result of a magical event lived for 700 years and cannot die; he longs for death as he feels that nothing new happens and that his life is a continual repitition of past experiences. He has experienced that the whole can be less than the sum of its parts while she assumes that if each experience, considered by itself is good, then an infinite series of such experiences would be superb.[2]

In general, we may certainly experience situations where the evaluation of a system cannot reasonably be carried out by focusing on its specific properties. Wholes have emergent properties which cannot be observed by focusing only on the individual components and their relationships. In more "mathematical" terms, this leads to the conclusion that we may not in general be able to compare vectors of criteria values by serially looking at the individual criteria; from this analytical perspective, in order to determine our preferences we must simultaneously consider all the criteria, i.e. consider the vectors as "wholes". We will return to this important theme in chapters 6 and 7.

3.2. Conflicts

To focus our attention at this point on the preferences alone, let us assume that a decision maker's choice situation is characterized by a fixed set of alternatives which is known in advance. Thus, we are in the world of the Rational Ideal Model except for the complication that we now have n criteria instead of simply 1 criterion which measures his well-being.

[2] We could not resist introducing this notion of a whole being less than the sum of its parts. In all attempts we have seen to express the notion of synergy, it is done by arguing that the whole can be more than the sum of its parts. What matter of course, is that wholes cannot be described/experienced as an aggregation of their components.

Now, the existence of different measures of performance usually creates a **conflict.** The alternative which appears to be best with respect to f_1 may for example be rather poor with respect to f_2. In general, we can not expect to find one single alternative that simultaneously results in the best possible values of all the n criteria chosen to represent the decision maker's objectives. More precisely, for i=1,2, . . . ,n let x_i^* be a solution to

$$\begin{array}{ll} \max & f_i(x) \\ \text{s.t.} & x \in X \end{array}$$

For simplicity, let us assume that for all values of the index i this problem has a unique solution, i.e. one and only one alternative results in the maximal value of $f_i(x)$; no ties result. So, x_1^* is the alternative we would choose if we were only concerned about the 1'st criterion. Similarly, let $x_2^*, \ldots, x_n^*$ be the preferred alternatives from the points of view of the 2'nd, . . . ,n'th criteria, respectively. None, some, or all of these n preferred alternatives may in a given situation be identical. There is a **conflict** if **all** these choices $x_1^*, \ldots, x_n^*$ are not identical. Thus, a conflict emerges, unless the different points of view - as represented via the n criteria - unanimously point to the same alternative.

We can refer to such conflicts as **intrapersonal**, i.e. as conflicts of preference **within** a given individual. The emphasis on "intra" is intended to differentiate such conflicts from the more traditional concept of conflict as occuring **between** individuals due to differences in their preferences - or perhaps due to the imprecision of their communication. We will refer to such conflict as **interpersonal** conflict.

Although often ignored in the MCDM literature, this distinction is crucial. MCDM has been developed to cope with intrapersonal conflicts. Interpersonal conflicts create quite distinct problems. They can result for example in socalled "strategic" or opportunistic behaviour. That is, one person may attempt to influence the outcome of the group's collective choice by sending biased or false signals about his personal desires. The analysis of such interpersonal conflict calls for quite different methods. From a mathematical-analytical perspective, such conflict has been the object of analysis in the fields of "social choice" and "game theory". In chapter 11 interpersonal conflicts will also be viewed within the context of groups actively seeking to find a compromise solution that all can agree upon even though it may not be the preferred compromise solution to any single member's intrapersonal conflict.

We will also introduce a more comprehensive notion of conflict, - what we call **systemic conflict** - between those who make decisions based upon their preferences, and those who are on the receiving end. This way of viewing conflicts leads to a reorientation of our attention. We no longer focus solely on the individuals making decisions, the **decision makers**, but also include those parties who are affected by the decisions, the **decision receivers**. Such conflict is considered from a systems point of view. The underlying hypothesis is that in order for a social system in a pluaralistic society to be able to pursue its own objectives in the best possible way, it must support the objectives of its sub- and suprasystems. To be able to do so requires a radical change in the tasks and selfperception of the managment of an enterprise. Since its major concern is now the ability of the enterprise to pursue its own objectives as well as the capability of those affected by its decisions to pursue their own objectives, it must identify a) the enterprise, b) the parties who affect and are affected by the enterprise, and c) these parties' values. As will be seen, this takes the lid off Pandora's box; these tasks are existential in nature and require a whole new repertoire of language and tools. Furthermore, since the metaobjective of the enterprise becomes the attunement of decision maker and decision receiver values, the focus shifts from analysis to communication, from conflict to consensus, and from decision making to **ethics**. We will return to these new themes in chapter 11.

We return once again to the traditional frame of reference for MCDM, that of a single decision maker who is to make a choice between a number of alternatives, none of which simultaneously optimizes all of the criteria chosen to represent his objectives. A convenient way of indicating the extent of the intrapersonal conflict which occurs due to the presence of multiple criteria is by what we call the **cross-effect matrix** defined as

$$\begin{matrix} f_1(x_1^*), & f_1(x_2^*), & \ldots, & f_1(x_n^*) \\ f_2(x_1^*), & f_2(x_2^*), & \ldots, & f_2(x_n^*) \\ \cdot & & \cdot & \cdot \\ \cdot & & \cdot & \cdot \\ \cdot & & \cdot & \cdot \\ f_n(x_1^*), & f_n(x_2^*), & \ldots, & f_n(x_n^*) \end{matrix}$$

Moving down the diagonal, $f_1(x_1^*)$, $f_2(x_2^*)$, . . . , $f_n(x_n^*)$, we get the highest values of the different criteria given the set of alternatives X.[3] This vector of maximal values is often called the utopia or **ideal point.** It is only attainable if we are in a case of non-conflicting criteria, that is, a situation where the same alternative results in the maximal values for **all** criteria. Also, moving down a column like the first, $f_1(x_1^*)$, $f_2(x_1^*)$, . . . ,$f_n(x_1^*)$, we see how single minded focus on the first criterion will affect the fulfillment of the other (n-1) criteria. Similarly, moving along a row like the first, $f_1(x_1^*)$, $f_1(x_2^*)$, . . . ,$f_1(x_n^*)$, we see how single minded focus on the n different criteria will affect the first criterion.

3.3. Compromises

One way or the other - and a multiple criteria perspective suggests many different ways - we have to choose an alternative. Clearly, at the very heart of any such attempt we must somehow attune our attitudes towards the different criteria. More correctly, perhaps, we have to live somehow with the conflicts - in fact we might say that decision making here is equivalent to **choosing the most preferred conflict.** We must accept that in general it is impossible to accomplish all of our intentions optimally. Except in rare cases, the ideal point is not realizable. Therefore, we have,

---

[3] Note that the cross-effect matrix presented implicitly presumes that each of the n preference functions has a unique solution. If this were not the case, then there would be alternative matrices, each of which would have of course the same ideal point.

explicitly or implicitly, to make some compromise between our different interests as expressed by the criteria we choose.

In the Rational Ideal Model the outcome is called the optimal alternative, since it is determined by optimization. "Optimality" has no precise meaning when we move from one to several criteria. In multiple criteria planning therefore, we call the decision maker's preferred outcome the **compromise solution**, since it is determined as his most preferred compromise between the values of the different criteria[4].

One way to illustrate what compromising is all about is through **trade-offs**. No matter how the decision maker determines his choice of alternative, when the decision maker makes a choice, it corresponds to the implicit choice of a vector of criteria values as being the most preferred. And we can interpret the choice by saying that the decision maker implicitly trades off all the losses in some criteria for the gains in the others. To see this, let us assume that the decision maker ends up selecting the alternative x^*. He thus implicitly or explicitly believes x^* to be better than any other specific alternative available to him, say alternative x. Let us assume for ease of exposition that n criteria are chosen to characterize the alternatives and that the values of the first k criteria decrease while the values of the last n-k criteria increase when we move from x to x^*. Now, by preferring x^* to x the decision maker is basically saying or thinking that he is willing to accept the declines ($\downarrow$)

$$f_1(x) \downarrow f_1(x^*),\ f_2(x) \downarrow f_2(x^*),\ \ldots,\ f_k(x) \downarrow f_k(x^*)$$

in order to gain the improvements or benefits ($\uparrow$)

$$f_{k+1}(x) \uparrow f_{k+1}(x^*),\ f_{k+2}(x) \uparrow f_{k+2}(x^*),\ \ldots,\ f_n(x) \uparrow f_n(x^*)$$

---

[4] Some MCDM procedures employ optimization techniques as subroutines in their search for a compromise solution. In addition, the outcome of some MCDM procedures are actually optimal in the sense of optimizing a certain approximation of the Rational Ideal Model. Nevertheless, this difference in terminology - compromise solutions versus optimal solutions - is useful since it emphasizes the differences in the starting points of multiple criteria planning and the Rational Ideal Model.

We can thus interpret his choice of x^* by saying that he is willing to trade off the reduced performance with respect to the first k criteria in order to gain the improvements in the last n-k criteria.

It is worth noting here that although we may interprete the choice of x^* in terms of trade-offs, it need not correspond to the way an actual decision maker handles the choice problem. Note in particular that this interpretation presumes that all qualities characterizing the alternatives can be expressed in terms of n criteria that are sufficiently independent to allow more to be better than less. Also, note that in practice it may be a very demanding and even painful process to attempt to achieve a preferred compromise solution via pairwise comparison of criteria. In the airport development problem, for example, the decision maker may prefer an alternative where, according to the criteria chosen, the only difference with respect to another alternative is that it will cost an additional $1,000,000 per year, while the average noise level in the surrounding area will be reduced by say 10% or, even more provokingly, according to some statistical analyses, the expected number of passengers killed per year will be reduced by 1. Such an evaluation may be unavoidable. If we want to follow our basic values instead of some overly simple objective like cost minimization, we have to directly or indirectly investigate what our values and preferences are. On the other hand, this is not to say that a direct investigation of trade-offs is in general the most appropriate approach. We shall return to this in chapters 6-9 where we discuss different approaches to determining a preferred compromise solution.

This discussion of trade offs and compromise solutions leads to a crucial difference between traditional one-criterion optimization and multiple criteria planning. With the traditional one-criterion approach to decision making, there is really no content to the term "decision making". Once the optimization problem has been formulated and relevant data have been collected, the solution process does not involve the decision maker. In fact the "solution" is imbedded in the formulation; all that is required to make it visible is a series of computations, performed by employing an algorithm. The computational process may in some cases be extremely demanding, but this does not in any way alter the conclusion that once the optimization problem is formulated, in principle the decision maker is no longer a necessary participant in the solution process which is purely computational. Just the opposite is true in most approaches to formulating and "solving" multiple criteria problems. Here a decision maker is the only one who can provide the preference information which is required to determine the best compromise. Decision making is no longer a computational process, but is now a process of search, evaluation, communication and learning where the decision maker's values and preferences gradually become explicit. This is what M. Zeleny once refered to as "Letting the man back in".

3.4. An Example

Let us continue the example in section 2.2 by assuming that the company's president expresses interest in sales volume as well as in profit generation. He does so for several reasons. Sales volume can be considered to be a handy surrogate objective for the long run market position and hence profit potentials in the future as well. The volume of sales may also be a surrogate objective for stable working conditions and for prestige in the community. Finally, sales volume may be of direct importance as an end. The decision maker may consider it in a manner similar to the way he regards profits; he knows that from a logical point of view it is a means rather than an end, but on the other hand, it has achieved such symbolic importance, that it also becomes important in its own right.

We assume that the price of product 1 is \$5 per unit and the price of product 2 is \$10 per unit. As was the case earlier, we assume that the corresponding contributions to profit are \$2.5 and \$1, respectively.

Thus, we have a context characterized by a decision maker, a given set of alternatives but now two criteria instead of just one:

$$f_1(x^i_1,x^i_2) = 2.5x^i_1 + 1x^i_2 \quad \text{(profit)}$$
$$f_2(x^i_1,x^i_2) = 5x^i_1 + 10x^i_2 \quad \text{(sales)}$$

The performances of the six alternative plans with respect to these two criteria are calculated to be

Plan no. i	1	2	3	4	5	6
Prod.levels (x^i_1, x^i_2) Mill. units	(0,10)	(3,8)	(4,9)	(6,5)	(7,3)	(8,0)
Profit $f_1(x^i_1, x^i_2)$ Mill. $	10	15.5	19	20	20.5	20
Sales $f_2(x^i_1, x^i_2)$ Mill. $	100	95	110	80	65	40

We see that the best plan according to the profit criterion is plan number 5 while the maximization of sales volume alone would point in the direction of plan number 3. Thus, we have a non-trivial case of conflict.

The extent of this conflict and the possibilities facing the president may be indicated by the following cross-effect matrix:

$$\begin{array}{c} \\ f_1 \\ f_2 \end{array} \begin{array}{cc} x^{1*} = x^5 & x^{2*} = x^3 \\ \left[\begin{array}{cc} 20.5 & 19 \\ 65 & 110 \end{array} \right] \end{array}$$

We may illustrate the two-criteria case as in figure 3.1 below. In figure 3.1a we have a reproduction of figure 2.1 except that we have now supplemented it with an iso-sales-curve; we recall that an iso-curve indicates those values of the underlying decision variables which result in the same value of the attribute in question. We see that the values of the two criteria are increasing in different directions and this leads to contradictory proposals, i.e. x^5 and x^3 respectively.

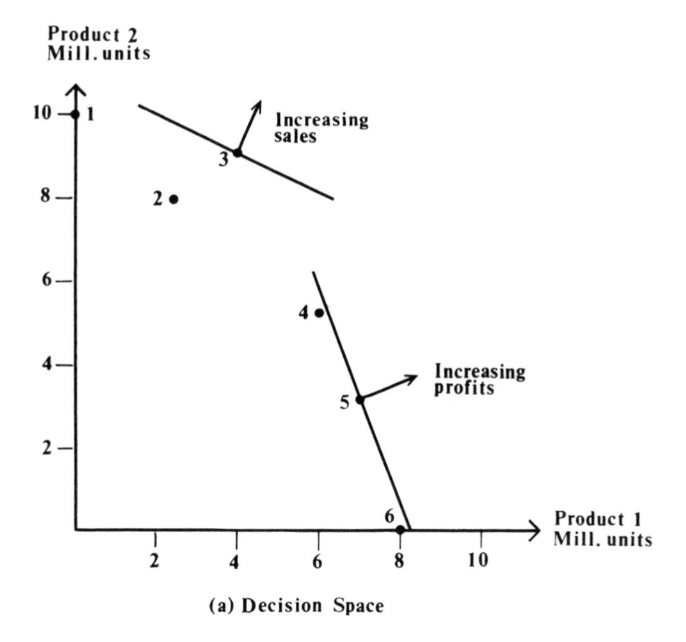

(a) Decision Space

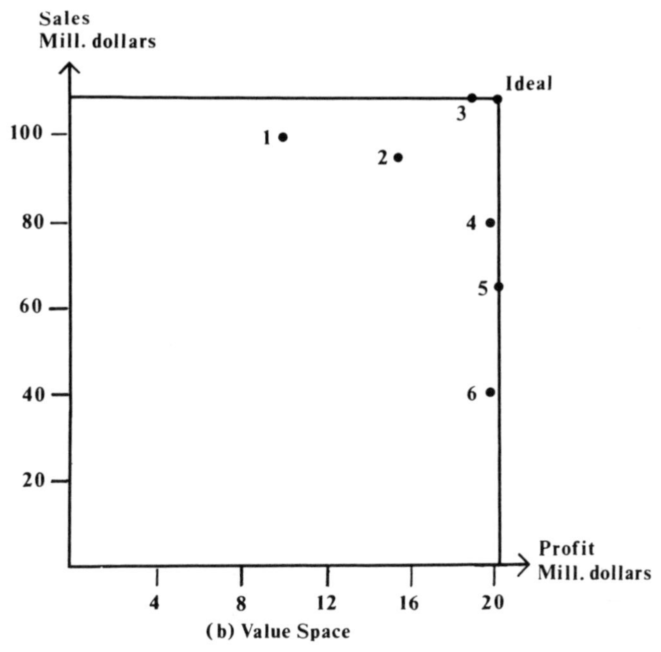

(b) Value Space

Figure 3.1 Two-Criteria Production Planning

In figure 3.1b, we have transferred the whole picture into what we refer to as "criteria space". In this space, we ignore the operational details of the feasible plans. We confine our attention to the attributes that appear to matter for the president - namely profits and sales. Thus, the different plans are now simply identified with the profits and sales they generate.

Faced with these conflicts, the president has to make a compromise. Initially, he may of course eliminate the alternatives 1, 2 and 6. In each of these plans it is possible to obtain more of both criteria by choosing another plan. However, to choose between the remaining alternatives 3, 4 and 5, he has to make some kind of compromise. Should he go for the high sales alternative 3 at the cost of a reduction in profit level of \$1.5 million compared to the high profit alternative 5? Or should he trade the other way around? Or should he take a more middle-of-the-road standpoint accepting lower levels of fulfillment in both criteria compared to the - unattainable - ideal of (20.5,110) by choosing alternative 4? Or, perhaps, based upon this information attempt to create new and better alternatives? Certainly, there are no a priori, self-evident answers to these questions; only the president can decide.

Is there no way the analyst could help the president? Yes, of course. Indeed, he has probably already been useful by helping to structure the problem formulation, gathering the data, and exposing the choice possibilities as above. In more complex cases, the analyst may engage in an interactive communication whereby the picture is successively presented to the president and whereby he is helped to structure his compromise and trade-off considerations.

In addition, if the dialogue regarding the planning context leads to the awareness of new, relevant values, objectives and criteria or to the replacement of an existing surrogate criterion by more relevant criteria, he could modify the model accordingly. Finally, the new insights as to the nature of the criteria and the impact they have on the decision maker's preferences could also lead to a search for new and more attractive alternatives.

3.5. Risk and Uncertainty

We have assumed above that the performance of a given alternative $x \in X$ with respect to a given criterion f_i can be represented by a real number $f_i(x) \in \Re$. Thus, for example, we have assumed that we can calculate the profit generated by different production plans, i.e. that there exists a function

$$f_1(x) = \text{profit of } x$$

Implicit in this formulation is the assumption that consequences can be calculated with certainty.

In reality, however, consequences will almost never be known with certainty and precision. The profit of a firm will almost always depend on a series of more or less unknown factors, like demand, competition, and productivity. Also, it may not be clear exactly how these factors affect the firm's profit. And finally, "profit" is a very loose term, also from an accounting point of view, as any study of annual reports will make quite clear. One may wonder, therefore, whether our formulations above and our exposition below is really relevant in such cases. Let us comment here on this fundamental problem.

First, let us observe that the assumption of **certainty** may indeed be useful. Although the consequences of different actions are probably never certain, the uncertainties involved may not always be a major concern and it may therefore be a useful, analytical simplification to simply ignore this complication. A major part of the literature on planning and decision making, especially that related to traditional mathematical programming approaches, is based on such a simplification and has in many cases proved useful. This is certainly our own experience from numerous applications.

Next, let us emphasize that we shall constantly be concerned with the problem of **hidden information**. That is, as expanded upon in the next chapter, we generally allow that the alternatives, their consequences, and the evaluation of these are not immediately available. Rather, information about these basic ingredients in a choice problem is "hidden" and thorough investigation and communication are needed to bring it to the surface. In fact, just how these investigative and communicative activities are to be performed is a major theme of the book.

Thirdly, let us consider cases with substantial **risk and uncertainties** in planning. The hidden information assumption may leave the impression that we are will in the end be able to perfectly forsee the consequences of given actions, we just have to work hard enough. Whether this is the case is a somewhat philosophical issue but it is certainly not the idea on which we base this book. From a practical point of view, even if such perfect descriptions may be developed, their value may not motivate the efforts required to generate them. In reality, therefore, we have to allow for the possibility that consequences are uncertain and risky and that the extent of these uncertainties and risks may be so important as to require explicit consideration. Let us emphasize therefore that the complications are not ruled out by the multiple criteria formulations used in this book. To the contrary, the multiple criteria perspective enables us to explicitly introduce some of the difficulties arising due to uncertainties.

Imagine for example that the profit f_1 which will result from a production plan depends intimately on the level of demand. Assume for the sake of simplicity that the management is considering two rough scenarios, one based on low (L) demand and one based on high (H) demand. Assume too that we do not know which of these scenarios will be realized. In this case, we could substitute two criteria f_{1L} and f_{1H} for the single profit criterion f_1, i.e. we could introduce

$$f_{1L}(x) = \text{profit of x under "low" demand}$$
$$f_{1H}(x) = \text{profit of x under "high" demand}$$

reflecting that the decision maker would like to generate a large profit whatever the market conditions turn out to be. Similarly, depending on the data available, it might be reasonable to describe the profit generated by x by a socalled random variable, i.e. a description of the possible profit levels and their associated probabilities. We could then for example substitute the mean profit f_{1M} and the precision f_{1P} with which the profit can be foreseen for f_1, i.e. we could introduce two new criteria

$f_{1M}(x)$ = mean profit of x
$f_{1P}(x)$ = precision of the profit of x

This reflects that we cannot foresee the exact profit which will be generated by x but that the decision maker would like both a large average profit, and that he would like the variability of the profit to be as small as possible. These two intentions will most likely be in conflict. Typical examples of such a conflict between expected gains and variability are provided by the stock market: those stocks which may give a very high expected return on investment are often characterized by considerable volatility.

It follows that we have not ruled out uncertainties and risks per se. The introduction of new criteria as above allows - at least in an ad hoc fashion - for the possibility that uncertainties may be significant and may require explicit consideration. It remains to be noted, however, that we do not keep these matters at the forefront of the presentation. This is a matter of exposition and a necessity to avoid too lengthy discussions. Also, it reflects that large parts of the literature on MCDM have their roots in the mathematical programming tradition. A major limitation of our treatment is therefore that it does not cover the substantial literature developed to tackle uncertainties per se. In particular, this is clear in chapter 7 and appendix 2 where we discuss the modelling of preferences and where we do not discuss many important models of preferences for uncertain results. These models, however, build on the groundwork presented here.

Finally, we should probably comment on what is somtimes referred to as genuine or **fundamental uncertainty**. This refers to the fact that in some cases, we are not even able to delineate the set of possible consequences. When considering the implementation of a new gene-technology, for example, it may be virtually impossible to even list the possible effects. This is tightly related to the problem of listing all relevant criteria and we shall return to this issue at several points. Indeed, the omission of relevant criteria is a very fundamental problem and it appears that this problem cannot be handled within the confines of a formal model. As we shall argue, however, the multiple criteria perspective allows us at least to protect against such fundamental "ignorance", e.g. via the introduction of thresholds as explained in chapter 7.

3.6. Summary

We have argued that the necessity of considering a multiplicity of objectives and criteria is an inherent property of most real-world planning problems. The multiple criteria may be intrinsic expressions of the decision maker's values and/or an induced property due to incomplete modelling. In the later case we focus upon surrogate objectives which are used in place of other objectives which are more expressive of the decision maker's underlying values, but which are more difficult to measure and express. Multiple criteria usually cause intrapersonal conflicts since it is rare that all a decision maker's criteria can be optimized simultaneously. This calls for the decision maker to make what may be difficult - even painful - compromises which implicitly or explicitly trade off some intentions against others. Since making compromises is an essential part of any multiple criteria planning process, we refer to the outcome as a preferred compromise solution. Indeed, the process of determining a preferred compromise distinguishes traditional one criterion optimization from real-world planning where introspection, search, doubt, learning and compromise are keywords. No longer can decision making be reduced to a computational procedure where the optimal solution lies embedded in the formulation like an undeveloped film, only waiting to be revealed; the decision maker's preferences and value structure must now be considered and the responsibility - and the authority - is once again in the hands of people and not computers.

3.7. Bibliographic Notes

We will return to most of the subjects introduced above in later chapters. In particular, we return to the nature and definition of criteria in chapter 7, to the nature and role of compromises and trade-offs in chapters 6-9, and to the distinctions between intrapersonal, interpersonal and systemic conflicts and the methods they call for in chapter 11. Appropriate references are provided in these chapters.

Chapter 4

MULTIPLE CRITERIA PLANNING AND DECISION MAKING

We end this first part of the book by describing more precisely what multiple criteria planning is all about, i.e. by delineating its context and purposes.

4.1. The Context

As an introduction, we commence with a brief summary of some basic characteristics of real-world planning contexts which are identified in previous chapters.

The first characteristic is

* **Incomplete information about preferences**

In a given planning context our values receive expression as objectives and these objectives are operationalized by the definition of appropriate measures of performance or criteria. The existence of multiple criteria which are incommensurable and in conflict with each other lead to intrapersonal conflict. The appropriate compromise or trade-offs between these different intentions, e.g. as could be determined via the use of a preference function, is not known in advance. The choice of an alternative corresponds to the culmination of a learning process where values, objectives, criteria, alternatives and preferences continually interact and redefine each other and lead - explicitly or implicitly - to a compromise which dissolves the intrapersonal conflict. From this perspective, preferences are context-dependent and therefore dependent on the set of alternatives being considered.

The second characteristic is

* **Incomplete information about the set of alternatives**

It is extremally rare that the set of alternatives and the consequences they generate are well defined in advance. This information can be costly and/or time-consuming to generate. More decisive however is the realization that it is essentially impossible for the decision maker to generate and comprehend such information unless he is able to relate it to his - incomplete - knowledge about his preferences. So, in effect, we have the mirror image of the situation regarding preferences: the delineation of the set of alternatives depends upon our - incomplete - information about our preferences.

To make this context more precise, it is useful to introduce the idea of **a basic decision problem within a context of decentralized and not-immediately-available information.** This defines a framework within which most of multiple criteria planning can be conceptualized.

4.2. The Basic Decision Problem

The **basic decision problem** is given by

$$\begin{array}{ll} \max & F[f_1(x), f_2(x), \ldots, f_n(x)] \\ \text{s.t.} & x \in X \end{array}$$

where X is the set of feasible, i.e. currently available, alternatives, $f_1, \ldots, f_n$ are real functions measuring each criterion currently of relevance to the decision maker, and F is his unknown preference function.

We assume for sake of presentation that our awareness of our preferences develops during the planning process, at least subconciously, and that this insight in the form of F can be **implicitly** employed when the decision maker participates in the planning process.

Assuming the existence of an overall preference function is convenient: it simplfies the presentation but will in no way delimit our approach. This cannot be stressed sufficiently strongly. We do not say that such a function consciously exists in the head of a decision maker or that it is necessary for it to be explicitly defined in order for a decision maker to make decisions which are consistent with his underlying values. What we do say, is that we can present our conceptual framework for planning with multiple criteria in a much more concise and precise form if we assume that such functions implicitly exist. For by so doing, we are able to develop reasonable and useful definitions and deductions which otherwise would be practically impossible to develop in a consistent manner. In other words, this assumption is of axiomatic importance as a starting point for our theoretical development, just as the assumptions as to the existence of "values" is fundamental to the development. Neither values nor preference functions exist in the sense that stones exist; they are both intangible products of our intellect and whether or not it is reasonable to assume that they exist can solely be determined by the extent to which they contribute to our understanding and our ability to behave in harmony with our desires.

So the conceptual model simply says that we should choose the alternative x that gives the decision maker the highest possible value as measured by $f_1, \ldots, f_n$ and F. Also, we will assume that F is increasing, i.e. higher values of the criteria give higher values of F. Often this assumption is without loss of generality, cf. chapters 3 and 7 and appendix 2.

Furthermore, it may at some point be useful to transform the basic decision problem into what we refer to as **criteria space.** This concept, briefly introduced in section 3.4 in connection with Figure 3.1, will now be made more precise. If the decision maker subscribes to the model above, he is by definition only interested in the criteria values generated by the alternatives, and not in the alternatives themselves. We can therefore, without loss of information, identify an alternative x by its criteria values $[f_1(x), \ldots, f_n(x)]$ and forget any operational details involved in defining x. We denote the set of alternatives in n-dimensional criteria space as the set of points

$$Y = \{[f_1(x), f_2(x), \ldots, f_n(x)] \mid x \in X\}$$

Hence, each alternative in criteria space corresponds to at least one alternative in decision space. Two or more alternatives in decision space might be characterized by exactly the same criteria values and from this perspective be considered equally preferable though not identical. We can now restate the basic decision problem in criteria space as

$$\begin{aligned} &\max \quad F(y) \\ &\text{s.t.} \quad y \in Y \end{aligned}$$

The use of criteria space representations will ease our exposition considerably. More profoundly, though, it may be very useful in real world planning to focus attention on the **criteria alternatives** rather than the underlying **decision alternatives.** The decision alternatives may be very complex and may be characterized by a great many technical and economic details. Although seldomly explicitly presented in this perspective in the literature, the basic idea of multiple criteria methods can be interpreted as focusing attention on a few summary statistics represented by the criteria values $[f_1(x), \ldots, f_n(x)]$ rather than on the underlying decision alternatives.

At this point, the reader may feel that we have returned to the Rational Ideal Model to which we have devoted several pages of criticism. Indeed it might appear that we have simply made the additional assumption that only n properties $f_1(x), \ldots, f_n(x)$ of the alternatives are relevant to the decision maker instead of all the possible properties involved in a complete description x of a plan.

However, it was not the Rational Ideal Model as a mental framework which we criticized. Rather, what we rejected was naive planning based on the direct application of this model without consideration of the complexities introduced by multiple criteria as well as by incomplete information as to preferences and alternatives. We have already argued that a preference function can with advantage be assumed to be implicitly employed when making choices which are in harmony with our values. We hope to demonstrate that it is possible to cope with many of the complexities of multiple criteria within the broad conceptual framework of the Rational Ideal Model without having to accept its idealization of optimizing man.

4.3. Decentralized, Hidden Information

To define the relevant aspects of the **planning context** we will now assume that **information about the preference function F and the set of alternatives Y is decentralized and not immediately available.** More precisely, we will assume that one agent, the decision maker (**DM**) "knows" about F, while another agent, the analyst (**AN**) "knows" about Y. By this we do not mean that they have explicit expressions for F and Y, respectively. We simply mean that they are able to investigate F and Y, i.e. to answer certain questions about the preferences and the alternatives in criteria space.

To clarify, let us expand this characterization of the planning context.

The assumption of **two role-players**, a decision maker and an analyst, in charge of values and alternatives respectively, is mainly a terminological convenience which should not be taken too literally. In particular, the analyst may be anything from a computer, a production technician, an operational researcher to the decision maker himself. Similarly, the decision maker may be anything from the chairmman of the board who is only interested in receiving summary statistics and verbal orientation from top management, to an economist with considerable analytical talents and who actively participates in analyzing the problem at hand. So, the AN and the DM should simply be thought of as two "systems", the AN system producing information about the alternatives, and the DM system producing information about the values and preferences.

Although we allow substantial freedom in the interpretation of the AN and the DM roles, there are nevertheless some implicit assumptions hidden in this terminology. First, in those cases where the AN and the DM roles are performed by different people - which is an underlying assumption in much of what follows - the elimination of divergent interests and strategic behavior is quite a strong assumption. When those structuring the problem formulation and supplying information about the alternatives are themselves affected by the final choice, they may well feel inclined to manipulate the information supplied. So the analyst, who supplies the information as to the alternatives, represents the ideal of a civil **servant** who is loyal, objective, value-neutral and obedient, who does not try to influence the outcome but only to assist the decision maker to achieve his objectives - while the decision maker represents the ideal of a **masterful politician** who is only interested in basic values, while decisions are only considered to be means to achieving these ends and have no intrinsic value. This picture may not only be unrealistic, it may also be challenged on ethical grounds - and will be so later on in the book.

Secondly, and closely related to the above assumption, it is implicitly assumed that one may - at least abstractly - distinguish between objective alternatives and subjective values. This is a part of the Rational Ideal Model paradigm. This has previously been challenged when we considered bounded rationality and the concepts of satisficing behavior and aspiration levels. In addition, the whole conceptual framework for planning presented above highlights the contextual interdependency of preferences and alternatives.

The assumption about the analyst and the decision maker being able to undertake **certain unspecified investigations** of the set of alternatives and the preference function may seem much to loose in a definition[1]. What we want to emphasize here is simply that different multiple criteria planning approaches make different assumptions about the investigations and hereby about the DM's and the AN's capacities for production and processing of information. We want to encourage the reader to look for and care about these assumptions, which seldomly are explicit in the planning and MCDM literature. Is the DM asked to choose between only two alternatives at a time, for example, or is he asked to specify how much of one criterion he is willing to give up to obtain one unit of another criterion? Is the AN supposed to solve, say, linear programming problems during the search process, or is he supposed to employ more complex optimization or heuristic routines, and is he supposed to use interactive graphics, simulation, or spread-sheet analyses in his attempts to help the DM to obtain greater insight as to his preferences and as to the choice to be made? Clearly, these questions are important in delineating the burdens imposed on the DM and the

[1] Using the concepts of information systems from statistical decision theory, we could be more precise. Athough this could be interesting and point towards new research topics, it will not be attempted here since our main message would drown in technical notation.

AN, and hence the kind of information processing and analytical capacities each must be assumed to possess.

4.4. The Purpose of Multiple Criteria Planning

The notion of a basic decision problem within a context of decentralized and not-immediately-available information is an attempt to delineate the mental framework of multiple criteria planning. It is the world in which we will find ourselves for some time to come.

Within this broad mental framework we consider the **purpose of multiple criteria planning** to be the **design of whole investigation - communication - choice modes** which support a decision maker contemplating action within the context of decentralized and not-immediately-available information.

From a narrow, decision oriented point of view, multiple criteria planning should help him identify an optimal alternative y^* in the basic decision problem: max $F(y)$ s.t. $y \in Y$. However, reflection leads to another conclusion more in line with the train of thought of bounded rationality than that of the rational ideal model.

First of all, the "optimal solution" y^* is a rather transient, utopian concept. Our values and possibilities change with time as we plan and learn[2]. Therefore the very search process affects the position of y^*. It follows that if we instead set our sights on identifying an alternative $y^\#$ which is a "good" approximation of the transient y^* itself we are in reality describing the planning process in a far more meaningful way than provided by an ideal of optimization. From this point of view we continually aspire to approach a target which is forever elusive. Since planning is a decision-oriented process and not description-oriented, making a "best compromise choice" is primary to identifying a "best" solution and from this planning perspective, it is rational to attempt to identify $y^\#$ rather than the ephemeral y^*. The paradoxical conclusion is

[2] We have previously noted in chapter 1 that the time gap between decision and action may lead to adaptive behavior and to action which deviates from the optimal decision.

that trying to identify an optimal alternative may lead to far poorer decisions than trying to plan optimally and to seek a best compromise solution.

Secondly, and more concretely, multiple criteria planning deals with far more than choosing a most preferred alternative from Y. As discussed in chapter 2 we have neither a complete, comprehensive description of the set of alternatives nor of the decision maker's preferences.

Since neither F nor Y are givens, **investigations** are needed. And since also our knowledge of F and Y co-develops during the planning process, the perspective introduced above as to the relationship between $y^{\#}$ and y^{*} is also relevant here. It follows that Y and F can best be interpreted as ideals to be sought after rather than as truth to be uncovered.

This requires the **communication activity** in the planning process to be far more than just technical discussions between the DM and the AN. It requires both parties to carry on introspective monologues with themselves and interactive dialogues with each other as to both what they want and what possibilities they have.

Therefore, the **choice activity** is not simply an analytical task which can be left to an economist or operations researcher - or a computer program and a data base[3]. From this perspective, a choice is simply a temporary synthesis which occurs at a more-or-less definable instance during a planning process. It represents an explicit expression of what a DM has learned about his preferences and his possibilities. Planning is a continual process of decision making which does not start with the sudden existence of a "problem" and does not terminate with the sudden identification of a "solution"[4].

---

[3] We distinguish here between insignificant, repetitive choices and planning problems. It may be quite realistic to develop an automatic multiple criteria procedure for sorting defect return beer bottles from non-defects. This "decision" may be made by a brewery a million times a day and it would be nonsense here to speak of "whole investigation - communication - choice modes". Note however, that the design of such a sorting routine and its integration with the whole production process could represent a multiple criteria planning problem.

[4] We note that in this context the notion of "a continual process of decision making" does not only refer to the choice of a substantive alternative, but also to all the introspective, investigative and communicative activities surrounding the collection and processing of information, identification of criteria and alternative actions, model building, analysis and implementation. In other words, to the ongoing process of cognition, search and compromise which we participate in to create desirable future states of a system.

We conclude that what really matters in multiple criteria planning is our ability to determine whole investigation - communication - choice modes. The essence of the multiple criteria planning process is to design and constructively utilize such modes.

Our attempt to define the purpose of multiple criteria planning leads therefore to a new, meta-level multiple criteria problem of deciding which cost and benefit elements of the investigation - communication - choice modes to focus on. Thus, if one really wants to operationally define the multiple criteria planning problem in the spirit of multiple criteria analysis, it would probably run as follows: Consider the problem of choosing an alternative in the above setting of decentralized and not-immediately available information. Now, taking into account the different costs and benefits of supporting planning, what kind of investigation - communication - choice processes could we reasonably suggest? This is really the perspective we want the reader to have at this point. In chapter 10, this question will be taken up in far more detail.

4.5. Summary

We have tried to model - without being technical - some of the major characteristics of real-world planning contexts as identified in the previous sections. The properties focused on, i.e. incomplete a priori information about both the appropriate value system and the appropriate set of alternatives, were introduced within a context of decentralized and not-immediately-available information. A decision maker (DM) is able to investigate certain questions about the overall preference function (F), while an analyst (AN) is able to investigate certain questions about the set of alternatives (Y). This model is the mental framework to be employed in the sequel.

Also, we tried to delineate what it means to assist decision making in these kinds of contexts. We argued that it involves investigation, communication as well as choice activities. Also, all these activities have multiple effects. Hence, the very attempt to delineate the purposes of multiple criteria planning leads to just another multiple criteria problem at a meta-level. It follows that we cannot precisely define a multiple criteria problem without violating the whole idea of multiple criteria planning. We recommend that the reader keeps this in mind when studying the details of more concrete multiple criteria approaches in the following chapters.

4.6. Bibliographic Notes

There is no commonly accepted way to delineate the context and purpose of MCDM and therefore of multiple criteria planning as well. Indeed, most publications on MCDM are highly fuzzy on these fundamental questions - or else they completely ignore them and focus entirely on techniques, computer models and the like. Nevertheless, we have tried to be somewhat explicit in this chapter. We have drawn on some previous work in Bogetoft (1985a,85b,86) which was clearly inspired by the literature on multi-level planning based on mathematical decomposition theory, c.f. for example Burton and Obel (1984), Dirickx and Jennergren (1979), and Obel (1981).

Chapter 5

A TAXONOMY OF METHODS

In chapters 6 - 9 we describe a spectrum of multiple criteria planning modes, i.e. approaches to tackling the investigation - communication - choice activities arising from the process of planning with multiple criteria. That is, we discuss different ways in which a compromise solution to a multiple criteria planning problem may be sought. Our primary intention is to give a good idea of what the planning process may look like, with particular emphasis on the role played by the criteria which the decision maker chooses to represent his objectives, and on the alternatives he is to choose from in criteria space. For example, we consider how a decision maker might direct the search for promising alternatives, and how the analyst might make conjectures about the decision maker's wishes.

The specific results and models may often appear to be overly simplistic, naive or at least somewhat sterile. Together, however, they provide a useful intellectual framework for understanding and representing how a decision maker's intrapersonal value conflicts can be resolved. To set the stage for an overview of the existing methods, we now propose a taxonomy.

5.1. The Multiple Criteria Setting

Initially, let us recall the multiple criteria planning context discussed in chapter 4. We have as our conceptual model a basic decision problem as depicted to the left in figure 5.1 below. That is, we regard the decision maker's underlying problem as one of selecting an alternative y from the set of alternatives Y in criteria space so as to best achieve his objectives as reflected by the preference function, F(y). Things are complicated though by information being decentralized and not-immediately-available. Clearcut expressions of F and Y do not exist when the decision problem is formulated. As depicted to the right in figure 5.1, we imagine that one agent, the decision maker (DM), is able to investigate the preference function F, while another agent, the analyst (AN), is able to investigate the set of alternatives Y. We can look at the DM and the AN as being able to investigate, i.e. answer certain questions about, the contents of the black boxes containing F and Y, respectively.

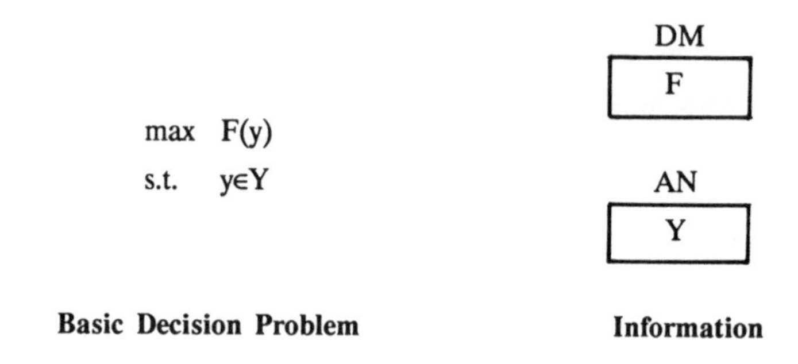

Figure 5.1. The Multiple Criteria Setting

Within this context of decentralized and not-immediately-available information, we do not know what F and Y are. Therefore we cannot start out attempting to choose an alternative as described in the basic decision model. Obviously we have to investigate the preference function F and the set of alternatives Y and integrate whatever we may learn. This requires communication, if the final choice of an alternative is to reflect an attunement of the wishes and possibilities delineated. In other words, to determine a preferred compromise solution we have to engage in **a planning process involving investigation, communication and choice activities.**

5.2. The Taxonomy

An incredible number of MCDM techniques has been proposed by now. To get an overview of these techniques as well as to structure our perception of intrapersonal planning, we now develop a categorization scheme based on the overall organization of the investigation - communication - choice activities characterizing multiple criteria planning. This taxonomy will structure the presentation in the five following chapters; its relevance will be considered in some detail in section 5.7.

A basic design issue when organizing the interaction between the DM and the AN involved in multiple criteria planning is

* **When to investigate F and Y**

At least two possible organizations of the timing may be distinguished. One is a linear or **phased** arrangement, where the investigations of F and Y are performed in two distinct phases. In the first phase, and largely detached from the concrete set of alternatives, an estimate or approximate representation of F, referred to as F#, is established. In the next phase we establish those aspects of Y that are relevant in view of the concrete F# from the first phase. Or vice versa.

The second possible arrangement is a cyclic or **iterative** approach. It consists of a sequence of alternating investigations of F and Y such that one constantly examines those details of F that are relevant in view of the information established so far about Y and vice versa.

Another basic design issue when organizing the interaction between the DM and the AN is

* **Who directs the search**

This is really a set of questions about who directs the investigations, accumulates the information and makes the final choice proposal. Although some delegation of these tasks may be envisaged, it simplifies the presentation immensely to let one agent be responsible for all these tasks. Furthermore, such an organization of the responsibility is quite natural since it is difficult to direct the investigations intelligently without keeping track of whatever has been learned so far, and it is necessary to merge the F and Y information generated in order to make the final choice. Two obvious arrangements are the **DM-directed** approach where the DM is in charge of all the tasks above, and the **AN-directed** approach where the AN is in charge of these tasks.

Certainly, other arrangements are possible. A third "mediator" could for example be introduced or a task-force composed of the DM and the AN could be in charge. It turns out, however, that to structure the multiple criteria planning process and to categorize the existing MCDM techniques, the two pure arrangements are sufficient.

Using the above design questions, we get a taxonomy distinguishing four overall organizations, or modes, of the the DM-AN interaction in multiple criteria planning. This taxonomy is depicted in figure 5.2.

Timing of investigation / Entity in charge	DM directed	AN directed
Phased	Prior articulation of alternatives DM ↑ ↑ ↑ ↑ ↑ AN	Prior articulation of preferences DM ↓ ↓ ↓ ↓ ↓ AN
Iterative	Progressive articulation of alternatives DM question↓ ↑answer AN	Progressive articulation of preferences DM answer↓ ↑question AN

Figure 5.2. A Taxonomy of Multiple Criteria Planning Modes

Before we discuss the appropriateness of this taxonomy some further clarification of the different organizations will be helpful.

5.3. Prior Articulation of Alternatives

One possible organization of the DM-AN interaction involves the prior articulation of alternatives. In the first phase, the AN undertakes rather extensive investigations of the set of feasible alternatives, Y, and he submits a set of proposals, say **Y#**, to the DM. In the next phase, the DM inspects the set of proposals, clarifies his preferences and makes a choice. This contemplative phase is carried out "inside" the decision maker. Specific MCDM techniques which can be classified as belonging to this organization do not describe how this may be done. The overall idea, though, is that the set of concrete alternatives may help the DM to focus his attention and sharpen his ideas about what he really wants.

Such a structuring of planning is often encountered in practice in hierarchical organizations. While routine tasks in most enterprises are handled by rules, programs and tradition, exceptions are usually handled by hierarchical referral. This involves a lower level submitting a limited number of alternative proposals to a higher level. This higher level has the authority to formulate organizational goals or at least is in a better position to judge how the different alternatives satisfy overall goals and how they may affect other parts of the organization. This approach to structuring decision making is also met in the context of public planning where civil servants perform analyses for politicians. In such contexts a typical procedure is: 1) for the civil servants - the AN - to generate a few alternative plans based upon some general instructions and expressions of preferences from the political leadership - the DM, and 2) for the politicians to simply choose between the alternative plans and to present the choice in the form of rules, guidelines or legislative proposals prepared by the AN.

5.4. Prior Articulation of Preferences

Another multiple criteria planning mode is characterized by the prior articulation of preferences. The aim of the first phase is to construct a model, say F*, of the DM's preferences, F. The AN accomplishes this by studying the DM's behavior in previous or, most notably, fictive choice contexts or by otherwise interrogating the DM or guiding his self-examination. In the next phase the AN couples this description F* of the DM's preferences with the actual set of feasible alternatives Y in an attempt to pick out the most preferred alternative or at least a reduced set from which the final choice will be made by the decision maker. In this way, the model represents a surrogate DM and planning is pretty much conceived of as in the rational ideal model; the analyst is now in charge and decision making, i.e. the determination of a most preferred alternative, is reduced to optimization. Note however that even in this model considerable time and effort are devoted by both the AN and the DM to the investigation and modelling of the DM's preferences.

If we take a liberal interpretation of this planning mode it should be clear that it is useful and encountered in many and quite distinct practical contexts. Consider again an organization where predictable routine tasks are governed by rules and programs while exceptions are handled by hierarchical referral. One area of application concerns referrals which are truly exceptional, one-shot, complicated issues to be resolved. This might well require the upper level to rethink its own rules and programs, or indeed the whole organization to clarify its objectives and its willingness to make trade-offs between them. To structure these activities, the approaches in this mode may be useful. However, the approaches may also be interesting for organizations where "exceptions" start becoming routine. To avoid overloading the organization's communication channels and information processing capacity, this may call for the upper level to supplement the rules and programs applied at the lower level by supplying it with additional information as to its preferences. Such an extension of the lower level's knowledge about the preferences of the higher level leads to improved screening and less referral. Finally, these approaches may also pave the way for decentralized planning and decision making. When the decentral planners have operational information on the preferences of decision makers higher up in the hieracrchy, they are better able to integrate their own preferences with those of the organization.[1]

5.5. Progressive Articulation of Alternatives

A third organization of the DM-AN interaction is based on the progressive articulation of alternatives. This is an iterative arrangement directed by the DM. In each round, the DM asks the AN about the set of alternatives, the AN answers and the DM evaluates the answer. He then decides either to continue the search by posing

[1] We will expand upon this perspective in chapter 11 where we question whether, and under which conditions, organizations meaningfully can be considered as having values, objectives and preferences.

new questions or to stop the search and choose one of the alternatives identified so far.

In specific MCDM techniques which can be classified as belonging to this mode, the AN's task is usually well defined. He simply has to answer the questions posed by the DM. Although well defined, it may of course be an extremely difficult task, particularly when the set of alternatives is complex or when identifying alternatives calls for innovative and creative activities. The DM's task however, is much less well defined. He has to investigate his preferences, the general idea being that it helps him to do so if he is faced with real alternatives. He has to accumulate information, and he has to direct the search for better, i.e. more preferred, alternatives by specifying desirable improvement of previous proposals and asking the AN to see if these wishes can be fulfilled. How all of this is carried out is usually left entirely to the decision maker to figure out, i.e. it is not an explicit part of existing models.

It should be obvious that a lot of actual planning proceeds along these lines. In a hierarchical organization, planning can be considered as involving several rounds, where the higher level iteratively asks the lower level to propose uses of a given budget or to propose activities in accord with some tentative priorities. Either way, the higher level seeks information about the lower level alternatives. It may of course involve several rounds of communication and modifications of the tentative plans to develop even a consistent overall plan, where for example the procurement department purchases at least what the production department needs in order to produce at least what the sales department has promised to deliver. Even more iterative adaption may be needed to determine profit maximizing activity levels or, perhaps most ambitiously, a good compromise between the multiple conflicting objectives of the organization.

5.6. Progressive Articulation of Preferences

Finally, a fourth possible organization of the DM-AN interaction involves the progressive articulation of preferences. Again, this is an iterative approach. However, this time the AN is in charge. In each round, he poses a question to the DM about his preferences and the DM answers. If the AN now knows sufficiently about the

DM's preferences to make a choice from the concrete set of alternatives, he proposes a final choice. Otherwise, the questioning continues.

The AN's task is usually well defined in methods which can be classified as belonging to this organization of the DM-AN interaction, i.e. they describe how he should define the questions, when to stop, and how to make the final proposal. Also, the DM's task is well defined as he simply has to answer the questions posed to him. In reality, answering may of course be difficult and painful by requiring an introspective journey into the unexplored territory of his basic values. Still, compared to the other interactive organization - the progressive articulation of alternatives - the DM performs a much more well-structured activity. He does not have to direct the AN and systematically accumulate information about the actual alternatives.

It should be noted that the first phase of the prior articulation of preferences approach may also involve iterative questioning of the DM. However, as will be seen, that mode employs simplified, fictitious alternatives in connection with this questioning, while the present mode involves progressive determination of preferences in the light of concrete, feasible alternatives.

From the point of view of a traditional, formal depiction of power and authority in a hierarchical organization, such a planning mode would be unacceptable. It gives lower level employees - the AN - the duties of questioning higher level employees - the DM - as well as the power to pick, or at least propose, the final alternative. If, however, we interpret the mode more liberally and consider the organization's informal procedures as well, it is most relevant. During repeated hierarchical referrals, it is likely that the lower level builds up a picture of the DM's preference which may be useful in its investigation and design activities. Furthermore, during a budgetting process, it is likely that the lower level may also pose questions about the higher level's intentions which provide it with information relevant for modelling the higher level's preference structure. Finally, when the set of opportunities is complex, as in the design of a prototype teapot, or in the development of a governmental policy, it is often the case that the AN makes some tentative proposals which the DM comments on. In this manner the AN iteratively collects information useful for modelling the DM's preferences. It is suggested that this is a general, although informal, characteristic of planning in larger organizations and typifies much of the interaction between leading civil servants and their political counterparts.

5.7. Relevance of The Taxonomy

The usefulness of any taxonomy depends on its purpose. Since we advocate multiple perspectives on planning in general and on investigation - communication - choice procedures in particular, the problem of developing a classification scheme for multiple criteria planning becomes a multiple criteria problem on its own. Rather than be formal here - and hence end up in a problem of infinite regress - let us be pragmatic and simply emphasize that we have proposed the above taxonomy because it seems interesting and constructive from several perspectives.

From a **pedagogical point of view,** it has its own logic when one considers the basic decision problem within a context of decentralized and not-immediately-available information. Also, it is possible to categorize existing MCDM techniques within this taxonomy. Furthermore, the classification underlines some of the basic ideas and themes in multiple criteria planning.

One such theme concerns the **possibility of distinguishing between values and alternatives** in the first place. Although the idea of objective alternatives and subjective values is basic to the rational ideal model, we have strongly challenged this view. A basic idea in the bounded rationality literature is that the desires people have - or at least express - are often heavily influenced by what they believe they may actually accomplish. With this in mind, it is worth noting that the phased arrangements seem to keep a sharp distinction between values and alternatives while the iterative arrangements in principle allow desires to be dynamically influenced by prevailing possibilities and vice versa.

Another theme concerns the idea of **"letting the DM back in"**. In the DM-directed arrangements the decision maker has certainly regained his central place in planning. Not only is the importance of his preferences explicitly recognized. He is also placed in charge of the search process. This implies for example that non-technical aspects concerning implementation, employee-motivation, ethical considerations, and the organizational culture may influence the process as he deems appropriate. So the DM-directed approach is definitely a break with the traditional rational (OR) approach to planning as a matter to mainly be undertaken by experts. Perhaps then the DM-directed arrangements may produce "better" decisions that are more easily implemented. On the other hand, it also puts additional burdens on the DM since it may be difficult and time-consuming to succesfully direct the whole investigation, communication, and choice process. From this prespective, the "letting the DM back in" theme has serious implications for the organization as well as for management's self-conception and the way it allocates its time and energy. These themes are far too extensive to be treated in depth here, although they will under various guises appear many times in the sequel.

Another way the taxonomy supports the "letting the DM back in" theme is by highlighting the importance of his wishes under the AN-directed arrangements. Here, we explicitly model and incorporate the DM's prefences, focusing on their multiple criteria aspects. So, also the AN-directed arrangements represent an improvment on the traditional optimizing or economic man approaches, because some single ad hoc criterion is replaced with a multiple criteria model of the DM's preferences.

Finally, from a **contextual point of view**, we believe the classification to be relevant in the sense that: a) the different costs and benefits of the planning process significantly depend on the approach which is chosen, and b) the relative importance of these cost and benefits depends on the planning context. Together, these factors provide a contextual basis for choosing between planning modes. For example, in a specific environment where the DM has very limited time to participate in the planning process, it may be advantageous to employ an AN-directed approach. Alternatively, if the issues at stake involve delicate or confidential value judgements, a DM-directed arrangement may be most favorable. The brief illustrative discussions of the DM's and the AN's duties in the different modes and of planning problems in hierarchical organizations emphasized such interdependencies between context and mode. We will expand on these ideas in chapter 10 where we discuss how to **choose** between different multiple criteria planning modes depending on the context.

Let us end by emphasizing once again that our taxonomy cannot be said to be "optimal" or "given" although we feel it to be a direct, logical extension of the presentations so far. The choice of a multiple criteria taxonomy is a higher order multiple criteria planning problem with no optimal solution.

We have sketched some potential virtues of our taxonomy above. It is appropriate to point out some of its limitations and hidden assumptions as well.

The taxonomy is methodologically rather than contextually oriented. This is in accordance with our belief that it is possible and meaningful to discuss planning as a general, intellectual activity without always having to focus on a specific planning context. On the other hand, it is clear that valid recommendations as to the choice of mode can only be achieved by considering an actual problem in an actual organization. This is as mentioned repeatedly our theme in chapter 10.

Although the taxonomy is not contextually oriented, we cannot claim that it is context independent. It is clearly structured around our perception of real world planning problems as problems involving decentralized and hidden information about wishes and possibilities. Although we have attempted to justify this perception and our representation of it in terms of the DM-AN dichotomy, it may of course be that these characteristics are not the most salient ones in some contexts. Some times, the real decision maker is the person in charge of investigations of both the preferences and possibilities. In principle, this is accommodated in our set up by letting the "DM" and the "AN" be two interacting subsystems of the real decision maker. Still, in such cases our approach offers but little support for how, for example, an external planner could assist in this case. Our presentation throughout implicitly assumes that the communication activities referred to are carried out by an AN (e.g. an operations researcher and/or a computer program) that is distinct from a DM.

As a matter of fact, we did consider structuring the presentation around contextual taxonomies such as:

1) A taxonomy based upon the type of planning problem. For example: a) strategic, tactical or operative, b) one-shot or repetitive, and c) private or public.

2) A taxonomy based upon the type of decision maker. For example: idealistic, participative, bureaucratic, manipulative, charismatic, tycoonic or autocratic.

3) A taxonomy based upon the type of conflict. For example: intra-personal, inter-personal or systemic conflicts.

Thus, for example, we could have chosen to discuss a series of more context specific problems, e.g. how a bureaucrat should handle a one-shot, strategic multiple criteria planning problem involving inter-personal conflicts. We think that studies along these lines could potentially be very valuable, but that this would not be a very efficient or pedagogical way to present our main ideas. We shall, however, return to many of these contextual characteristics as we proceed, especially in chapters 10 and 11.

5.8. Summary

Since we want to accomplish many different things when we plan, the choice of a multiple criteria decision mode is itself a multiple criteria problem. Similarly, since different objectives of planning may call for different groupings of the possible approaches, the development of a useful taxonomy may also be considered to be a multiple criteria problem. By "useful" we mean that the taxonomy improves our ability to structure and to communicate as to planning approaches.

With this in mind, we proposed a specific taxonomy that **distinguishes between phased and iterative arrangements.** This dichotomy is pertinent since it distinguishes the kind of support required and the information available when investigating the preferences and alternatives. Additionally, this temporal dichotomy emphasizes to what extent the definition of preferences and alternatives are co-dependent and to what extent investigation and communication are required to define the preferences and alternatives.

This in turn leads to another operationally significant distinction; the taxonomy **distinguishes between DM-directed and AN directed procedures**. This dichotomy is important from the points of view of who directs the investigations, who accumulates information, who makes the final proposal and to which degree "soft", non-modelled considerations enter the planning process.

Using these two classification principles, we identified four different modes:

* Prior articulation of alternatives
  - the phased, DM-directed mode

* Prior articulation of preferences
  - the phased, AN-directed mode

* Progressive articulation of alternatives
  - the iterative, DM-directed mode, and

* Progressive articulation of preferences
  - the iterative, AN-directed mode.

We now turn to a more concrete description of the different multiple criteria planning modes. We start out by describing the phased arrangements. Not only are they approaches to planning in their own right. The basic models and results considered also contribute to the foundation on which the iterative arrangements rest.

5.9. Bibliographic Notes

The taxonomy presented here is a specialization of a more general classification of problems with decentralized information developed in Bogetoft(1985). In MCDM, a classification based solely on the timing of the elicited value information has sometimes been used, c.f. e.g. Evans(1984) and Hwang & Masud(1979). We introduced the "Who is in charge" perspective and integrated it with the "when" perspective. This structuring of the taxonomy is more in line with the planning framework introduced in chapter 4 based on investigation - communication - choice processes, then with the narrower decision making perspective characterizing tradtional MCDM. In the more technique-oriented literature, alternative distinctions are made based upon such factors as whether the alogrithm employed presumes discrete or continuous problem formulations, linear or non-linear optimization routines etc. However, as underlined in the introduction where we stated our intention of focusing upon the main ideas and insights as to planning with multiple criteria, since such means of classifying modes is algorithmically rather than insight-oriented, we will desist from further comment here. We refer to Steuer(1986) for an in-depth treatment of such computational aspects and note that to the best of our knowledge, no broadly accepted taxonomy exists based upon these technical aspects. An interesting description of planning and decision making in hierarchical organizations can be found in Arrow(1974). An attempt to develop a multiple criteria approach to the problem of selecting a multiple criteria method depending on the characteristics of the problem and the organizational context is given in Bogetoft(1990) and Bogetoft and Pruzan(1990) and is also discussed in chapter 10 of the present book. Finally, in a broader context, our approach has much in common with the literature on "multiple perspectives", where planning problems are viewed from technical, personal and organizational perspectives. This approach has been developed during the past decade, notably by Linstone(1984), see also Linstone(1989) for a brief survey.

Chapter 6

PRIOR ARTICULATION OF ALTERNATIVES

We will now structure an organization of the multiple criteria planning process based on the prior articulation of alternatives. This is a phased, DM-directive planning mode. In the first phase the AN investigates the set of feasible alternatives and submits a set of proposals to the DM. In the next phase, the DM inspects the list of proposals, sharpens his opinions about his wishes, and makes a choice.

In terms of theory, the main question during the investigation phase is how the AN can find a relevant set of alternatives to present to the DM. The guiding principle is usually that of efficiency. First we define the concept and discuss its relevance. Then we turn to different ways of generating and characterizing efficient alternatives; we focus on methods with simple economic and managerial interpretations. As noted previously, these methods do not describe more precisely how the second phase should be undertaken. It is supposed to be carried out "inside" the decision maker. We shall return to this issue more thoroughly in the subsequent chapters. For now, the general idea is simply that by presenting the decision maker with a reduced set of concrete, promising alternatives - as determined for example via a screening based on the efficiency concept - the analyst may help him to sharpen his idea of what he really wants.

We emphasize that although we will be focusing upon the more analytical multiple criteria aspects, we will continually do so within the investigation - communication - choice framework for planning. This holds true not only for the present chapter but for chapters 7 - 9 as well, all of which deal with the four approaches to multiple criteria planning delineated in the discussion on taxonomy in chapter 5.

6.1. Efficiency

Consider the following context. A set of feasible decisions, X, has been identified. The DM does not know about X, but the AN does. By this we mean that the AN is able to explore X, i.e. he is able to answer questions about the alternatives. In practice, this knowledge may range from having a neatly typed list of alternatives with detailed technical and economic descriptions to a mathematical formulation of X in terms of equations and inequalities.

Additionally, the AN has - presumably after some initial consultations with the DM as to his objectives - established a list of n attributes of the alternatives that the DM cares about. These are described by n criteria $f_i:X\rightarrow \mathfrak{R}$, $i=1, \ldots ,n$ which are assumed to measure the different attributes in such a way that more is preferred to less. We will return to this "more is better than less" assumption in section 6.2 while the problem of establishing such sets of criteria is discussed in chapter 7.

Now, given the set of alternative actions X and the criteria $f_1, \ldots ,f_n$ of relevance to the DM, the problem is: which proposals should the AN submit to the DM. The key concept here is that of efficiency or, synonymously, non-dominance. The single principle generally employed to delimit the set of relevant alternatives is that the AN should only submit proposals based on efficient alternatives. In cases where the number of efficient alternatives is large, he may choose to present a well-chosen subset of the efficient alternatives. We will see in section 6.2 that this principle can be deceptive and can have some rather significant flaws.

Definition 1

An alternative $x\in X$ is dominated by an alternative $x'\in X$ if and only if x' improves at least one criterion, say j, without worsening any of the others, i.e.

$$f_j(x')>f_j(x) \text{ for some } j$$
$$f_i(x')\geq f_i(x) \quad i=1, \ldots ,n$$

An alternative $x\in X$ is **efficient,** or, equivalently, **non-dominated,** if and only if it cannot be dominated by another alternative $x'\in X$. o

We denote the set of efficient alternatives

$$X_E = \{x \in X \mid x \text{ efficient}\}$$

and the representation of these alternatives in criteria space

$$Y_E = \{(f_1(x), \ldots, f_n(x)) \mid x \text{ efficient}\}$$

Figure 6.1 illustrates the efficient alternatives in criteria space in both a "discrete" and a "continuous" example.[1] In the discrete case, A is dominated by B, since B improves f_1 and keeps f_2 constant, and E is dominated - in fact strictly dominated - by C, since C gives higher values of both f_1 and f_2 than E does. On the other hand, neither B, C nor D are dominated, as there are no feasible alternatives to the northeast of these points. So B, C and D are all efficient.

In the continuous case, the set of efficient alternatives consists of all the points on the heavily shaded part of the perimeter of Y.

We do not claim that efficiency is in general something good nor that it makes the DM happy. Efficiency is not a sufficient condition for optimizing; in fact, it is in general not even necessary. To illustrate, consider figure 6.1(a) and assume that the DM puts all his heart in f_2. Then, he would rank the five alternatives as $A \approx^* B >^* C >^* E >^* D$ where the symbol "$\approx^*$" indicates preference indifference, i.e. it is equivalent to the statement "equally as good as". We see that the inefficient alternative A beats the efficient C and D. Also, E is inefficient and still it beats D. So efficiency is not enough - in fact, the worst alternative from the DM's persepective, D, is efficient. This is important to stress since efficiency is often confused with something desirable in its own right.

---

[1] Instead of providing precise mathematical representations of these two terms at this point, we will simply use "discrete" to characterize the case where there are a countable number of alternatives. By "continuous" we refer here to those cases which are not discrete.

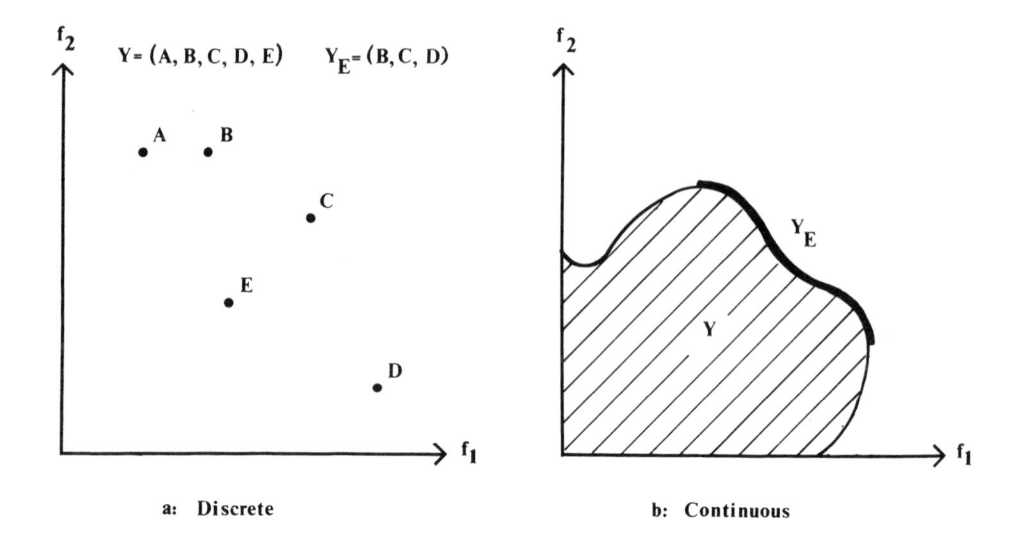

Figure 6.1 Feasible and Efficient Alternatives

Consider for example planning in the hospital sector. Here, establishing clear objectives involves delicate ethical issues. Therefore, it is tempting to focus entirely on the efficient use of given resources as a technical - surrogate - means of avoiding the difficult - but necessary - discussions as to basic values and preferences. This is definitely not the kind of use of the efficiency concept which we advocate. Filtering alternatives with efficiency is just intended to be a preliminary step that may aid the essential activity - that of helping the DM to choose in accord with his preferences.

Efficiency is just intended as a **filtering device**. It provides a natural guide as to which proposals to make to the DM.

First of all, it seems **safe to ignore inefficient, i.e. dominated alternatives.** The DM who prefers more to less will, in principle, always be at least as happy choosing an alternative which dominates other alternatives as choosing any of the alternatives dominated by it. So, in this case, there is no need to include dominated alternatives in the set of proposals to the DM.

Secondly, it is **impossible to exclude any of the efficient alternatives a priori**. For any given efficient alternative it is conceivable that exactly this alternative represents the combination of attributes which the DM likes best among all feasible combinations. In figure 6.1(a), for example, we cannot exclude B a priori, since it is conceivable that the AN puts almost all his interest in f_2. Similarly, D cannot be excluded, since the DM might primarily be interested in f_1, and C cannot be excluded, since the DM may be almost equally interested in f_1 and f_2.

Summarizing, X_E or its equivalent in value-space, Y_E, seems to be the **smallest, sufficient set of alternatives** to consider. This intuition is made precise in Theorem 1 below, where the description of a preference function as "weakly increasing" means that if the value of a criterion increases, then the value of this function either increases or remains unchanged. A proof of the theorem is provided in appendix 1.

Theorem 1

Imagine a DM who has an implicit preference function F: $\Re^n \rightarrow \Re$ which is some weakly increasing function, i.e. he weakly prefers more to less of all the n attributes $y_1, \ldots, y_n$. Ideally, therefore, his most preferred choice could be identified by solving the basic decision problem

$$(P) \qquad \max_y \; F(y) \qquad \text{s.t.} \quad y \in Y$$

i.e. by choosing the alternative in criteria space Y giving the highest value of F(y). Now,

(i) For any solution y to (P) there exists an efficient alternative $y' \in Y_E$ which is at least equally good

(ii) For any efficient alternative $y' \in Y_E$ there exists a preference function F such that y' is the unique solution to (P). o

According to theorem 1, part (i), inefficient alternatives can be ignored a priori, since the DM is always at least as well off choosing among the efficient alternatives. On the other hand, by part (ii), no efficient alternative can be ignored a priori, as it may turn out to be the DM's single most preferred alternative. This justifies - at least in a limited sense - the idea of submitting all efficient and nothing but the efficient alternatives to the DM in the present planning mode.

6.2. Questioning the Relevance of Efficiency

Although convincing at first sight, the above reasoning is nevertheless amenable to some serious criticism. This necessitate two qualifying or at least clarifying remarks.

First, should one really present all the - perhaps huge number of - efficient alternatives to the DM? According to the above reasoning it is necessary to do so in order to avoid the possible cost of forgone opportunities, since each and every efficient alternative may turn out to be the single most preferred one.

On the other hand, it is obvious that this may be a demanding task. In simple cases like figure 6(a) where we have only few efficient alternatives it should be easy to perform. However, when the set of efficient alternatives becomes larger and the number of criteria exceeds two or three, and hereby makes it impossible to use simple graphical representations, it soon becomes a major task, even for the discrete case, for the AN to generate and communicate all efficient alternatives and for the DM to comprehend, evaluate and choose among them. And in the continuous case, considerable communicative effort and talent may be required if **all** the efficient alternatives are to be presented to the DM in such a form that he can comprehend, evaluate and choose among them. Most likely, the AN will have to perform some - more or less arbitrary - selection among the infinite number of efficient alternatives so that a manageable number are presented to the DM.

Therefore, when we take into account the effort involved in generating, communicating and comprehending alternatives, the idea of submitting all efficient alternatives becomes less convincing. Of course, there are many other costs and benefits involved in the planning process than those mentioned above. For example, by introducing the benefits accruing from learning we might again be pulled in the direction of full disclosure. Similarly, if the potential opportunity costs of a final plan in terms of forgone opportunities are large compared to the costs of investigation, communication and comprehension in the planning process, full disclosure of the efficient alternative may be favourable. And vice versa.

Still, it seems reasonable to conclude that **prior articulation of alternatives is most attractive when the set of alternatives is small and easily represented.** Therefore, in many cases, we cannot expect to present all the efficient alternatives to the DM. Rather, a hopefully **representative subset of the efficient alternatives might be submitted.**

In the sequel, we will encounter several ways to alleviate the problems arising from the investigation, communication and comprehension of a "large" set of efficient alternatives. At this point let us simply note that the presentation of alternatives in criteria space Y_E as opposed to a perhaps far more complex decision space X_E will reduce the DM's burdens considerably. Also, a set of "representative" alternatives supplemented by information about the opportunities associated with the "neighbors" to these alternatives may be a useful substitute for complete disclosure. Finally, we might of course switch to a different planning mode, such as for example "progressive articulation of alternatives" in which the DM is sequentially presented with only a subset of the efficient alternatives .

Secondly, is it really safe to ignore inefficient alternatives? According to the above reasoning it is, since a DM would be equally well off choosing simply from the set of efficient alternatives instead of choosing from the whole set of alternatives. This reasoning should not go unchallenged.

Several factors will be important with respect to this question. We commence by considering the assumption underlying theorem 1 that the individual criteria each have the "more is better than less" property such that the implicit preference function F is an increasing function. This "more is better than less" assumption implicitly underlies almost all the literature on MCDM, and in particular, the concept of efficiency, which dominates most of this literature. As discussed in section 3.1, the assumption is rather general. It does not exclude ordinal properties, nor does it exclude cases where "less is better than more" or cases where a particular criterion value is sought. But simply assuming that "more is better than less" also implies that our preferences with respect to any one criteria can be evaluated independently of the values of the other criteria. This may be quite a reasonable assumption in many cases. For example, most would agree that a house which is most beautiful, has the best location, requires the least upkeep, has the lowest purchase price, has the best number of rooms, etc. would most likely also be the "best" house to purchase. However, as was exemplified in the discussion of "the perfect woman" in section 3.1, one can also meet cases where we may not be able to presume that if each of the criteria values characterizing one alternative is better than the corresponding criteria values characterizing another alternative, then the first alternative is better than the second.

Therefore, if the "more is better than less" assumption with respect to the individual criteria is violated, the concept of efficiency loses its discriminatory power. In such cases, a DM's preference for one alternative over another can only be determined by comparing the vectors of criteria values as wholes, which roughly corresponds to the saying **"the whole is more than the sum of its parts"**. In such cases, there may be no analytically derivable filters which can differentiate between more attractive and less attractive alternatives. Thus, even though the assumption appears to be reasonable in most practical planning problems, it will be important to recall that it is a necessary condition for Theorem 1 to hold, and therefore for our being able to ignore dominated alternatives. If this condition does not hold, then there may be opportunity costs associated with disregarding dominated alternatives.

In addition to the "more is better than less" assumption, another fundamental - and implicit - assumption underlies the assertion that it is safe to ignore inefficient alternatives. This is the assumption that all relevant criteria have been identified. In case of **omitted criteria,** inefficient alternatives can certainly not be eliminated a priori. For example, if just two criteria were thought to be relevant, and if there only are two feasible alternative actions under consideration, A and B, with corresponding criteria values A:(1.2, 30), B:(1.1, 28), then it would appear that B is strictly dominated and that therefore action A should be chosen. If, however, there were in fact three relevant criteria and the corresponding criteria values are A:(1.2, 30, 14), B:(1.1, 28, 56) then neither of the two alternative actions dominates the other, and B may in fact be the solution preferred by the DM.

Let us therefore consider this condition of not omitting relevant criteria in greater depth. We have previously discussed the role of criteria and emphasized that they often are surrogate measures for the DM's underlying organizational and personal values. It is our experience that decision makers become confused when they realize that their gut feelings as to the desirability of some action are in apparent discord with the values of the criteria they choose to characterize the alternatives. This can be due to the fact that the set of criteria does not adequately represent all the DM's objectives and thereby are not sufficient to measure the degree to which his values are fulfilled. A great many criteria may be required to even approximately represent our objectives, making a complete description inoperational. Even more problematical, it may simply be impossible to define appropriate measures, e.g. as regards aesthetic, existential or ethical considerations; we are not used to expressing ourselves and measuring such matters as beauty, quality of life, sincerity and power. In all such cases, employing the concept of efficiency to filter the set of alternatives may prohibit the DM from selecting a preferred alternative since it may have been filtered away. Thus, if relevant criteria are omitted, there are potential opportunity costs associated with assuming that it is safe to ignore dominated alternatives.

Before proceeding to the consideration of a third and final argument why it may not be safe to ignore inefficient alternatives, let us note that there may be a close relationship between the reasonableness of the "more is better than less" assumption and the assumption that all relevant criteria have been included. In some cases where the "more is better than less" assumption appears to be unreasonable, we may be able to justify the assumption by introducing additional criteria to supplement the original set.

For example, in selecting between applicants for a job, let us suppose that a DM has decided to place primary emphasis on the applicants' scores on a series of specially designed tests and to personally interview only those applicants whose vectors of score tests are efficient. Here it would at first glance appear reasonable to accept the assumption that "more is better than less". Nevertheless, the DM may have his doubts about this filtering process since he has experienced that choosing employees from the set of efficient applicants often has led to bad results. An investigation leads to the conclusion that applicants who are dominated given the existing criteria but who nevertheless have both reasonable test scores **and** are not extremely good in any particular field, may be more proficient and dependable workers than efficient applicants who also have exceptional scores on one or more of the tests. He may then choose to supplement the vector of test scores by another criterion which measures the equity of scores, e.g. as measured by the inverse of the standard deviation of the scores. In this case, the "more is better than less" assumption may now be fulfilled by taking into account an omitted criterion and all the attractive workers are now to be found amongst the efficient set[2]. Note however, that we cannot in general expect to be able to guarantee the applicability of theorem 1 in this manner. It is for example extremely difficult to conceive of such an approach working in the case of the "create the perfect woman" project.

Finally, we will consider a situation in which it is not really safe to ignore dominated alternatives even though no criteria have been omitted. This is the situation where a DM is considering the choice of not just one but possibly two or more alternatives. This may for example be the situation in the case where one or more new employees is to be hired. Suppose that the management of a firm advertises after a new salesman and that applicants are to send in data corresponding to a series of criteria (reflecting age, experience, style etc.) and that all the "ineffecient" applicants are rejected before inviting the efficient applicants to an interview. Suppose too, that during the interviewing process it is decided to hire two new salesmen. In this case, the elimination of the "inefficient" applicants may result in an opportunity loss; a potentially attractive applicant e.g., the second best, may have been eliminated during the first, technical screening. This candidate could have been dominated by the most attractive candidate for employment, but if the best candidate were hired and thereby removed from the set of feasible alternatives, then the second best candidate would then become efficient, i.e. a member of the nondominated set. Another such case

---

[2] A related example where "the more is better than less" assumption may not appear to be reasonable, but may be so after introducing a new criterion, concerns situations where several persons have to agree on a choice. In such cases it is not evident that only the socalled Pareto-efficient alternatives, i.e. those in which no individual can be better off without another being worse off, should be considered. It is not unlikely that agreement can only be reached on alternatives that also make the individuals rather equally well off.

could be found in the area of investment decisions, for example when an individual is to purchase one or more stocks from a list of stocks.

To illustrate this graphically, consider again figure 6.1(a) and assume that there is an alternative, C', which lies slightly to the southwest of C and therefore is dominated by C. Assume too, that C is the DM's most preferred compromise solution. If the DM decides to select two alternatives, and if the dominated solutions have been filtered away before the set of "relevant" solutions is presented to the DM, then he will not be able to choose C', as he will not be aware of its existence. And he might greatly prefer C' to say B or D. Note too, that C' becomes efficient once C is chosen. We note that this criticism can be considered as redefining the "rules of the game". The efficiency concept may again be useful if we define the set of alternatives as the set of pairs of the original alternatives. Our point is however, that during a given planning process, the DM may more or less spontaneously decide to chose two - or more - alternatives.

The **moral** is: The principle that inefficient solutions may be ignored implicitly presumes a) that the DM's preferences can be measured via a set of "independent" criteria, b) that all the relevant criteria have been identified, and c) that only one choice is to be made from the set of alternatives. Determining whether these conditions are fulfilled in a particular case may be difficult and place considerable demands on the time and energy of both the DM and the AN. We note that the MCDM literature more or less blindly adheres to the notion of efficiency and essentially ignores these matters.

6.3. Generating Efficient Alternatives

Now, having defined efficiency, argued its relevance, and clarified its proper application, let us turn to **different ways of generating and characterizing efficient alternatives.** Numerous approaches are available. Here, we restrict attention to approaches with simple economic and conceptual interpretations in terms of **budgets, prices, and targets.** The motivations for considering various approaches are as follows:

First, from a computational perspective, the approaches provide different ways of generating the efficient alternatives.

Secondly, and more generally, they provide an intellectual framework which is useful when trying to understand and propose alternative strategies for searching for good opportunities.

Thirdly, from a more conceptual perspective, the different approaches provide different ways of interpreting and hence understanding the efficiency concept. In particular, we will see how the practices of thinking in terms of varying constraints (budgets) and importance weights (prices) may be related to broader concepts of rationality.

Finally, the approaches differ in their assumptions as to the information which is available and communicated. This perspective is important for the determination of which approach to employ in a given planning environment. Thus, we provide background material of relevance for the choice of multiple criteria planning mode dependent upon the contextual setting.

A few remarks on the interpretation of the mathematical formulations are relevant here. Several mathematical optimization formulations, socalled mathematical programs, will be encountered. For example, we may write

$$\max_{x} \ f_1(x)$$
$$\text{s.t.} \quad x \in X$$

meaning that among the set of all alternative actions X we want to find one that gives the highest value of the first criterion. In many cases, finding such an alternative corresponds to an exercise in mathematical optimization. For example, we may imagine a production plan being determined by solving a linear programming problem where profit is to be maximized. In other cases, however, very different skills may be needed. For example, a potential purchaser/producer of a chair may face the problem of selecting/designing a most comfortable chair subject to certain resource constraints.

This process can hardly be computerized. In general, we simply look at mathematical programs as an expedient way of expressing an investigation question. We do not assume that a specific method is used to find the answer.

Truly, this is a very liberal interpretation of mathematical programs. We might therefore suggest the following reading guide: Initially, consider the problems as genuine mathematical optimization problems. In particular, imagine that X is defined by enumeration $X=\{x_1, \ldots, x_n\}$ or by inequalities and equations $X = \{x\in \Re^s \mid g_j(x)\leq 0,\ h_k(x)=0,\ j=1, \ldots ,q,\ k=q+1, \ldots ,m\}$ and that $f_1, \ldots ,f_n$ are concrete mathematical functions. Then, all the concepts and manipulations encounted below are well defined. Next, try to be open minded - and critical - about the possible extensions to softer, more complex, and less well defined settings. The details do not generalize, but the general ideas and approaches often do. In the sequel we will try to support this process by suggesting alternative interpretations.

A final remark about the interpretation of mathematical programs is relevant here. We typically work in criteria space in the sequel Thus, for example, the above formulation of an optimization problem will be represented by

$$\max_{y} y_1$$
$$\text{s.t.} \quad y\in Y$$

meaning that among the set of alternatives Y described in terms of criteria vectors, we seek the one that gives the highest value of the first criterion.

We have already in chapters 3 and 4 argued that working in criteria space will in most cases support the planning process from the point of view of the DM. It allows him to focus on a limited number of important consequences of a decision rather than having to work with all of the operational details of the underlying plan x. From the point of view of the AN, however, things may be reversed. Delineating Y requires him not only to describe X , but also to determine how the different underlying x plans perform according to the chosen criteria. In many cases, therefore, our simple representation of problems in criteria space may give a false impression of the difficulties faced by an AN. In particular, this will be the case when the alternatives have to be designed or created.

In the chair problem, where the DM might be a producer and the AN might be an architect, x may be a description of an alternative in terms of materials used, the number of legs, the size, the color, etc., while y may characterize the result in terms of comfort, beauty, costs and the like. Hence, what appears to be simple in the mathematical formulation, to select the $y \in Y$ with the highest comfort value y_1, may in fact be a tremendous task for the AN involving the creative selection of materials, size, color, etc. for a chair - as well as somehow translating the physical characteristics of the chair into a measure of "comfort".

6.4. The Constraint Approach

One way to generate efficient alternatives is by what we call the constraint approach. This involves solving ordinary, that is, single criterion, optimization problems of the form

$$
(P_\epsilon) \qquad \begin{array}{ll} \max\limits_{y} & y_1 \\ \text{s.t.} & y_2 \geq \epsilon_2 \\ & \cdot \\ & \cdot \\ & y_n \geq \epsilon_n \\ & y \in Y \end{array}
$$

where $\epsilon_2, \ldots, \epsilon_n$ are minimum requirements imposed on n-1 of the criteria. So, among all alternatives in criteria space Y, we only consider those giving at least ϵ_2 of the second, ϵ_3 of the third, . . . , and ϵ_n of the n'th criterion, and we discard all those alternatives which do not simultaneously live up to these demands. Among the set of such alternatives, i.e. the alternatives which are **feasible** for P_ϵ in that they fulfil the demands, we pick the one giving the highest value of the first criterion. The choice of the first criterion as the one to be maximized is completely arbitrary here, and is only made to simplify notation.

The constraint approach is illustrated for n=2 in figure 6.2 below. The set of feasible alternatives in value space Y is the set delineated by OAB. Now, the constraint $y_2 \geq \epsilon_2$ implies that we must be to the north of the horizontal line CD. So, the set of feasible solutions to P_ϵ are those delineated by CAD. Finally, the one among these doing best according to the first criterion, i.e. the solution y^* to P_ϵ is D.

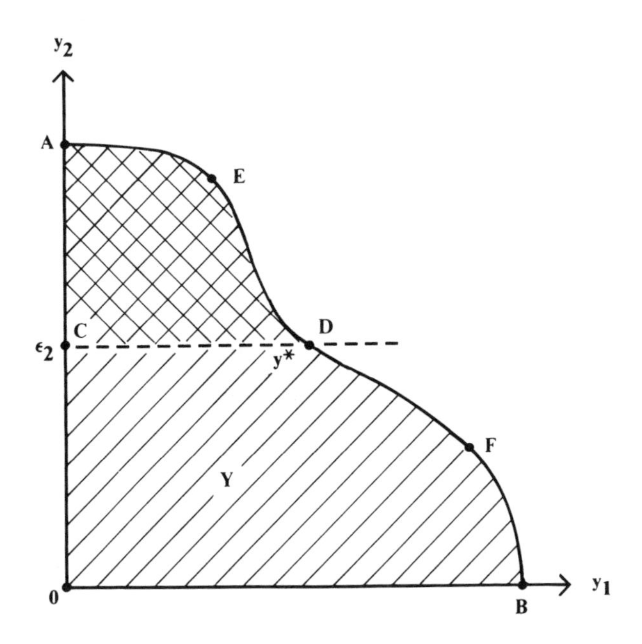

Figure 6.2 The Constraint Approach

By varying the constraints $\epsilon_2, \ldots, \epsilon_n$ it is possible to trace out the whole set of efficient alternatives. This is intuitively clear in figure 6.2. By varying ϵ_2 from 0 to A we generate all the points on the curve between B and A as solution to the problem P_ϵ. This is the efficient set Y_E. In general, we have the following result, an extended version of which is proved in appendix 1.

Theorem 2
If y^* is efficient, there exist values of $\epsilon_2, \ldots, \epsilon_n$ such that y^* is an optimal solution to P_ϵ .

The idea of coping with multiple intentions by maximizing one criterion, for example f_1, while constraining the acceptable values of the remaining criteria $f_2, \ldots, f_n$ is far from new. Long before MCDM crystallized as a discipline, practical economists and operational researchers had recognized the usefulness of explicitly working with **subjective, ad hoc policy restrictions** like $y_2 \geq \epsilon_2, \ldots, y_n \geq \epsilon_n$ as well as with the **objective, physical, technical and economical restrictions** reflected in the definition of Y. These subjective, "soft" restrictions were introduced to make the solution to a traditional "hard" optimization problem more reasonable by making it conform with certain additional, more or less explicit, subjective desires. Note though, that the motivation was not to generate the set of efficient solutions, as is the case here.

For example, the production planning problem of chapters 2 and 3 might be approached as follows. Initially, simple profit maximization leads to plan number 5. Inspecting this plan it is felt that it involves too single minded an involvement in the market for product 1. To prepare for future opportunities or to protect against future changes in the market, the president expresses a desire for diversity. One way to incorporate this desire into the analysis is by introducing an ad hoc "soft" restriction on the sales of product 2 such that a minimal participation in the market for product 2 is assured. This restriction is quite different in its interpretation from a "hard" restriction due for example to a contractual agreement to deliver a certain minimal number of product 2; symbolically, the restrictions may be identical, but their motivation is quite different, as will be the interpretation of the solution to the problem so formulated. However, no matter whether the restriction is soft or hard, by varying the restriction on product 2, the whole set of efficient solutions can be generated.

Another example of a context where the constraint approach may be applicable and economically interpretable is planning in a multilevel organization where budget or resource directive planning procedures are employed. In such a context, each lower level unit typically is to maximize its contribution to profit. The constraints to be varied under the constraint approach represent "soft" tentative budgetary restrictions and/or "hard" restrictions on actual consumption of certain shared production factors having limited capacities. Varying the constraints here will not only lead to the development of the set of efficient production plans at the decentral level, but will also provide valuable information at the headquarters level on the role played by both the "soft" and the "hard" restrictions it has established.

To give yet a third interpretation of the constraint approach, we might note that in the planning literature a problem with the structure P_ϵ is sometimes interpreted as an (ad hoc) reflection of bounded rationality and satisficing behavior. The idea typically presented is that to be satisfactory, an alternative need not be "best", it need only fulfill certain minimum requirements. From this perspective, the constraint approach can be interpreted as follows: among the alternatives satisfying these minimum requirements, select one, more or less arbitrarily, e.g. the alternative doing best according to the first criterion. This interpretation is closely related to the idea of soft constraints above. We should like to emphasize, however, that in our view this interpretation does not pay due respect to the deeper notions and ideas of bounded rationality and satisfying behavior, c.f. our discussion of these matters in chapter 2.

Thus, while the basic idea underlying the constraint approach is not new, it takes on a new significance within a multiple criteria planning perspective. Traditionally, it emphasizes the possible importance of constraints expressing "softer" subjective desires instead of simply considering "harder" objective restrictions which reflect physical and economic realities such as machine capacities and contractual obligations. In our context, the idea of varying constraints is extended to include generating the set of efficient solutions within an economically interpretable framework. Additionally, theorem 2 shows that this use of constraints is theoretically safe in the sense that this practice does not exclude any efficient alternatives a priori.

6.5. The Weighting Approach

Another way to generate efficient alternatives is by the weighting approach. This involves solving ordinary (single criterion) optimization problems of the form:

$$(P_\alpha) \qquad \max_{y} \sum_{i=1}^{n} \alpha_i y_i \quad \text{s.t.} \quad y \in Y$$

where $\alpha_1, \ldots, \alpha_n$ may be interpreted as importance weights - or prices - assigned to the n different criteria. So, among all the feasible alternatives which constitute the set Y, we pick the alternative y* giving the highest value of the compound criterion $\Sigma\alpha_i y_i$ formed by assigning importance weight α_1 to the first, α_2 to the second, . . ., and α_n to the n'th criterion.

Note that, in effect, we identify an efficient alternative as the alternative that would be optimal in the Rational Ideal Model **if** the decision maker's desires could reasonably be described by a preference function

$$F(x) = \sum_{i=1}^{n} \alpha_i f_i(x)$$

which is linear in the individual criteria. Although suggestive, this preference function interpretation is far too restrictive. As referred to many times earlier, it is not in general possible to condense a decision maker's multiple, incommensurate and conflicting criteria into a single measure of utility or well-being which can then be mechanically employed as the basis for determining an optimal solution. Furthermore, even if it is possible to determine such a preference function, it is quite unlikely that it will have the form of F(x) above. And finally, even if such a preference function could be said to exist implicitly, it will in general be unknown to us and require considerable effort to "uncover" it and to determine its parameters.

Therefore, our aim here is **not** to determine a procedure whereby such an "optimal" alternative can be computed. Rather we intend to **utilize P_α as a convenient - and economically interpretable - means of generating efficient alternatives.** A preferred compromise solution will be identified by first solving P_α for varying values of the importance parameters and by then actively involving the DM in the problem of choosing a preferred solution.

This approach is illustrated in figure 6.3. The set of feasible alternatives Y is delineated by OAB. The straight lines are iso-value curves depicting (y_1,y_2) combinations which give the same values of the compound criteria $\alpha_1 y_1 + \alpha_2 y_2$. Figure 6.3 illustrates the case of equal, positive importance weights, $\alpha_1 = \alpha_2$. Higher values correspond to movements to the north-east. The feasible alternative touching the highest iso-value curve, i.e. the solution to P_α, is y*

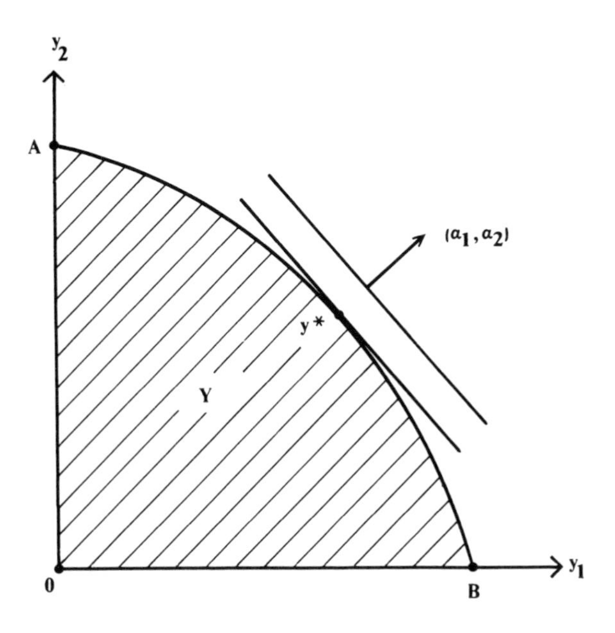

Figure 6.3. The Weighting Approach

Now, by varying the importance weights $\alpha_1, \ldots, \alpha_n$ it is possible to generate different efficient alternatives. In figure 6.3, for example, by setting $\alpha_1 = 1$ and letting α_2 vary from zero to infinity, the iso-value curves shift continuously from vertical to horizontal lines and the solutions generated trace out the complete set of efficient alternatives, i.e. the curve between B and A which is the "north-east" frontier of the set Y. Thus, in this example, the weighting approach is able to generate all the efficient alternatives. In other cases, however, this is not the case. Consider for example figure

6.2. Here, efficient alternatives in the middle section of the efficient frontier, for example y*, cannot be generated by the weighting approach. No linear function takes its maximal value at this point as may easily be seen by drawing some linear iso-value curves in a trial-and-error process. Intuitively, the weighting approach does not work when we have "holes in the efficient frontier", i.e. when the efficient frontier "bends inwards".

Therefore, to make the weighting approach work in general, we need additional regularity assumptions. Let us briefly comment on these. Readers unfamiliar with convex analysis may choose to ignore these remarks regarding what we refer to as a "convex setting" and simply note that additional assumptions are needed here so as to avoid an "inwards bending" frontier. Such readers can proceed directly to section 6.6, "The Mixed Approach".

Recall that a convex set Z is defined by the property that $\delta_1 z_1 + \delta_2 z_2$ belong to Z whenever z_1 and z_2 belong to Z and δ_1 and δ_2 are nonnegative real numbers summing to one. So, a set is convex if and only if any weighted average of points from the set does itself belong to the set. Now, one way to avoid "holes" in the efficient frontier is to have Y convex. The problem in figure 6.2 is precisely that Y is not convex. Any weighted average of the points E and F falls outside Y.

But even if Y is not convex, we may still avoid "holes" in the efficient frontier if the criteria functions are concave. Recall that a concave function $g: Z \rightarrow \mathbb{R}$ is defined by the property that $g(\delta_1 z_1 + \delta_2 z_2) \geq \delta_1 g(z_1) + \delta_2 g(z_2)$ whenever z_1 and z_2 belong to Z and δ_1 and δ_2 are nonnegative real numbers summing to one. Thus, a function is concave if and only if its value on a weighted average of points from a set is at least as high as the weighted average of its values on the individual points. The effect of concave criteria is therefore to make the efficient frontier "bend outwards".

Summarizing, we define a **convex multiple criteria setting** as one in which Y is convex or in which X is convex and $f_1, \ldots, f_n$ are concave. The intuition above suggests that the weighting approach is generally applicable in convex settings. This intuition may be made precise by the folllowing theorem, an extended version of which is proved in appendix 1.

Theorem 3
Consider a convex multiple criteria setting. Now, if y* is efficient, there exist values of $\alpha_1 \geq 0, \ldots, \alpha_n \geq 0$ such that y* is an optimal solution to P_α.

So the weighting approach is generally applicable in convex settings, i.e. in such settings all efficient alternatives can be generated by varying the importance weights assigned to the different criteria. To economists and operations researchers convexity assumptions are familiar. An important example of convex settings is linear programming models where all criteria and constraints are linear, i.e. both of the conditions sufficient for defining a convex setting apply.

Still, the assumption of a convex setting assumption does exclude many cases. Let us therefore emphasize that the weighting approach may be very useful in non-convex multiple criteria settings as well. First, it is often conjectured that the weighting approach allows us to generate if not all then at least a reasonable subset of the efficient alternatives. Therefore, the costs in terms of forgone opportunities due to restricting attention to alternatives generated by varying importance weights may not be overwhelming. In particular, this reasoning may often be convincing in discrete problems. If we only have a finite or countable set of alternatives, the assumptions of theorem 3 fails; X, and therefore Y as well, are discrete and hence not convex sets. Still, as in figure 6.1(a), it is often possible to generate all efficient alternatives by the weighting approach. The subset of the efficient alternatives which may be generated by the weighting approach is sometimes called the set of **non-convex-dominated** alternatives, c.f. appendix 1.

Secondly, it is often conjectured that a DM's - unknown - preference function is in fact linear in the n criteria. Sufficient conditions for this to hold are discussed in chapter 7. In such cases, it suffices to consider the non-convex-dominated alternatives since for any other alternative there will always be a non-convex-dominated alternative which is preferred. Indeed the non-convex-dominated alternatives constitute the smallest sufficient set of alternatives to consider in this case, just like the set of non-dominated, i.e. efficient, alternatives is the smallest sufficient set of alternatives to consider when the overall preference function is only known to be weakly increasing. In chapter 9 we will encounter several applications of this kind of reasoning.

6.6. The Mixed Approach

The constraint and weighting approaches represent somewhat stylized approaches to generating efficient alternatives. They may be modified, combined and generalized in numerous ways. Let us just note one possibility, namely mixed approaches based on the solution of ordinary (single criterion) optimization problems of the form

$$\begin{aligned} \max_{y} \quad & \sum_{i=1}^{k} \alpha_i y_i \\ \text{s.t.} \quad & y_{k+1} \geq \epsilon_{k+1} \\ & \cdot \\ & \cdot \\ & y_n \geq \epsilon_n \\ & y \in Y \end{aligned}$$

In this formulation the first k criteria are "steered" by importance weights while the last n-k criteria are regulated by constraints. Note that k=1 gives the constraint approach and k=n gives the weighting approach. In a convex setting, as indeed in many other settings, we might generate all efficient alternatives by solving this problem for varying values of the importance weights and constraints, c.f. appendix 1.

Mixed approaches can be said to be "realistic" insofar as they often will reflect a decision maker's conceptual model of a choice situation.

One typical case where we may consider such a formulation to be realistic is where the first k criteria are **soft**, expressing general concerns and intentions while the remaining n-k criteria are **hard**, expressing physical needs and therefore tightly controlled by constraints. When planning the design of a microchip, for example, intentions like low costs and small size may be soft - corresponding more to wishes than to restrictions - while the electronical performance standards may be hard constraints - corresponding more to technical requirements than to intentions or wishes.

Another example is the case of production planning in a particular plant of a multi plant firm. The general intention is to produce high output levels with low input consumptions. For some of the inputs and outputs, such as general purpose machines and final products respectively, there may exist external markets. Therefore it is not necessary to control these factors precisely, since slack may always be sold or bought in the marketplace; they may be coped with using weights rather than being delimited via "hard" restrictions. For other factors like highly specialized labor and firm-specific intermediate products, external markets may be unreliable; the firm is not willing to consider them as a means of regulating its inputs and outputs. To make the firm's overall production plan physically consistent in this case, it may be necessary to control these factors internally and to do so rather precisely. This may point to the use of constraints establishing minimal requirements, rather than weights to govern these factors.

We note too, that in general the mixed approach presented above is just one rather simple way of combining the ideas of regulation via weights and constraints. In general, some - or all - of the factors, may appear both in the weighting function and in the restrictions. This may be natural for example in the case where there exist certain minimal production requirements for an intermediate product due to the existence of sales contracts for the finished goods it is a part of, while production above the minimal level so established has potential market value and/or value to the firm as inventory. Using such an approach, it is once again possible, assuming regularity conditions similar to those considered above, to develop all the efficient alternatives by varying the weights and/or constraints; reference is made to appendix 1 for further discussion.

6.7. The Target Approach

As a final general approach to the problem of generating efficient alternatives, let us briefly sketch what we might call the target appproach. In the MCDM literature specific examples of this general idea may be found under headings like reference point and goal programming methods. Within this approach, proposals are generated by solving ordinary (single criterion) optimization problems of the form:

$$(P_{d,y^o}) \qquad \min_{y} \; d(y,y^o) \quad \text{s.t.} \quad y \in Y$$

Here, the **target** y^o is a - possibly infeasible - point in criteria space. For example it might represent a production target. The **deviation function** d(.,.) measures how severely an alternative y deviates from the target y^o. So, the idea of P_{d,y^o} is that we search through the set of feasible alternatives Y looking for the alternative $y^* \in Y$ which deviates least seriously, min $d(y,y^o)$, from the target y^o. By varying y^o and/or d(.,.) it is usually possible to generate all efficient alternatives in general - not necessarily convex - multiple criteria settings, c.f. appendix 1.

The target is often interpreted as an expression of the decision maker's goal or optimistic guess concerning the outcomes of the n criteria. Indeed, many authors appear to adhere to such an approach to modelling a decision maker's preferences in the same way as the constraint approach may be interpreted as a (crude) modelling of satisficing behavior. However, for our purposes, the target approach is purely instrumental. It is employed solely as a means of generating efficient solutions and **not** as an expression of preferences. In other words, the idea underlying the target approach is **not** to employ it to determine an "optimal solution" as that which minimizes the deviation from the target for a given value of the target and for a given deviation function. Rather it is to generate the set of efficient alternatives via varying the deviation measure and/or the target.

Just to give some flavour of what the target approach may look like, let us consider a few examples. In the spirit of the socalled goal-programming method, one might measure the deviation by

$$d^G(y,y^o) = \sum_{i=1}^{n} (\delta_i^+ d_i^+ + \delta_i^- d_i^-)$$

Here, d_i^+ equals y_i-y^o_i if this is positive and $d_i^+ \equiv 0$ otherwise. Similarly, d_i^- equals y^o_i-y_i if this is positive and 0 otherwise. So d_i^+ measures the degree of overfulfillment and d_i^- measures the degree of underfulfillment of the goal y^o_i for the i'th criteria. Also, δ_i^+ and δ_i^- are parameters describing how unpleasant these deviations are considered to be. The use of this deviation measure with $\delta_1^- = 3\delta_1^+$ and $\delta_2^- = 3\delta_2^+$, i.e. where underfulfillments are considered by the DM to be three times as unpleasant as overfulfillments, is illustrated in figure 6.4(a) below. The kinked curve is the highest level curve of d^G which intersects Y, and y^* is the feasible solution which deviates least seriously from the target y^o. We note that the slope of the level curve is -1 to the south-west of y^o, reflecting the equal severity of underfulfillment in both directions. The numerical value of the slope decreases as y_1 increases beyond its target value, reflecting the fact that overfulfillment is penalized with 1/3 of the weight as underfulfillment. Similar comments apply for the case of y_2 exceeding its target value.

As another example often encountered in the reference point literature, consider measuring the deviation by socalled p-norms:

$$d^p(y,y^o) = [\sum_{i=1}^{n} |\beta_i(y_i-y^o_i)|^p]^{1/p}$$

where $\beta_1 \geq 0, \ldots, \beta_n \geq 0$ are parameters defining how severely deviations from y^o are in the different coordinates. For $\beta_1 = \ldots = \beta_n = 1$ and $p=2$, this deviation is simply the ordinary Euclidian distance between y and y^o. The use of d^2 in the target approach is illustrated in figure 6.4(b), where the circle around y^o is an iso-level set of d^2.

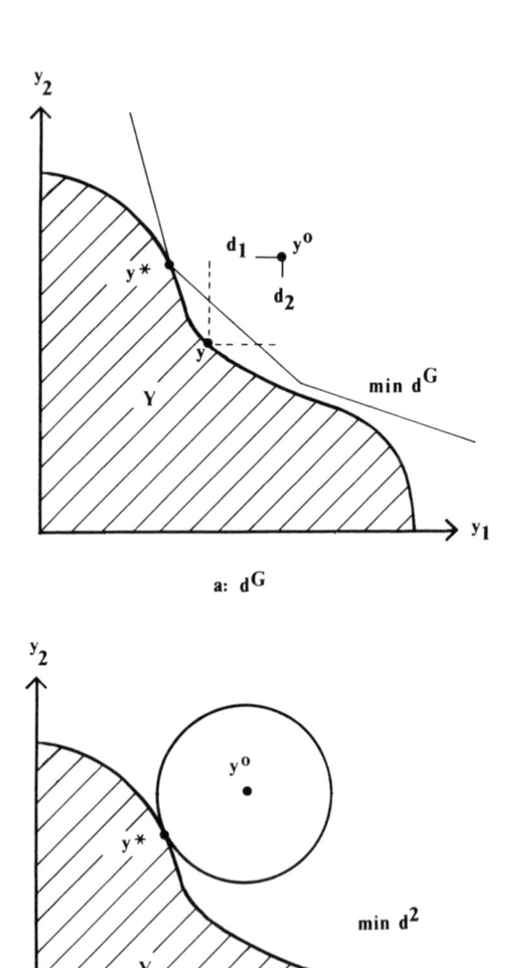

Figure 6.4.(a)-(b) The Target Approach

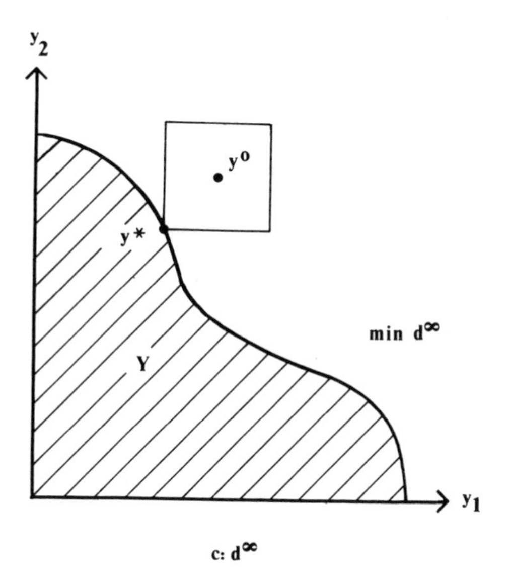

Figure 6.4.(c) The Target Approach

Another interesting case of d^p obtains when p becomes very large. Then, only the maximum value of $|\beta_i(y_i-y^\circ_i)|$, $i=1, \ldots, n$ matters. Therefore, the deviation measure becomes

$$d^\infty(y,y^\circ) = \max_{i=1,\ldots,n} |\beta_i(y_i-y^\circ_i)|$$

and the target approach problem becomes one of determining the alternative y whose largest weighted deviation is the smallest, i.e. P_{d,y° minimizes the maximal weighted coordinate distance. This is illustrated in figure 6.4(c) for the case $\beta_1 = \ldots = \beta_n$. Note that the level sets are now sharply kinked. This reflects the fact that the distance is constant as long as the largest deviation is constant. On the horizontal line segments, the largest distance is in the y_2 coordinate and on the vertical line segments, the largest distance is in the y_1 coordinate. In the case of unequal weights, the square in figure 6.4(c) becomes a rectangle.

6.8. Trade-Off Information

In many concrete problems, the set of efficient alternatives is very large. This may prohibit the analyst from submitting all the efficient alternatives to the decision maker. As indicated previously, one useful modification of the planning mode in this case may be just to submit a hopefully representative subset of the efficient alternatives to the DM. Also, a more fundamental modification may be to change the whole approach from one of a priori to one of progressive articulation of alternatives. In this mode, to be considered in depth in chapter 8, the DM successively learns about alternatives; this allows him to successively clarify his wishes and hence more precisely to direct the search for promising alternatives. Whichever modification one makes, it may be important to supplement the description of a given efficient alternative with information about the possibilities in its neighborhood. Using the specific proposal as an anchor point, descriptions of the neighboring possibilities often take the form of **substitution or trade-off information**. That is, information about how much one has to give up of one criterion in order to gain a certain increase in another criterion.

Within mathematical programming, trade-off information is referred to as **dual information** while it is often refered to as **Langrange multipliers** in regular convex settings. In economics, substitution information is usually given as **prices**. Market prices, for example, essentially tell us how much to sell of one commodity to be able to buy one unit of another commodity. Also, in everyday life we are used to thinking in terms of trade-offs. How much present consumption do I have to give up to be able to go to the Bahamas this coming summer? Thus, trade-off and substitution concepts are natural and time-honored constructs and one should not be surprised to find that they may be highly useful in multiple criteria planning as well. Presently, we are concerned with the possibilities (Y) available to the DM. Therefore, we are going to talk a little about **substitution possibilities**. In the next chapter, we focus on the DM's wishes (F) and hence we discuss there **substitution wishes**. Finally, in chapter 8 and 9 we will see how a large part of the interactive methods evolve around the idea of balancing substitution wishes against substitution possibilities.

To get a more concrete grasp of what substitution information may look like and how it may be be used, let us consider a setting where we assume that Y is as depicted as in figure 6.5 below; we note that this setting is what we earlier have referred to as a convex setting. One of the efficient alternatives is y*. Now, the classical way to describe neighboring alternatives, i.e. the substitution possibilities around y*, is by a **linear approximation** to Y at y*. The line ℓ - and more generally in n-dimensional criteria space, a socalled hyperplane supporting Y at y* - is the geometrical counterpart of the mathematician's multipliers and the economist's prices.

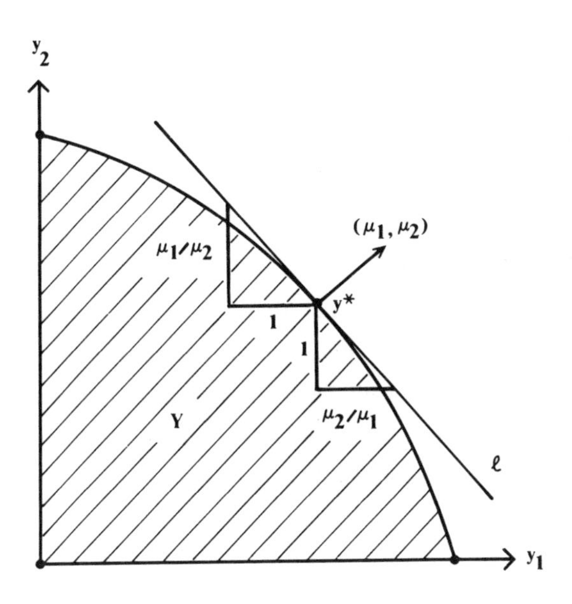

Figure 6.5 Substitution Possibilities

To construct the linear approximation ℓ:$\mu_1 y_1 + \mu_2 y_2 = c$, we need the vector of coefficients, (μ_1, μ_2). For the ease of future reference we denote this the vector of **substitution possibilities coefficients at y*** and use $\mu(y^*) = (\mu_1, \mu_2)$ as a shorthand notation. Let us note that if the efficient alternative y* is generated by solving a mathematical program like P_ϵ, P_α or P_{d,y^o} above, knowledge of $\mu(y^*)$ is usually generated as a sideproduct in terms of optimal Langrange multipliers, c.f. appendix 1.

The **interpretation** of the substitution possibilities coefficients $\mu(y^*) = (\mu_1, \mu_2)$ is straightforward. As illustrated in figure 6.5, they tell us that by giving up one unit of

y_1 we can gain at most μ_1/μ_2 units of y_2. Similarly, if we forego one unit of y_2 we can gain at most μ_2/μ_1 units of y_1. We see that the substitution possibilities pictured by ℓ are **locally rather precise but globally somewhat optimistic**. They are optimistic by being approximations from the outside of Y, not from the inside. The ratio μ_1/μ_2 exaggerates the possible gain in y_2 from giving up one unit of y_1. Similarly, μ_2/μ_1 somewhat overstates the increase in y_1 made possible by decreasing y_2 by one unit. Summarizing, we might say that the substitution coefficients $\mu(y^*)$ give a locally precise and globally exaggerated picture of the substitution possibilities around y^*.

Now, let us see how trade-off information in terms of substitution possibilities coefficients may be **useful**. Imagine two cases as illustrated in figures 6.6(a) and (b) below, where information on Y is not available. In case (a) the DM is simply informed about a given efficient proposal y^*, that is, he does not know the shape and content of Y. The fact that y^* is efficient simply tells him that there are no feasible alternatives to the north-east of y^*. He can only infer therefore that the rest of Y must be found somewhere in the shaded area. In contrast, case (b) illustrates a setting where the AN submits to the DM not only an efficient alternative y^* but also the substitution coefficients $\mu(y^*)=(\mu_1,\mu_2)$. This allows the DM to ignore all points to the north-east of the line ℓ; he can infer that all feasible alternatives are in the shaded area to the south-west of ℓ.

It is of course easier for the DM to comprehend a specific proposal y^* than to understand and process the information contained in a report $[y^*,\mu(y^*)]$ on both a proposal y^* and the neighboring possibilities as delineated by $\mu(y^*)$. Still, as illustrated by the reduced shaded area in case (b), the improved inference from this report may make it worthwhile. This explains why a useful alternative to the submission of all or many efficient alternatives to the DM may be simply to submit a few proposals with accompanying substitution information. Taking the argument a bit further, let us assume that the DM has a relatively precise picture of his overall wishes with respect to the two criteria as represented by the preference function F. Specifically, let us imagine that he regards his indifference curve through y^* to be the $F=F(y^*)$ curve drawn in figure 6.6. Therefore, potentially better alternatives must be sought in the shaded areas above $F=F(y^*)$. In case (a), there seems to be room for substantial improvements. Also, the DM cannot really say whether or not the value of the first criterion should be decreased or increased. In case (b), however, the remaining potentially attractive alternatives are very limited. The DM may feel satisfied immediately. If not, he may at least give directions for the subsequent search for improvements since they must clearly involve an increased value of y_1. This illustrates once again how the improved inference from substitution possibilities information may be valuable in a prior articulation of alternatives planning mode[3].

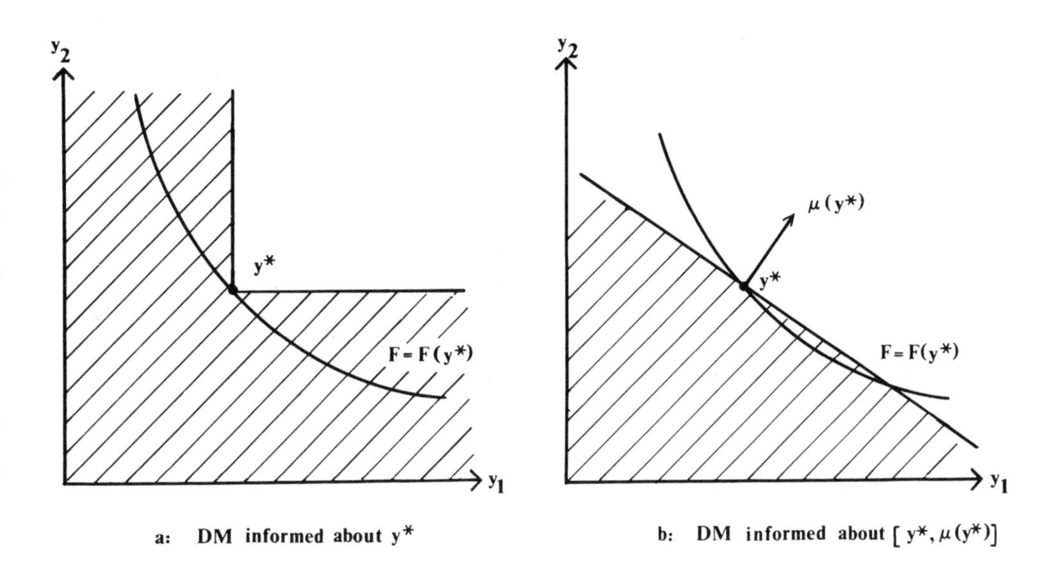

Figure 6.6 Use of Substitution Information

We have focused above on substitution possibilities information in its purest form as represented by the substitution coefficients μ. Although this is definitely an important type of substitution information, we do not want to leave the impression that it is the only such information which can be employed, nor that it is in general the most valuable such information. Theoretically, substitution coefficients are only useful in convex settings since in non-convex settings we cannot presume the regularities assumed here as to the shape of Y. References to more general types of dual information are given in appendix 1.

---

[3] It also indicates how substitution information may aid the DM in choosing search directions in a progressive articulation of alternatives planning mode to be considered in chapter 8.

In practice, we may not have a convex setting, or, perhaps more likely, we do not know whether the setting is convex or non-convex. In addition, we may not be able to generate proposals by programs like P_ϵ which automatically provide us with the substitution coefficients, or the AN may simply hesitate to reveal the coefficients to the DM, since he may expect the coefficients to be too hard to understand. In all such cases, the AN might instead give some less refined information about the substitution possibilities to the DM in terms of, for example, the ideal point, a subset of "nearby" efficient alternatives, the cross-effect matrix or other aggregate and crude trade-off expressions. Also, in some situations the AN might have great faith in the DM's information processing capacity and try to provide him with more detailed information than contained in the substitution coefficients. In a linear programming setting, for example, he might describe the substitution possibilities around an extreme point solution by the "efficient trade-offs", i.e. the trade-offs occurring when we move to neighboring corner solutions. These and other alternatives to substitution coefficients have been suggested in various MCDM techniques. Seen from the perspective of multiple criteria planning, such more informative signals may assist the DM and the AN in their search for a compromise solution.

Summarizing, we do not here advocate the use of a specific type of substitution information. Rather, we simply want to note the potential usefulness of this kind of supplementary information. The proper implementation of this idea must be developed by the AN in direct response to the concrete context, including the characteristics of the set of alternatives and the DM's personality and preferences, as well as his analytical and communicative talents.

6.9. Summary

In this section we considered one of the four principle multiple criteria planning modes, that of "prior articulation of alternatives". Additionally, we did a lot of groundwork useful in subsequent chapters. This planning mode involves two phases. First, the AN investigates the set of alternatives and presents some of them to the DM. Next, the DM makes a choice. Therefore, the basic issues discussed in this section were how to investigate the set of alternatives and which alternatives to submit to the DM.

The guiding principle was that of efficiency. An alternative is efficient if we cannot find an other alternative that can improve the value of any criterion without deteriorating the value of one or more of the remaining criteria. We argued that, if certain fundamental assumptions were fulfilled, it was safe to ignore inefficient alternatives, but potentially costly to exclude any efficient alternatives. Primary amongst these conditions were the "more is better than less" assumption and the assumption that all the criteria relevant for a DM's evaluation have been identified. We stressed the importance of these assumptions and the need for establishing their validity in practical contexts; if they are not reasonably justified, ignoring dominated alternatives may result in opportunity costs since potentially preferred solutions may be filtered away. Also, we argued that although efficiency may be a useful screening principle, it is not a necessary and certainly not a sufficient principle for choice of an alternative. Attempts to avoid delicate value judgements by simply going for efficiency would be in direct conflict with the philosophy underlying multiple criteria planning.

Having clarified the interpretation and use of the efficiency principle, we turned to different ways to search for efficient alternatives. We described: a) the constraint approach based on varying minimum requirements imposed on the different criteria, b) the weighting approach based on varying importance weights assigned to the different criteria, c) the mixed approach based upon a combination of the constraint and weighting approaches, and d) the target approach based on varying target values for the different criteria. We defined these different approaches, discussed their abilities to generate efficient alternatives and we emphasized their conceptual and economic interpretations. These approaches provide a useful intellectual framework for structuring the search for alternatives.

Finally, we emphasized the possible relevance of substitution or trade-off information in multiple criteria planning contexts. In realistic planning situations, the set of efficient alternatives may be so large, that presenting all of the efficient alternatives to the DM may make it very difficult for him to utilize his knowledge as to his preferences, F, to choose from among this set. Such a situation could be disasterous for the planning process, and might lead the DM to great frustration and to return to more ad hoc behavior. In such cases, a subset of the efficient alternatives, supplemented by information about the substitution possibilities around them, may give a good overall picture of the set of efficient alternatives. This may provide the DM with adequate information to make a choice which is consistent with his overall wishes. Alternatively, such information may be useful to guide the search for alternatives in an intelligent manner, as we will see in chapter 8.

6.10. Bibliographic Notes

Most of the formal concepts and results in this chapter are pretty well established in the general literature on economics and mathematics. In many cases, however, special versions have been developed in the MCDM literature. Thus, for example, modified notions of efficiency have been introduced by among others Burkard, Krarup and Pruzan(1984), Geoffrion(1968), Lowe, Thisse, Ward and Wendel(1984) and White(1985). Results on the relevance of the efficiency concept along the lines of theorem 1 have been developed by - among others - Soland(1979), who also provides a very nice overview of different ways to generate and characterize efficient alternatives. The specific possibility of generating efficient solutions by the constraint approach may be attributed to Haimes(1970), Yu(1974), or Haimes, Hall and Freedman(1975). Results along the lines of theorem 3 date back to at least Arrow, Barankin and Blackwell (1953), DaCunha and Polak(1967), Geoffrion(1968) and Kuhn and Tucker(1951). Generalized results are given in Bogetoft(1985a,b,86) and in Bogetoft and Tind(1990). The use of mixed approaches here is inspired by the literature on multilevel planning. In MCDM, hybrid approaches have been suggested by - among others - Corley(1980), Soland(1979) and Wendel and Lee(1977). Regarding the target approach, numerous references are again possible. e.g. Chankong and Haimes(1983a), Yu(1973) and Zeleny(1973). The generation and use of trade-off information like the substitution possibilities coefficients is discussed by e.g. Bogetoft(1985a,b,86), Bogetoft, Hallefjord and Kok(1987), Bogetoft and Tind(1990), Haimes and Chankong(1979), Kok(1984) and Nakayama and Sawaragi(1984). Despite the length of these references, they do not cover all of the important contributions. The reader is recommended to consult more textbook-like presentations, e.g. those referred to in chapter 1, for more complete bibliographic notes. Also appendix 1 offers some additional references.

Chapter 7

PRIOR ARTICULATION OF PREFERENCES

Another multiple criteria planning mode is characterized by prior articulation of preferences. In the first phase of such an approach, and largely detached from the concrete set of alternatives, the AN constructs a model of the DM's preferences. This is accomplished by studying the DM's behavior in previous or, most notably, fictive contexts or by otherwise interrogating him or guiding his self-examination. In the next phase this description of the DM's preferences is coupled with the actual set of feasible alternatives in an attempt to identify the best alternative or at least a reduced set from which the final choice will be made.

Within this general organization of the planning task there is a wide spectrum of possible approaches. One may make more or less demanding investigations and assumptions in the first phase leading to more or less forceful prescriptions in the second phase. In general terms though, the mode is unchanged. In the first phase one enriches the dominance relation by introducing new information about the DM's intentions and in the second phase one exploits the extended dominance relation to eliminate some of the available alternatives from further considerations.

Before presenting an overview of the prior articulation of preferences mode some warnings are called for. Such an approach, for the main, implicitly attributes several rather demanding rational characteristics to the DM. Included are the assumptions that his preferences are internally consistent and stable, may be completely represented by a series of objectives, and may be completely evaluated via a series of criteria chosen to represent the objectives, and that he is able to perform a preference evaluation for any relevant set of such criterion values. Furthermore, it might appear that via some hokus pokus we have returned to a single-criterion planning mode which consistently subsumes all information as to basic values, objectives, criteria and preferences within a simple preference function.

It is important at this stage to emphasize therefore, that there is a significant difference between the multiple criteria planning approach to the modelling of preferences and traditional single-criterion modelling typically met in microeconomics and operations research. The DM is very much a part of the planning process in this mode, even though he appears to be decoupled from the here-and-now choice aspect of the planning. That is, he participates quite actively in the investigation and communication phases surrounding the choice phase. Also, the explicit, demanding investigation performed here to estimate a DM's preference function will be of value per se; very likely, it will be of greater value for the DM than the resulting analytical expression of his preference structure.

However, an additional warning is called for just because of his active participation in the investigation and communication activities. This participation may lead to - perhaps unwarented - faith in the AN-controlled choice phase and to a virtual evasion of decision making responsibility. That final phase is, at least according to the rather prototypical presentation of the prior articulation of preferences mode, left to the AN. The DM appears to be at the mercy of the AN and to be transformed into some sort of answering service, providing the AN with the information he requests, and relinquishing his decision making responsibility.

This picture is certainly frightening - but highly exaggerated. An experienced leader will only seldomly relinquish control to the extent depicted in the formal presentation of the prior articulation of preferences mode. Although he may willingly e.g. promote the development of decentralizing decision rules for more tactical decisions, he will not simply leave the choice phase to the AN in complex, significant, strategic planning situations. The prototype methods which are presented here and which appear to lead to such a sharp division of responsibility, must simply be considered as templates for the real world planning environment; the DM is still the decision maker, but here after considerable consultation with and support from the AN. Both are now participants in extended and on-going investigation-communication-choice activities in the multiple criteria planning process.

A final "warning". In general, a DM's preferences may not be stable but may change with time when he learns more about his underlying values and preferences, and when the state of the system changes. Thus, detailed modelling of the DM's present preferences may be both inadequate and inappropriate if decisions made now have long-term consequences. In such cases, overreliance on the formalisms presented here may lead to the unconscious rejection of intuition and creativity, which are vital for coping with such planning situations.

There is a substantial theory supporting this planning mode.

In disciplines like consumer behavior and marketing, many **descriptive** models have been proposed. The aim is to build models capable of emulating observed behavior. This is often approached by statistically estimating a family of preference functions on some previous behavioral data. Although multiple attributes is a distinct characteristic of many such models, these approaches do not live up to our characteristic of multiple criteria planning as processes of investigation - communiation - choice.

Within the context of multiple criteria planning, decision making is a **normative** discipline. The aim is to determine concepts, assumptions and procedures that may be used to **prescribe** how the DM should proceed, i.e. investigate, communicate and choose, so as to behave in accordance with his preferences. Although descriptive validity may be considered desirable it is not indispensable here. First of all, we doubt that unguided choices in the past necessarily were good choices. If they were, then there very likely would be little need for the rather demanding approaches considered here. Secondly, it is highly problematic to separate the DM's picture of wishes (F) and possibilities (Y) in the past and hereby to produce the data on which to estimate a preference function. In fact one of the major themes underlying this book is that it is only via the continual interaction between our preferences and our possibilities that we may both generate good alternatives and make good choices among these alternatives. Thirdly, many planning problems are nonrepetitive by nature so no history of past behavior or mistakes exists.

Finally, let us mention that most methods in the present mode are **axiomatic**. The basic idea underlying this mode is that it pays to build a complex model in parts. Reality in all its dimensions is believed far too complex to be dealt with in its totality, even though we aspire to be "holistic" in our planning behavior. Therefore, simple and necessarily hypothetical questions may be useful to focus on basic attitudes and it makes sense for the DM simply to accept certain assumptions, i.e. axioms, as part of the rationality he wants his behavior to conform with. Consistently putting together these different parts gives the overall model. Of course, there must be a reasonable balance between hypothetical simplicity and realistic complexity. After all, it is usually held that realistic questions have the advantage of being taken seriously by the DM and of leaving him more comfortable. Therefore, adherents of this approach argue that one should not only check the basic assumptions repeatedly. Rather the total model employed should also be confronted with realistic, complex problems to see that the hypothetical questioning does not contribute to systematical errors.

The outline of the following sections is as follows. We commence with a short discourse on the relevance of preference theories, since they often are the subject of heated discussions. Next, we turn to a very fundamental issue in any normative modelling of a multiple criteria preference structure, namely how to construct a useful set of criteria. This theme is of course of interest not only for the prior articulation of preferences approach, but for all the four approaches identified in our taxonomy. We discuss this in section 7.2. The next fundamental issue is how to compromise the DM's different desires, i.e. how to incorporate information on the relative importance of the different criteria to give a comprehensive preference structure. The classical theory here is the so-called multiple attribute utility theory, often abbreviated in the literature as MAUT. A basic assumption underlying MAUT is that the DM is willing and able to make extensive comparisons and trade-offs and to behave in accordance with several axioms of rationality. The result of all this is usually a complete, functional description of the DM's wishes, his preference function F. Multiple attribute utility theory is the subject of sections 7.3 - 7.10. Finally, in sections 7.11 - 7.13, we turn to several newer, notably European, approaches, the so-called outranking methods. These presume that in complex and significant planning situations a decision maker not only will accept - he will also prefer - less extensive compromising than permitted by a complete identification of his preference strucutre. In particular there is room for some amount of incomparabilities of alternatives. Of course, the resulting prescriptions in the second phase are then more modest. Typically, these models only allow us to isolate a subset of alternatives from which the final choice must be made by whatever means available. Still, as a first cut into the preference structure, this may be very useful.

7.1. On the Relevance of Preference Theories

As the prior articulation of preferences approach is often the subject of heated discussions between theoreticians and practitioners, e.g. between mathematical economists and designers of decision support systems, we will briefly summarize the major contents of such discussions and present our own point of view.

Briefly speaking, there are theoreticians who argue that in order to justify an analytical-quantitative approach to decision making, it is necessary to presume the existence of a preference function. Furthermore, in order to operationalize such an approach, it is necessary in the given context to define the function. If such explicitness is forgone, decision making is reduced to unaided intuition and to ad hoc impulsive behavior with no reasonable assurance that decisions will consistently reflect a decision maker's preferences.

The practitioners take the opposite point of view. They argue that no one has ever "seen" a preference function, that ordinary people do not behave in accordance with the rather strict axioms underlying the existence of such functions, and that attempts to develop them in practice lead to wastes of time and energy as well as to poor decision making, i.e. decisions which do not reflect the DM's preferences. They support these arguements by refering to the apparent dearth of publicized and successful applications. Instead they argue that decision "technology" should support a decision maker in his quest for help in structuring and integrating the complexities charactering a planning context. These include uncertainty as to objectives, the possible means of promoting these objectives, and the criteria to evaluate the substantive and procedural qualities of a decision. This, they argue cannot be achieved by attempting to develop mathematical expressions of value, but by designing attractive environments which permit the DM to investigate his own doubts, possibilities and preferences.

We agree with much to be found in both standpoints. In the sequel, we will therefore be selective and include perspectives based on elements from both of these two extremes.

For example, we strongly support the point of view that it is valuable for any theory-supported approach to decision making to be based on knowledge as to the axiomatic foundations of preference theory and therefore as to the limitiations in such theory as well. Just how important such knowledge is can be seen by considering the market for decision support systems. There exists an abundance of PC-oriented program packages which facilitate what appear to be reasonable man-machine dialogues to help a DM make his decision based on common sense questions as to his priorities and the like. When such approaches are supported by well functioning graphic interfaces, it is very natural for a decision maker to assume that the methods are "scientifically sound" and that the resulting decisions are, if not "optimal" then certainly "good" and based upon state-of-the-art theory. In fact, most of the software we are acquainted with make strong, fundamental, but most often implicit, assumptions as to the DM's preference structure. And if the DM and/or AN are not knowledgeable as to preference theory, they may participate in such a computer steered dialogue in the belief that this will support recommendations which are in accord with the DM's underlying preferences. We therefore consider it to be of considerable importance that planning experts are knowledgable as to the theory, even if they do not actually use it in practise to construct such preference functions.

Furthermore such theory underlies most of the models employed in the interactive approaches to planning with multiple criteria to be presented in chapters 8 and 9. It is therefore necessary to have a reasonable "hands on" level knowledge of the theory as to prior articulation of preferences in order to be able to understand and select among the various modes of multiple criteria planning.

On the other hand, we tend to agree with the practitioners' arguments as well. In general, "significant" decisions are not just left to an individual. Therefore approaches to support systems should underline the group and communication aspects, factors which are ignored by the functional approach to preference theory. In addition, as indicated earlier, values, objectives and in particular preferences are in general non-stationary. They tend to change with the context and with the state of the system; we would not be surprised if the values, objectives and preferences of a poor student who works as a taxi driver in all his free time change rather abruptly if he learns that a distant aunt has left him an inheritance of 40 million dollars. Thus, vagueness as to goals, means and measures together with the uncertainty and non-stationarity characterizing decision making environments, tend to point in the direction of flexible support systems, which do not presume the elegance of complete and consistent descriptions of a DM's preference structure.

As we shall see towards the conclusion of the present chapter, considering both perspectives can lead to flexible preference modelling. In order to interpret and criticize such modelling requires, however, a knowledge of the possibilities and limitations associated with more traditional preference modelling.

7.2. Specifying Objectives and Criteria

The question of how to specify the set of objectives and the criteria used to measure the degree to which an objective is met, is a very important one. So far, we have assumed the specification to be available to us at the very outset. Hereby, the problem we face is simply how to utilize the criteria to determine which choice among the alternatives best corresponds to our preferences. However, this is not the case in reality, and if we are to take preference modelling seriously, we must necessarily confront this question of how to specify the objectives and criteria. Unfortunately, this is also a question for which there does not exist precise theory. The process is basically creative in nature and there exist, at best, rules of thumb. One of the difficulties is that the subject seems to be rather context specific. Therefore, the best way to learn the art, except from by doing it, is probably through case-studies and examples. Nevertheless, let us try to specify here whatever little we can at a general level.

We seek a set of objectives, i.e. intentions expressed in terms of everyday language, and associated attributes, i.e. operational criteria which allow us to measure the degree to which an alternative contributes to the achievement of the objectives. These objectives and criteria must possess at least the following properties. They must ideally be **complete**, so as to cover all important aspects of the problem, **operational**, so as to be understandable to the DM, while facilitating explanation to others, **nonredundant** so that double counting of impacts can be avoided, and, closely related, **minimal** so that a problem's dimension is kept as small as possible. Furthermore, we would like them to be at least somewhat **independent**, a term to be made precise in section 7.9, so as to allow the evaluation of trade-offs to be decomposed. The problem is now how to strive towards this ideal.

Initially, the AN could generate a lot of ideas as to potentially relevant objectives and criteria by whatever means are available. A starting point may be casual empiricism. One might consider what the DM immediately suggests to be at stake, what people in the organization talk about, and how they justify their decisions. More systematically, it may be useful to examine relevant descriptions of similar problems to see if others have documented objectives of relevance to the problem at hand, to make surveys of what the DM's peers find crucial, and to consult knowledgeable experts to identify the diversity of implications the planning process may have. In addition, as soon as one starts doing analytical work, building a model of the system, identifying inputs and outputs etc., it is highly likely that objectives and criteria originally omitted by intention or oversight come to the front. In general, **objectives and criteria are not specified once and for all.** As we have emphasized earlier: planning is not a linear but a cyclic process.

Furthermore, the apparent clear distinction between means (alternatives) and ends (objectives) may turn out to be rather muddy and quite context-dependent. In fact, many means may be ascribed existential qualities per se by the DM; they may have value in themselves, and are not just mechanisms producing criteria values.

Finally we may note that our **preferences are seldom stationary**, i.e. unchanging with time. When we become older, wiser and more experienced we tend to realize that rather significant reorientations in our perspectives and fundamental values may occur.

Similary, and as referred to in the introduction to this chapter, our preferences may change - even rather abruptly - with the state of the system, i.e. with changes in the values of the criteria which characterize our present situation. Once again, the cylical, learning aspect of planning becomes predominant.

Now, faced with a **preliminary** set of objectives and criteria, most likely varying widely in scope, detail, and explicitness, the problem becomes one of structuring these elements and hopefully detecting serious omissions and inconsistencies. Perhaps the most natural approach at this point is to **build the preference structure hierarchically**. At the top, we have the overall, all-inclusive reason or reasons for caring about the problem in the first place. The labels used here reflect what we earlier referred to as the DM's underlying values; the term "labels" is used here to underline that words are not the things they represent, a realization which is particularly relevant at the value level. Usually, these will be much too vague for operational purposes. They may include wellbeing, happiness, quality of life or the like. As we move down the hierarchy, we successively clarify the meaning of higher-level objectives by subdividing them into lower-level objectives and criteria of more detail. Also, one may look at lower objectives as the means to the higher objectives, which can be viewed as their ends. Every time we subdivide, we must be careful to have all facets of the higher level objective accounted for by one of the lower-level objectives. In this way, each level of the hierarchy ideally provides a complete, comprehensive description of the DM's possible concerns. In figure 7.1 below we indicate some of the values, objectives and criteria that may enter a university professor's choice between employment at neighboring universities.[1]

---

[1] We note that such a hierarchical representation of the preference structure is the starting point for one of the most well-known and used MCDM techniques, the socalled Analytical Hierarchy Method, originally developed by T.L. Saaty.

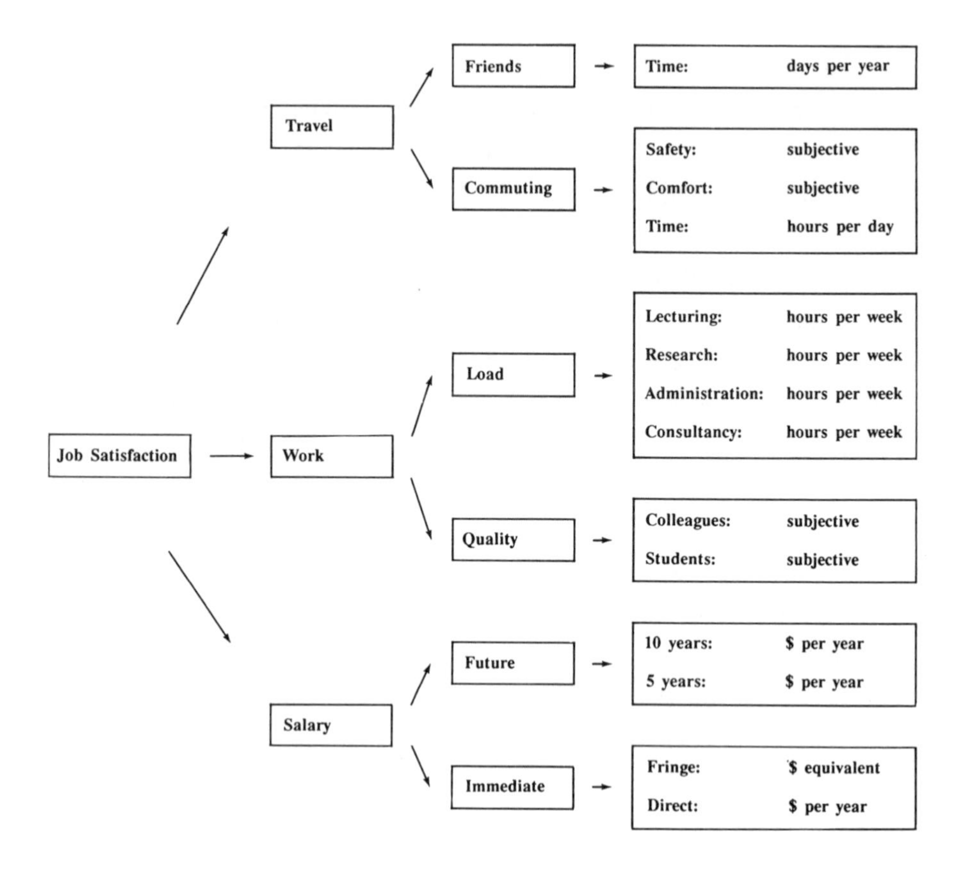

Figure 7.1. A Hierarchy of Values, Objectives and Criteria

One of the hard problems when setting up a hierarchy of values, objectives and criteria is when to stop the horizontal and vertical expansion. At the top, we have a natural stopping point in the all-inclusive reasons for being concerned in the first place. At the bottom, however, we do not have a natural stopping point, and one has to be pragmatic. On the one hand we want many dimensions to get an operational and yet comprehensive picture, on the other hand we only want the important ones to be included so as to keep things tractable. Different measures like the use of proxy attributes and subjective indices may alleviate us, cf. below. However, they do not eliminate the issue, and in the end, experience, rules of thumb, an open mind and in particular a feeling for the context determine the appropriateness of the specification. If, for example, the DM and the AN coincide, then an index expressing the DM's subjective evaluations of an attribute might be reasonable; if this is not the case, more objective measures may be advantageous. Also, for example, an attempt to reconcile viewpoints may call for substantial decomposition into objective measures so as to identify the points of disagreement.

In most cases, we cannot even imagine the DM's basic values decomposed into a comprehensive set of objective, directly measurable criteria like dollars and hours of transportation. Furthermore, even if such a breakdown is conceivable, we would not expect it to pay off since the costs of measuring and communicating and processing the details would become overwhelming. So, whether by necessity or choice, we must live with hierarchies based upon stopping the decomposition short of providing a complete picture in terms of objective, directly measurable quantities. This calls for the use of proxy attributes, subjective indices and direct preference measurements.

A **proxy or surrogate attribute** is one that reflects the degree to which an associated objective is met without directly measuring it. Theoretically, all criteria are probably proxies, but from an applied point of view, they are so to a varying degree, and the concept at least points to some important considerations. Proxies may be related either to the factors contributing to or the results following from achievement of the basic objective. If, for example, one plans the operation of an emergency service like ambulances, a basic objective may be to optimize the conditions of patients at the arrival at the hospital. One may proxy for this, for example, by one of the causes, average response time, or one of the effects, proportion of patients dead at arrival.

Also, observe that certain proxies are so commonly used that we almost believe them to be intrinsic, i.e. what basically matters. In macro-economic planning, for example, it is common to regard gross national product, inflation, unemployment, and the balance of payment as the things we really care about even though the population's (economic) wellbeing is what really matters. Also, at the micro-economic level we are so used to focusing on revenues, costs, market shares and the like that it is often forgotten that these measures probably just proxy for such intangibles as prestige, power to implement ideas, security, degrees of freedom and present and future consumption - all of which profit and market share may help us to achieve.

It is important to note the effect of using proxies with a somewhat remote relation to the DM's basic concerns. It implies that the DM has to take over some of the AN's problems of relating variables and characteristics to objectives. The DM has to do some of the synthesizing, he has to develop and carry part of the total model in his head. Thus, in the ambulance example, if response time is selected as one of the criteria to measure the quality of the service, the DM implicitly is required to predict the patients' conditions for given response times.

Most of the concrete criteria above, like profit, gross national product, and response time, are said to be objective in the sense that there exist reasonably well defined, commonly employed and understood procedures for their calculation. Other attributes, like the comfort of a car, the beauty of a product or the quality of a health service have no well defined measurement standards. Therefore, in order to use formal evaluation procedures, one may have to construct a **subjective index**, where the DM or some other individual or group subjectively defines a correspondence between the alternatives (characteristics) and an attribute level ranging for example from 0 (bad) to 1 (good). The DM may be asked, for example, to subjectively describe the aesthetic appeal of alternative buildings on a scale ranging from 0 to 1. Another example deals with the question of noise. Noise can be measured scientifically on a decibel scale. This presumes however that the proper instrumentation is available **and** that what really matters is the noise intensity and not the feeling of discomfort due to noise which may be experienced by say neighbors to a proposed new airport. If either of these conditions is not fulfilled, it may be more relevant to simply have a representative group of neighbors to the forthcoming airport express their feelings of discomfort with respect to simulated noise from alternative airport designs.

We do not want to be more precise here, since we mainly want to stress the general idea. Instead of expanding the hierarchy forever in an attempt to give a comprehensive picture of the DM's intentions in terms of objectively measurable characteristics, we might use subjective measures at a higher level. Of course, this really requires the DM to aggregate some of his multiple intentions. Therefore, we are in fact beginning the aggregation of multiple criteria that lies at the heart of preference modelling and to which the next sections are devoted.

7.3. Preference Modelling

We have discussed above how one may develop a first, crude description of the DM's preferences in terms of n different criteria. This may be a difficult process, involving as it does an investigaation into the DM's basic values. Still, delineating the relevant criteria does not suffice to guide choice. As observed repeatedly by now, we cannot in general simultaneously maximize several criteria. Different objectives call for different alternatives. Therefore, to decide on a specific alternative, a compromise must be made. To do so in a systematic, rational manner, we must somehow introduce information as to the relative importance of the different objectives. From this vantage point, we must, one way or the other, extract information about the DM's willingness to trade-off achievements in the different criteria. This is the kind of investigations to which we now turn.

Before attempting to build a more detailed model of the DM's preferences, it may be useful to reduce the set of circumstances that it must be able to cope with. Any model will be an approximation and it is important to know where we want it to approximate well. Assuming that the set of criteria is complete, we might safely shift attention from the original, often very complicated decision space X to criteria space $Y=\{(f_1(x), \ldots, f_n(x)) \mid x \in X\}$. Furthermore, we can use the results of chapter 6 and eliminate dominated alternatives. So, in theory at least, we have come up with a reduced set Y_E, the set of efficient alternatives in criteria space. What we need now is more information about the DM's attitudes towards the elements of Y_E.

However, the approaches below actually involve preference modelling over some possibly much larger set Y' containing Y_E. This reflects the tendency of the present planning mode to study preferences quite detached from the particular set of alternatives at hand. There may be good reasons to do so.

First, we might not know X,Y and Y_E precisely to begin with. Secondly, we may want our preference model to be useful in repeated choice contexts with possibly varying sets of alternatives. Thirdly, we might want to generate preference information using simple, and therefore perhaps hypothetical questions. We might for example ask the DM about his willingness in a hypothetical context to decrease the value of one criterion in order to achieve a unit increase in another criterion, even though no pair of real alternatives involves this trade-off. In effect, therefore, we model the DM's preferences not only on Y_E but on a larger set Y', which contains hypothetical alternatives as well.

In the following, then, we shall be concerned with the problem of modelling a DM's preferences towards the - possibly infeasible, future, or hypothetical - alternatives in Y'. To avoid overloading the notation, we shall not, however, distinguish between Y' and Y. We simply write Y and just remind the reader that this may be a set of alternatives that is distinct from the actual set, but which at least contains the actual set of efficient alternatives.

In the previous chapters, we have often thought of the DM's preference model in terms of some underlying, but unknown preference function $F:\Re^n \rightarrow \Re$ such that

$$y' >^* y'' \Leftrightarrow F(y') > F(y'')$$

where $>^*$ once again means "preferred to". The preference function F essentially aggregates the n different criteria. We will encounter this kind of representation shortly, where we will discuss when modelling in terms of F is possible and relevant. However, for reasons which will become apparent, we start at an even more basic level here. We commence by discussing properties of the underlying, primitive evaluations like "preferred to".

7.4. Completeness

A basic property of preference structures is that of **completeness**. In the preference models developed in economics and operational research it is usually stipulated that the DM is able to compare any pair of alternatives, say y' and y" in Y and to determine whether he (1) likes the first better than the second (y' strictly preferred to y", $y' >^* y''$), (2) the second better than the first (y" strictly preferred to y', $y'' >^*$

y') or (3) feels equally comfortable about them (y' indifferent to y", $y' \approx^* y''$). Exactly one and only one of these statements must be true for a given pair of alternatives.

We might note immediately that this may be a rather demanding assumption. There is no room for incomparabilities, for hesitation or for vague judgements. If the DM does not express a strict preference for one of two possibly very different plans, it is taken to mean that they are equally good. Also, he is not allowed to be unclear about whether or not a minor modification of a plan represents a significant improvement and hence a strict preference as opposed to an indifference. We will loosen these assumptions in sections 7.11 - 7.13. It will be seen that this results in more flexible models which, however, are not able to provide as precise delineations with respect to preferences and therefore do not allow as forceful prescriptions as to which alternative to choose.

7.5. Transitivity

The second assumption in classical, so-called ordinal, preference models is that of transitivity. This assumption permits us to rank not only two, but any number of alternatives in a consistent manner.

The best way to understand it is probably in terms of weak preferences. Let us define: y' weakly preferred to y", $y' \geq^* y''$, to mean that y' is strictly preferred to y" ($y' >^* y''$) or y' is indifferent to y" ($y' \approx^* y''$), i.e.

$$
\begin{aligned}
y' \geq^* y'' &\Leftrightarrow \text{y' weakly preferred to y''} \\
&\Leftrightarrow y' >^* y'' \vee y' \approx^* y''
\end{aligned}
$$

where the symbol "V" represents the conjunction "or". So, $y' \geq^* y''$ means that the DM feels at least as well off choosing y' as y", i.e. that y" is not strictly preferred to y'.

Now, the second assumption is that "weakly preferred to" is a transitive relation, i.e.

$$y' \geq^* y'' \wedge y'' \geq^* y''' \Rightarrow y' \geq^* y'''$$

So, for example, if we weakly prefer a Saab (y') to a Volkswagen (y") and we weakly prefer a Volkswagen (y") to a Honda (y'''), we must also weakly prefer a Saab (y') to a Honda (y''').

This assumption seems innocent at first. Indeed, it is the kind of ordering property we naturally would suggest preferences to have. If we are happy (or at least not unhappy) to go from y' to y", and happy (at least not unhappy) to go from y" to y''', we must also be happy (at least not unhappy) with the whole shift from y' to y'''. Also, it is clear that transitivity of at least the strict preference $>^*$ is necessary to avoid a total breakdown of our attempt to pick out a good alternative. Without transitive preferences we may have y' $>^*$ y" $>^*$ y''' and yet y''' $>^*$ y', i.e. the ranking may cycle. This may imply that no choice (or all choices) can be justified. Any proposal can be beaten.[2]

Nevertheless, the assumption is not innocent. We assume not only transitivity of strict preferences but also transitivity of weak preferences $\geq^*$. Together with the first assumption this implies that indifference $\approx^*$ is assumed to be transitive. So, to take a classic example, if you do not care whether your coffee contains 1 og 2 grams of sugar and if you are not able to distinguish between 2 or 3 grams, you must also be equally well off having 1 or 3 grams in your cup. And so on. In other words, the assumption as to transitivity does not allow small insignificant differences to accumulate into something important - which may be quite unreasonable if it leads to indifference between say black coffee and a cup of pure sugar. Clearly then, assuming transitivity requires the DM's evaluation apparatus to be extremely well developed in order to avoid results similar to those which could be derived from the coffee example. We will discuss methods to cope with such issues in sections 7.11 -7.13 below.

---

[2] Such cycling can be met if we temporarily leave our domain of intra-personal conflict. We consider a group of individuals, each of whom has transitive preferences, who agree to settle their disagreements by using democratic rules. A classic example is the case of 3 decision makers: I, II and III who are to choose amongst 3 alternatives: A, B and C where I prefers A to B to C, II prefers B to C to A and III prefers C to A to B. If they agree to abide by majority rule, then A is preferred to B, B is preferred to C and C is preferred to A!

7.6. A Classical Preference Model

In essence then, **the classical, ordinal preference model** traditionally employed in economics and operations research views the DM as capable of making (1) **complete** comparisons, i.e of comparing any two alternatives in (2) a **transitive** manner consistent with the idea of having an ordering from worst to best.

Readers with a more mathematical inclination should note that using the terminology of measurement theory, this may be expressed as the assumption that the DM has a relation $>^*$, interpreted to mean strictly preferred to and assumed to be a so-called **strict weak order**. Equivalently, it may be expressed in terms of a relation $\geq^*$, interpreted as meaning weakly preferred to and assumed to be a so-called **weak order**. Reference is made to the more formal exposition presented in appendix 2.

For readers without such a background, the best way to think of the model is probably in terms of the intuitively appealing notion of indifference mappings. When we are indifferent between two alternatives, i.e. when we cannot say that we prefer the one to the other and vice versa, they lie on the same indifference curve; such points are said to be indifferent - even though it is the DM of course who is indifferent. In our context of "more is preferred to less", higher level indifference curves correspond to more preferred alternatives. We have already encountered several instances of indifference mappings in earlier chapters and there is no need to provide new examples at this point. To relate the two interpretations, it is useful to emphasize that the formal model underlying the usual geometry of indifference mappings is in fact the classical, ordinal preference model, possibly supplemented by some additional properties like nonsaturation and continuity, c.f. below.

There is a close relation between the classical ordinal preference model and our previous use of an aggregate utility or preference function F. This is the content of theorem 1, where it is assumed that Y is finite. Proof of a generalized version is provided in appendix 2.

Theorem 1

Let us assume that Y is finite. Then the DM's preference relation $>^*$ is a classical, ordinal preference structure if and only if there exists a function F: $Y \rightarrow \Re$ such that

$$y' >^* y'' \Leftrightarrow F(y') > F(y'') \qquad \forall \; y', y'' \in Y$$

○

The proof of theorem 1 is straightforward. Given $>^*$ we might define F(y) as the number or cardinality of the alternatives worse than y, i.e.

$$F(y) = \text{cardinality}\{ y' \in Y \mid y' {}^*\!< y \}$$

Using the properties of the classical, ordinal preference model, it is easy to show that F takes larger values on better alternatives. On the other hand, given F, the relation $>^*$ defined by the bi-implication in theorem 1 inherits its properties through the equivalent properties of the relation larger than > in the real numbers.

According to theorem 1, we impose the same kind of regularity on the DM if we stipulate that he conforms with the classical, ordinal preference model or if we assume that he has some underlying, unknown preference function F. Furthermore, the theorem emphasizes what we implicitly require when we assume the existence of criteria having the property that the DM prefers more to less. Substituting f_i for F, we see that the DM's evaluation according to his i'th criterion must conform with the assumptions of the classical model. In particular, when judging the alternatives' performances in the i'th dimension, there must be no instances of incomparabilities, hesitation, vague judgements and no cases of minor, insignificant differences accumulating to significant ones.

Finally, we might add that the preference function F in theorem 1 is not uniquely defined; if we **rescale** F but maintain its "ordering", then the results of theorem 1 are still valid. This is a reminder that ordinal utility numbers have only limited meaning. They simply give a ranking. They cannot be added, multiplied or otherwise manipulated; only direct comparisons involving >, = and < are meaningful. It is meaningless, for example, to say that y' is twice as good as y", $F(y')/F(y'')=2$, since by a change of scale this ratio can be manipulated to give any other number larger than 1.

So far, we have discussed preference structures at a rather abstract level. It seems natural now to look at some concrete structures and in particular at the role of trade-offs.

A somewhat extreme case of the classical preference model, i.e. of a complete and transitive ordering, is the **lexicographical ordering.** In this model, the different criteria are given strict priorities such that, for example, f_1 is all that matters when alternatives are to be compared unless there is a tie here, i.e. several alternatives are equally attractive according to f_1, in which case f_2 is all that matters, unless there is a tie here too, in which case criterion 3 is decisive, and so on. So, a less important criterion enter the picture if and only if all more important criteria are unable to distinguish between the alternatives. In the case of two criteria, the lexicographical ordering may be formally defined as

$$y' >^* y'' \Leftrightarrow y_1' > y_1'' \vee [y_1' = y_1'' \wedge y_2' > y_2'']$$

So, the lexicographical ordering organizes the alternatives in the same way as subjects are organized in a lexicon or dictionary.

The lexicographical ordering is very easy to describe. In elementary first aid, for example, one is taught to secure respiration first and foremost, next to care about blood circulation, and when all this is done, to prevent chock. This virtue of the ordering, its naive simplicity, is at the same time its drawback. In practical first aid, for example, no one would seriously focus on a slightly reduced respiration level if the victim of a car accident is suffering from a heavy blood drain. Similarly, in a business context, although the emphasis on the "bottom line" could lead us to believe that profits simply come first as long as the decisions are legal, it is rather difficult to conceive of a decision maker who would not be willing to trade off say one additional cent of profit for huge increases in say worker satisfaction and recognition from one's peers and the local community, vastly improved safety and environmental results.

More generally, the lexicographical ordering models a very extreme attitude towards trade-offs. There is absolutely no willingness to trade-off performance in one criterion against performance in other criteria. A decrease in f_1 can never be compensated by an increase in f_2. To be preferentially indifferent, two alternatives must do equally well in all respects. This implies that the indifference regions are single points; indifference curves as such do not exist! All different points represent different performance levels.

When there is only a finite number of points in Y, we can represent a lexicographical ordering by a preference function F as explained in theorem 1. However, when Y is a "continuous" set, for example the plane $\Re^2$, this is not possible. Since no two different points in $\Re^2$ are indifferent in the lexicographical ordering, a preference function should assign different numbers to all different points in the plane $\Re^2$, and this is clearly not possible. Technically, we cannot construct a "one-to-one" mapping of $\Re^2$ to $\Re$. Identical results hold of course for any number of criteria leading to the conclusion that a lexicographical ordering on a "continuous" set cannot be represented by a preference function.

7.7. Trade-Off Information

An important property when trying to construct preference models is the DM's willingness to make trade-offs, i.e. his ability to identify alternatives that he is preferentially indifferent to. As soon as we leave the simple cases with a "discrete" set of alternatives, the DM's willingness to make trade-offs is crucial for the construction of a preference function which can map his preferences into the real numbers. This is quite obvious since the preference function must take different values on different indifference regions. Therefore, the existence of a preference function is basically a question of having a set of indifference regions with a simple one-dimensional ordering, since these are the orderings we can represent by real numbers. This explains the problem of representing the lexicographical ordering in terms of a preference function. In this ordering, the indifference relation has no bite whatsoever. All points constitute different indifference regions. So, no simplicity is gained from attempts to make trade-offs and no representation in terms of a preference function exists when Y is not finite, or at least so-called "countable", c.f. appendix 2.

However, in other cases it is possible to reduce a higher dimensional problem to at least a lower dimensional one by introducing trade-offs. In general, this procedure is known as that of **cancelling out the indifference relation** or **pricing out attributes.** Imagine, for example, a decision problem characterized by n criteria where y_1 is some monetary benefit and y_2 is some other benefit. Now, one way to start examining the preference structure may be to price out y_2. For any point $y \in Y$, one may ask the DM how large an increase p(y) in y_1 he requests to reduce y_2 to some base level y_2^*, assuming that the values of all the remaining n-2 criteria remain unchanged. Thus, the "price" p(y) is the increase required in the first criterion y_1 to balance a reduction of the second criterion from y_2 to y_2^*.

More formally, we define p(y) by

$$(y_1, y_2, \ldots, y_n) \approx^* (y_1 + p(y), y_2^*, y_3, \ldots, y_n)$$

i.e. by the requirement that the two alternatives lie on the same indifference curve.

This procedure for determining p(y) is illustrated in figure 7.2 below for the case n=2. It is worth observing that having priced out y_2, we might return to the initial step of eliminating dominated alternatives. The dominance relation has more bite now that we have introduced information about the relative importance of y_1 and y_2. In figure 7.2, for example, y' and y" could not be compared initially. However, knowing p(y') and p(y") and observing $y_1' + p(y') < y_1'' + p(y'')$ the (extended) dominance relation allows us to discard y'.

More generally, we see that knowing the price p(y) for all $y \in Y$ enables the original n dimensional problem to be reduced to a n-1 dimensional one. Since for all $y \in Y$ we may substitute $(y_1 + p(y), y_2^*, \ldots, y_n)$ for $(y_1, y_2, \ldots, y_n)$, we have effectively fixed and hence eliminated or cancelled out the second coordinate. Only n-1 dimensions remain. Indeed, if we could successively price out all the last n-1 criteria in our original model we would be back to a traditional, one-criteria optimization problem.

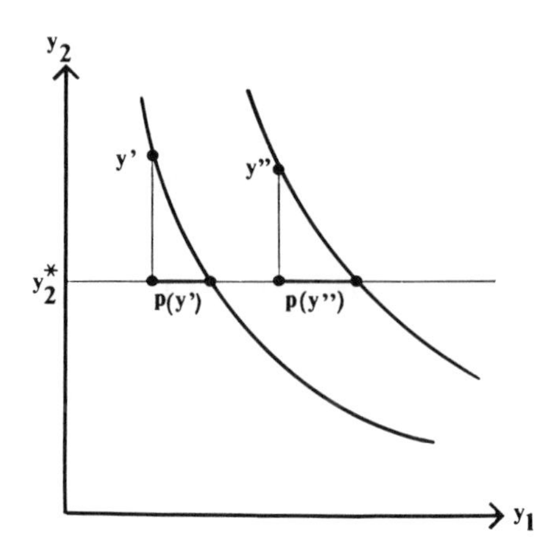

Figure 7.2. Pricing Out

It is important to emphasize that the price p(y) in general will depend on the whole bundle of criteria values $y=(y_1, \ldots, y_n)$. In particular, this will be the case if the decision which is being contemplated can result in significant changes in the values of some or all of the criteria.

To exemplify this, consider first a simple two criteria problem where an employee whose preferences are defined by his remuneration and hours of free time is being considered for promotion to a job with higher pay. He would be willing to work one hour extra a week for say $20, but if the new job required 5 additional hours a week, he would not be satisfied with a wage increase of less than $150. In other words, the salary increase he requires to offset an hour's reduced free time depends on the level of his free time.

To give another example, consider a restaurant guest who has to choose a menu as described by three criteria: price (as measured in $), wine (as measured by red=1, white=0) and the main course (as measured by beef=1, fish=0). Hence, we assume that he prefers red wine to white wine and beef to fish. Now, while considering a main course of steak, he may be willing to pay an extra $5 to accompany this meal by red wine instead of white wine. If, however, he considers having fish, he may only be willing to pay $1 extra to have red wine rather than white wine.[3]

The striking characteristic of this example is that the criteria are not "preferentially independent", a term to be made precise in section 7.9 below. The value of one criterion, here the main course, affects the trade-off between other criteria, here price and wine.

In theory, such dependencies do not invalidate the pricing out procedure. However, they do imply that we must allow p(y) to depend both on the current values of the two criteria involved as well as on the values of the remaining n-2 criteria. Therefore, in practice it will be a tremendous task to determine p(y) for all $y \in Y$. The DM must in principle be interrogated about his p(y) for all possible alternatives just to reduce the problem from one involving n criteria to one involving n-1 criteria. In practice, therefore, the procedure will not be useful unless we impose additional assumptions to simplify the determination of p(y), or more general, to simplify the delineation of indifference curves. We return to such assumptions in section 7.9.

Furthermore, a DM may feel awkward if he is asked to price-out in situations where the transformation process does not correspond to his normal way of thinking. This may for example be the case if a DM faces a choice involving a new, costly but highly effective technology. If the new technology is introduced, it will require major changes in the whole production process and the existing organization. It may be "unnatural" for the DM to be asked to state the cost reduction he would require to counterbalance the changes in the organization and its culture.

If on the other hand the decision situation is only expected to lead to marginal changes in the criteria values, then a simple interrogation of the DM's willingness to price out one criterion with respect to another may be quite reasonable; this corresponds to the economist's typical "everything else being equal" assumption.

---

[3] **Indeed, if he is old-fashioned, he would probably require a reduced price for having to live with red wine rather than white wine here.**

In this chapter we are concerned with preference models as developed in axiomatic theories. Therefore, we are focusing on exact trade-offs and the willingness to substitute as defined by two points belonging to the same indifference curve. In many applications, however, and in particular in interactive investigative procedures, it suffices to look at approximate trade-offs. For ease of future reference, we therefore insert a short digression on this subject here. Similar to the case of substitution possibilities which we considered in the previous chapter, the classical way to describe **approximate substitution wishes** is by linear approximation.

Consider a DM with indifference curves as depicted in figure 7.3 below. You might think of them as level curves of some preference function F.

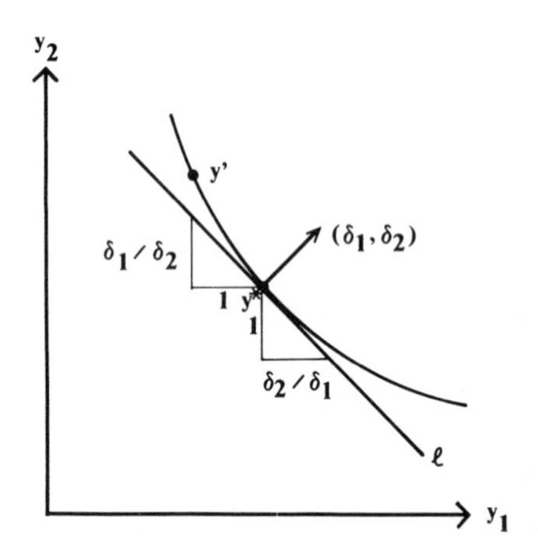

Figure 7.3. Substitution Wishes

Exact trade-off wishes are defined by two points belonging to the same indifference curve. The DM above is exactly willing to substitute the decrease of y_1^* to y_1' in the first criteria for the improvement of y_2^* to y_2' in the second criteria. Approximate trade-offs wishes are defined by the linear approximation ℓ: $\delta_1(y_1-y_1^*)+\delta_2(y_2-y_2^*)=0$ to the indifference curve through y*, i.e. by the normal vector (δ_1,δ_2). If we have an explicit expression of the preference function F and if F is well-behaved, partially differentiable to be precise, this normal vector may be defined as $(\partial F/\partial y_1, \partial F/\partial y_2)$. In analogy with the terminology in chapter 6.7 we might call $\delta(y^*)=(\delta_1,\delta_2)$ the **substitution (wishes) coefficients** at y^*. In economics, the ratio δ_2/δ_1 is often called the local, **marginal rate of substitution** of y_1 for y_2.

The **interpretation** of these coefficients is simple. As illustrated in figure 7.3, they tell us that to give up 1 unit of y_1, the DM requires at least δ_1/δ_2 units of y_2. Equivalently, to give up 1 unit of y_2, he requires at least δ_2/δ_1 units of y_1. Note, that the substitution coefficients give a locally rather precise picture of the DM's willingness to substitute. Globally, however, they give a somewhat optimistic picture, since the approximation is from below. In fact, the DM normally requires more than δ_1/δ_2 units of y_2 and, correspondingly, more than δ_2/δ_1 units of y_1. Summarizing, we might therefore say that the marginal rates of substitution, give a locally precise but globally exaggerated picture of the DM's willingness to substitute around y^*.

7.8. A Compensatory Model

As underlined in section 7.6, preference structures cannot in general be adequately modelled by lexicographical stiffness. Therefore, we will proceed by looking at compensatory models, i.e. models where genuine trade-offs between criteria are indeed possible. First, we will go to the other extreme, assuming that nothing can be extremely good or important, and nothing can be extremely bad or unimportant. Then, in sections 7.11-7.13, we will discuss models allowing both compensation as well as some degree of vetoing or lexicographical stiffness.

Economists and operational researchers often work with a slightly **specialized version of the classical, ordinal preference model.** If, e.g., $y=(y_1, \ldots, y_n)$ represents the consumption levels of n different goods, they assume that a DM always wants more, i.e. they accept the **non-saturation** property

$$[\forall i: y_i' \geq y_i'' \wedge \exists j: y_j' > y_j''] \Rightarrow y' >^* y''$$

That is, it is always attractive to increase the consumption of any good, however slightly. Also, it is assumed that it makes good sense to take weighted averages (convex combinations) of consumption bundles, and that any intermediate level of satisfaction may be obtained this way. In other words, we accept the **continuity** property

$$\forall\, y' >^* y >^* y'' \; \exists\, \lambda \in [0,1]: \; y \approx^* \lambda y' + (1-\lambda) y''$$

These properties are easiest to understand in terms of indifference mappings. The first property, the dominance or non-saturation property, says that indifference curves cannot be "thick". The second, the continuity or Archemedian condition, says that the line between any two commodity bundles intersects the indifference curves correspon-ding to all intermediate utility levels.

If the DM can accept these axioms in addition to the previous ones, it is generally possible and indeed easy to construct a specialized version of the classical, ordinal preference function. This is the content of theorem 2 below. Note that while theorem 1 dealt with the case of a finite number of alternatives, theorem 2 deals with the case where there is an infinite, in fact a multiple dimensional, continuous set of alternatives in criteria space. We assume for simplicity here that all the elements in any vector $y \in Y$ may take on values in the range from a to b, i.e. that $Y = [a,b] x \ldots x [a,b] \subseteq \Re^n$, where $a<b$ are arbitrary, real numbers.

Theorem 2

Let us assume that $Y = [a,b] x \ldots x [a,b] \subseteq \Re^n$, where $a<b$ are arbitrary, real numbers. Also, let us assume that the DM's preference structure constitutes a specialized, ordinal preference model, i.e. in addition to the classical, ordinal preference model, he accepts the non-saturation and continuity assumptions. Then, the DM's preference structure can be modelled by a preference function F, i.e. for all y', y'' ∈ Y

$$y' >^* y'' \Leftrightarrow F(y') > F(y'') \qquad \circ$$

The constructive proof of this theorem, presented in detail in appendix 2, is sufficient-ly educating to be sketched here. Consider any alternative $y=(y_1, \ldots, y_n)$. It easily follows from the non-saturation and continuity assumptions that there is exactly one alternative y' of the form $(\alpha, \alpha, \ldots \alpha)$, such that y and y' are equally attractive, i.e.

$y \approx^* y'$. Now, since alternatives that the DM is indifferent to must have the same value of F, i.e. $F(y)=F(y')$, we just need to construct F on the special alternatives of the form $(\alpha,\alpha, \ldots ,\alpha)$ where $\alpha\in[a,b]$. Again, by non-saturation, this is simple, since we must just ensure that $F(\alpha,\alpha, \ldots \alpha)$ increases with α. We might accomplish this for example by defining $F(\alpha, \ldots ,\alpha)=\alpha$. Summarizing, two steps are involved. First, define $F(\alpha, \ldots ,\alpha)=\alpha$ for all $\alpha\in[a,b]$. Next, for any alternative y not covered this way, determine α such that $y \approx^* (\alpha, \ldots ,\alpha)$ and define $F(y)=\alpha$. Observe how the second step requires the DM to make extensive trade-offs.

A clarifying remark may be useful at this place. In theorem 2, we assumed that the preference relation $>^*$ was given and from this we constructed the preference function F. In multiple criteria planning contexts however, neither $>^*$ nor F is known. In fact, it is this kind of information that we seek. The reader may wonder, therefore, if such results are really relevant for our present purpose. They definitely are. First, at the theoretical level, they illuminate the kind of regularities needed to safely claim, for example, the existence of a preference function. Next, and most important here, many of these results are proved in a constructive manner which may suggest ways of eliciting the preference structure from a real DM. The idea is simple. Whenever the construction requires knowledge about strict preferences or indifferences, ask the DM. For example, instead of using a known indifference mapping to find an indifferent alternative, ask the DM to do so. Part of the terminology used above already reflects this idea. In the pricing out example, we did not just define p(y) so as to give an indifference. Rather, we asked the DM to state p(y) so that he felt equally well off. Similarly, an articulation procedure structured around theorem 2 would require that the DM for each possible alternative $y\in Y$ states an alternative y' of the form $(\alpha,\alpha, \ldots ,\alpha)$, such that y and y' are equally attractive. Learning about α, the AN may then simply define $F(y)=\alpha$. Further illustrations of the DM's necessary involvement are provided below.

Before ending this discussion of the compensatory model, let us comment on an additional regularity, namely **convexity**, which appears quite natural, at least to economists. In economics and related disciplines it is usually assumed that the specialized preference function F is **quasi-concave**, i.e.

$$F(\lambda y' + (1-\lambda)y'') \geq \min\{F(y'), F(y'')\}$$

for all y'and y" in Y and all λ between 0 and 1, or equivalently that the contour sets

$$\{y \in Y \mid F(y) \geq F(y')\} = \{y \in Y \mid y \geq^* y'\}$$

for all $y' \in Y$ are **convex.**

When the DM accepts the non-saturation property, this implies that the indifference curves must be decreasing and convex. Indeed, this is how we have depicted indifference curves throughout this book. In conceptual terms, therefore, it is assumed that the DM's wishes do not get saturated and that his marginal rate of substitution is diminishing, i.e. the amount of y_i the DM is just willing to forego for a unit increase of y_j diminishes as the i-attribute gets more scarce and the j-attribute gets more affluent. This, the so-called law of diminishing marginal rate of substitution, is an empirical proposition, supposedly supported by considerable empirical evidence.

Finally let us note that it is often supposed that F is not only quasi-concave but indeed **concave**, i.e.

$$F(\lambda y' + (1-\lambda)y'') \geq \lambda F(y') + (1-\lambda)F(y'')$$

for all y' and y" in Y and all λ between 0 and 1. This is a stronger assumption and often quasi-concave preferences or convex contour sets in the sense defined above cannot be represented by concave preference functions. Necessary and sufficient conditions for a preference relation to be representable by a concave preference function are known but messy. It seems most appropriate, therefore to look at this latter property of concave representability simply as an analytical convenience which hopefully allows for reasonable approximations in applications.

7.9. Preferential Independence

A major drawback of procedures like the ones suggested in connection with the discussion of compensatory models in sections 7.7 and 7.8 is the extensive interrogations needed. In the pricing out procedure as illustrated in figure 7.2 for example, the DM must for each $y \in Y$ find a possibly fictive alternative with the baselevel performance $y_2{}^*$ that is equally as good as y. This need to trace out the indifference regions point by point follows from our limited a priori knowledge about the character of these regions. The obvious suggestion, therefore, is to introduce (and check) additional axioms allowing one to expect a more convenient, simple structure.

An important property in this context is that of **mutually, preferentially independent criteria.** To define this property, let us first introduce a bit of notation. Let M be any subset of the criteria, $M \subseteq \{1,2, \ldots n\}$, and let us use $(y'_{i \in M}, y''_{i \notin M})$ as a short-hand way of describing the performance profile $y \in Y$ that has $y_i = y_i'$ for $i \in M$ and $y_i = y_i''$ for $i \in \{1,2, \ldots ,n\} \backslash M$. So, $(y'_{i \in M}, y''_{i \notin M})$ is the - possibly fictive - alternative performing like y' with respect to the criteria in M and like y'' with respect to the remaining criteria.

Now, the assumption of mutually, preferentially independent criteria is the condition that for any $M \subseteq \{1, \ldots ,n\}$,

$$(y'_{i \in M}, y_{i \notin M}) >^* (y''_{i \in M}, y_{i \notin M}) \quad \text{for some } y,y',y'' \in Y$$

$$\Rightarrow (y'_{i \in M}, y^+_{i \notin M}) >^* (y''_{i \in M}, y^+_{i \notin M}) \text{ for all } y^+ \in Y$$

So, for any subset of criteria, preferences between actions that are only different on these criteria must not depend on the values of the remaining criteria. Whenever a change of performance in the M-criteria is attractive for some level of the remaining $\{1, \ldots ,n\} \backslash M$ criteria, it must be so for all other levels of these $\{1, \ldots ,n\} \backslash M$ criteria, too.

In practice, one need not check the preferentially independence assumptions for all subsets of M criteria. It is possible to deduce the general property above from less demanding conditions. Using lemma 1 in appendix 2, we might simply assume that the trade-off between y_i and y_j must be independent of the values of the other n-2 criteria for all possible values of y_i and y_j and all values of the indices i and j. Or even more simple, it suffices to assume that the trade-off between y_1 and y_i is independent of the remaining n-2 criteria for all $i=2, \ldots, n$.

For n=2, the independence assumption is rather weak[4]. It simply says that our preference ordering of y_1 values must be independent of the y_2 value and vice versa. This is basically our frequent assumption that more is preferred to less in all criteria. Of course, as referred to on several earlier occasions, even this is not a trivial assumption. It may be prohibited by interaction between the criteria. Thus, e.g., if (y_1,y_2) is a two-criteria description of menues where y_1 takes on the value 1(2) when we have beef(fish) and y_2 is 1(2) when we order red(white) wine, many "well-behaved" DM's would prefer $y_2=1$ to $y_2=2$ when $y_1=1$ and have a reversed ranking when $y_1=2$. This illustrates the necessity to set up the values-objectives-criteria hierarchy intelligently if one is to hope for independence. In this trivial, illustrative example, the overall objective, the quality of the meal, may, for example, be decomposed into attributes like harmony and calories instead, in which case independence is more likely.

For $n \geq 3$, the independence assumption is more powerful, and, as will be seen shortly, it leads to substantial simplifications when attempting to construct a preference function which reflects a DM's underlying preferences. However, the condition is also very demanding. Imagine for example a case of n=3, where y_1 and y_2 are some operational measures of performance for an emergency service, e.g. mean response time and variation in the response time, and y_3 is the cost of the service. The trade-off between the mean and variation of the response times may well be independent of the costs. However, the trade-offs between the variation in response time and costs of the service may easily depend on the mean response time; we may not be willing to pay nearly as much for a relative reduction in variation if the mean response time is low compared to the case where it is high.

---

[4] This explains the need for additional assumptions in this case, c.f. the appendix.

7.10. An Additive Model

An important extension of the classical, ordinal model is the decomposable or **additive preference structure.** In this structure indifference curves are linear, assuming perhaps that some of the criteria have been suitably rescaled. Several additional assumptions are needed to accept this additive preference structure.

Most profoundly, we need preferential independence. The necessity of preferential independence when we seek a decomposable preference function is emphasized by the following theorem. A set of sufficient conditions as well as some additional, necessary conditions are described in appendix 2.

Theorem 3
A necessary condition for the DM's preference structure >* to be represented by an additive preference function, i.e.

$$y' >^* y'' \Leftrightarrow \sum_{i=1}^{n} v_i(y_i') > \sum_{i=1}^{n} v_i(y_i'')$$

is that the criteria are mutually preferentially independent. ○

There is a large literature on concrete procedures that may be used to elicit a DM's preference function. As we have indicated earlier, such procedures implicitly assume that **all** information which is relevant for decisions can be subsumed in a formal expression, F(y). Although the purpose of these notes is not to describe concrete techniques, it seems natural to end this discussion of complete and transitive preference strucures by indicating what an application of the previous models may amount to. **A concrete procedure** may well contain the following three steps, all of which may involve substantial iterative questioning of the DM.

As **step 1,** one may try to **check the axioms** of some concrete model. To check transitivity, for example, may involve the DM in expressing preferences between y' and y'', y' and y''', and between y'' and y'''. Now, if the DM states y' >* y'' and y'' >* y''', he must also, to conform with the axiom, state y' >* y'''. Indeed, he must do so for many (all) possible triples of profiles. Other axioms can be checked along similar lines. It should be observed, too, that further checking naturally occurs throughout the subsequent steps. Of course, inconsistencies may well arise. Instead of discarding the model immediately, one may then request the DM to rethink his evaluation. In particular, the DM may well change his preferences during the procedure, and this may call for repetitions.

As **step 2**, one may try to **estimate the concrete model** preliminarily accepted by step 1. For example consider a case where two criteria are felt to be adequate for evaluating a group of alternatives and where the AN feels that, in the given context, the additive model will provide a reasonable support for the DM when making his choice. In this case the calibration may be accomplished by the so-called **lockstep procedure**. First, the AN fixes the origin as the minimal possible values of the criteria, i.e. by letting $y_i^0 = \min\{y_i | y \in Y\}$ for i=1,2 and defining $v_1(y_1^0) = v_2(y_2^0) = 0$. Next, he fixes the measurement unit by selecting some $y_1^1 > y_1^0$ and defining $v_1(y_1^1) = 1$. Now, to find the same value contribution from the second criteria, $v_2(y_2^1) = 1$, the DM is asked to determine the level of y_2^1 such that

$$(y_1^1, y_2^0) \approx^* (y_1^0, y_2^1)$$

Next, the AN asks the DM to specify y_1^2 and y_2^2 such that he can subscribe to

$$(y_1^2, y_2^0) \approx^* (y_1^1, y_2^1) \approx^* (y_1^0, y_2^2)$$

This defines the criteria values such that $v_1(y_1^2) = v_2(y_2^2) = 2$.

At this point, one may well check the additivity assumption by asking the DM if he agrees that

$$(y_1^1, y_2^2) \approx^* (y_1^2, y_2^1)$$

The AN now proceeds to the criteria values giving $v_1(y_1^3) = v_2(y_2^3) = 3$ by asking the DM to state values y_1^3 and y_2^3 such that he feels comfortable with the statements

$$(y_1^3, y_2^0) \approx^* (y_1^2, y_2^1) \text{ and } (y_1^0, y_2^3) \approx^* (y_1^1, y_2^2)$$

and so he continues. Having calibrated v_1 and v_2 this way for a certain number of points, the AN may now estimate handy functional approximations of v_1 and v_2.

Finally, as **step 3**, it may be useful to **check the total result** of all these minor and simplified investigations. One may ask the DM to state his preferences between some more realistic, complex criteria value combinations and to compare this with the prediction of the total model. Any major differences, which cannot be reconciled by the DM rethinking his statements, may be an indication that the decomposition approach and its substantial use of hypothetical questions has contributed to systematical errors, i.e. that the approach does **not** capture the DM's actual preferences.

7.11. Intransitive Preferences

In recent years, classical preference theory as outlined above has come under increasing attack. It is often felt that this paradigme is much too restrictive to aid real world decision making. One should not aim to make consistent, pairwise comparisons at all costs. In particular, strong arguments have been made that incomparabilities and intransitivities should be allowed. The point here is that we are imperfect mortals and lack the perfect consistency demanded by the classical theory.

Of course a slackening of the demands as to consistency of the preference model can be expected to lead to less forceful prescriptions. Using such a less demanding preference model on a given set of alternatives may not result in the identification of a preferred solution but simply in a reduced set of (efficient) alternatives from which the final choice should be made by other, presumably less formal and more intuitive means. Still, this should not discourage us. An initial screening of alternatives based on easily accepted value premises may be a good starting point, just as the efficiency concept provides a useful filter. In fact, this view of preference modelling

as a process of enriching the dominance (efficiency) relation so as to aid the solution of the choice problem, instead of attempting to solve it at all costs, conforms nicely with our view of multiple criteria planning as a cyclic process involving investigation, communication and choice.
Also, as mentioned earlier, incomplete preference models may be useful tools in an attempt to handle more repetitive choice problems. In a hierarchical structure, for example, it may be useful for higher levels to endow lower levels with such a partial description of intentions since it may reduce the frequency of hierarchical referrals.

In this and the subsequent two sections we give an introduction to such less demanding but perhaps more appropriate and operational preference structures.

The earliest attack on the classical preference models concerns the assumption of **transitive indifferences.** The example as to a cup of coffee and sugar which we referred to earlier illustrates the potential problems which follow in the wake of this assumption. There is no real room for vague judgements or limited discriminating power if indiffernces are to be transitive. In particular, small, insignificant differences cannot be permitted to accumulate into something important. Alternative models designed to overcome this problem have long been known. A detailed tretment of the basic properties of the DM's evaluations in such models is given in appendix 2 where we discuss so-called semi-orders and inverval-orders. The idea of these models is that to justify a strict improvement - from an overall perspective (F) or from a more restricted perspective (f_i) - the performance of the preferred alternative must exceed that of the less preferred alternative with a certain **indifference-threshold** value, say q. Thus, for example, we may have

$$y' >^* y'' \Leftrightarrow F(y') > F(y'') + q$$

From this it easily follows that y' and y'' are indifferent whenever $|F(y')-F(y'')| \leq q$, i.e. whenever their preference function values deviate by no more than q. This naturally leads to or reflects intransitive indifferences since small, insignificant differences, i.e. differences no larger than q, are allowed to accumulate. Thus, one may for example have $F(y')=F(y'')+0.75q$ and $F(y'')=F(y''')+0.75q$ so that $y' \approx^* y''$ and $y'' \approx^* y'''$, and yet $F(y')=F(y''')+1.5q > F(y''')+q$ so that $y' >^* y'''$.

As the representation above indicates, threshold structures allow us to model a DM with less discrimatory capacity than those previously studied. This is convenient since in most planning contexts there are probably, among the areas of firm conviction, hazy zones of uncertainty or halfheld beliefs. Instead of introducing these characteristics explicitly by probability models or so-called fuzzy models, it may be convenient to use thresholds, at least as a first attempt to filter away some alternatives. We note, however, that this improved modelling capacity is obtained via the introduction of a rather ad hoc parameter, q.

In particular, this may therefore be a reasonable approach when the data available is not too reliable or when we lack more precise knowledge of the relationships between our intentions and available statistics in terms of **proxies**. When, for example, we plan ambulance services and proxy for an injured patient's condition upon his arrival at the hospital by the average response time, we explicitly ask the DM to do a lot of cognitive modelling and synthesizing. He might well be quite uncertain about the relationship between response time and the state of arriving patients. He may even see conflicts as pushing for too prompt an average response time might increase the chance of ambulances being involved in accidents.

Also, the problem of **omitted criteria** seems important here. Realizing that the set of criteria chosen to characterize a choice problem can never really be complete, one may be reluctant to disregard an alternative which is only slightly dominated by an efficient alternative. One may fear that there is an omitted criteria where the inefficient alternative perhaps does substantially better. Consider for example the planning of a major food distribution system and in particular as regards the location of terminals. Let us imagine that two alternative approaches are being debated: a centralized plan with few terminals and a decentralized plan with many terminals. Assume too, that the centralized plan appears to be better with respect to all the modelled criteria. Suppose now that discussion of the plans leads to the realization that the focus has been on fairly easily quantifiable measures of performance and that the more qualitative objective, "flexibility", which could perhaps have been characterized by one or more surrogate criteria, appears to be omitted. Assume too, that the roundtable discussions which ensue point very clearly to the decentralized alternative as being best in this respect. In this case, one may well appreciate the use of thresholds. These ensure a certain safety margin and require that the plan chosen according to the original criteria is so superior with respect to these criteria, that it is likely that the plan chosen will be preferred, even after the DM becomes aware of the unexpected negative effect of centralizing.

We should probably emphasize at this point that two quite different perspectives on indifference thresholds are introduced above. One is the **theoretical perspective**, according to which thresholds simply reflect a lack of discriminatory power. Two alternatives, the performances of which do not deviate by more than q, are considered to be equally attractive. That is, if no strict preference is expressed, the DM is indifferent. The other is more of a **practical perspective** as reflected by the proxy and omitted criteria stories above. According to this perspective, two alternatives, the performances of which do not deviate by more than q, need not be equally good. The lack of expressed preference simply reflects that due to our doubts as to the adequacy of F we are not able to say decisively that one alternative is better than another. Presently, we do not know how to discriminate between such alternatives. Presumably, however, the DM will be able to do so by introducing additional viewpoints or by sharpening his evaluations.

Before we proceed to some additional modifications of the classical models, let us therefore comment briefly on how they may influence the kind of prescriptions one can make as to the choice of alternative. Readers with little taste for more methodological discussions may choose to skip the next four paragraphs.

Let us start by considering the concept of **optimality**. If F is the DM's preference function, then in the classical, ordinal preference model the AN is on firm ground by simply recommending any alternative maximizing F, i.e. any specific alternative in

$$Y^* = \{y \in Y \mid F(y) = \max_{y' \in Y} F(y')\}$$

If F represents the DM's preferences in the semi-order model above, then according to the theoretical perspective, the AN may safely recommend any alternative in

$$Y^{opt} = \{y \in Y \mid F(y) \geq \max_{y' \in Y} F(y') - q\}$$

Anyone of them appears to be equally good. In fact they cannot be distinguished or ranked as they deviate at most by the threshold value q. In particular, within our model, the AN is on firm ground by simply recommending any alternative maximizing F.

From the practical perspective, however, the DM is presumably able to make such discriminations among alternatives in Y^{opt} by introducing additional viewpoints or sharpening the evaluations. If we take this perspective, i.e. if we look at the so-called **semi-order** structure introduced here as a first attempt, as a first cut into the preference structure, we are naturally led to having the DM choose between all points in Y^{opt}. In the literature taking this perspective, Y^{opt} is often referred to as the **kernel** of the relation system $(Y,>^*)$. That is, a) Y^{opt} is a preference dominating subset of Y in the sense that for all $y \in Y \setminus Y^{opt}$ there exists a $y' \in Y^{opt}$ such that $y' >^* y$, and b) Y^{opt} is the smallest possible dominating subset since for all y and y' in Y^{opt} we can have neither $y >^* y'$ nor $y \,^*\!< y'$. We might note that in models like the semi-order structure where the preference relation cannot "cycle", a term which is made precise in appendix 2, a fundamental result from graph theory ensures the existence of a unique, non-empty kernel.

Also, let us comment on the **efficiency** concept in this kind of semi-order structure. Assume that the n different intentions are modelled by criteria functions $f_1, \ldots, f_n$ with thresholds $q_1, \ldots, q_n$. Now, from the theoretical perspective, one generalization of our previous dominance concept is to say that y' semi-order-dominates y whenever

$$y_i' \geq y_i - q_i \text{ all i}$$

i.e. y' is at least as good as y with respect to all the criteria. We could now define a set of semi-order-efficient points as the kernel of Y with respect to this semi-order-dominance relation. It is clear that since we may have y' semi-order-dominates y and y semi-order-dominates y', this kernel will not be unique. Also note that the AN is still justified in submitting the set of all efficient alternatives in the old sense, Y_E, since any alternative which hereafter is excluded will not be better than one of those included. So, if we believe the semi-orderings to be the ultimate possibility, the old efficiency principle is still useful although it may be improved to filter out more alternatives.

On the other hand, if we take the practical perspective and think of the semi-order model as just a preliminary description amenable to later refinements, some of the semi-order-dominated alternatives should not be excluded. The proper dominance concept in this interpretation is that y' dominates y whenever

$$y_i' > y_i + q_i \text{ for all } i$$

i.e. according to no criteria can y' ever turn out worse than y. By restricting attention to the set of alternatives that are non-dominated according to this concept, we will not exclude alternatives that, when refined measurements and evaluations are undertaken, turn out to be efficient.

After this methodological discourse, let us turn to a more recent but related attack on the classical models. It concerns the DM's ability to **distinguish between indifferences and strict preferences.** Even when developing the functions $f_1, \ldots, f_n$ and F to be used in semi-order models like the above, for any pair of alternatives y' and y" the DM must be able to state without hesitation either y' $>^*$ y", y" $>^*$ y' or y' $\approx^*$ y". However, using much the same arguments as above, one may expect the DM in some cases to hesitate between expressing a strict preference $>^*$ and an indifference $\approx^*$. It seems quite ambitious to assume that a strict superiority exists if and only if the difference exceeds a certain threshold value q. In a sense, the use of thresholds just pushes the problem to the next level, namely that of setting the threshold.

A more natural formulation would be to have increasing differences $f_i(y')-f_i(y'')$ or $F(y')-F(y'')$ signify increasing **intensities of preferences** for y' over y" as evaluated from the i'th perspective or the overall perspective. A formal model along these lines is the **pseudo order** structure discussed in appendix 2. In this structure there are three levels of preference intensity of y' over y": a zero level indicating indifference, y' $\approx^*$ y", an intermediate level interpreted as a "weak" preference, y' $\geq^*$ y", and an upper level indicating a strict preference, y' $>^*$ y". The representation of this model involves a

preference threshold p in addition to the above indifference threshold q. This representation for the preference function F is given by

$$
\begin{aligned}
y' >^* y'' &\Leftrightarrow & F(y') &> F(y'')+p \\
y' \geq^* y'' &\Leftrightarrow \quad F(y'')+q < & F(y') &\leq F(y'')+p \\
y' \approx^* y'' &\Leftrightarrow \quad F(y'')-q \leq & F(y') &\leq F(y'')+q
\end{aligned}
$$

Only when F(y')-F(y") exceeds p do we have a strict preference. When the difference is between the indifference threshold q and the preference threshold p, we have a weak preference. When the difference does not even exceed q, we have an indifference. Similar representations hold of course for the criteria functions $f_1, \ldots, f_n$.

In such a pseudo-order model one allows for both intransitive indifferences and intransitive weak preferences. Thus, for example, the DM is allowed to feel a weak preference for y' over y" and a weak preference for y" over y"' and yet feel a strong preference for y' over y"'. Minor differences justifying only weak preferences are allowed to accumulate into strong preferences.

7.12. Incomplete Preferences

Even more flexibility is offered by models allowing **incomparabilities.** In all previous models, the DM must be able to make preference statements regarding any pair of alternatives. In the pseudo-order model, for example, he must be able to subscribe to one and only one of the 5 different evaluations:

$$y'' >^* y', \quad y'' \geq^* y', \quad y'' \approx^* y', \quad y' \geq^* y'', \quad y' >^* y''$$

There is no room for incomparabilities here. According to the theoretical perspective introduced above, a lack of expressed strong or weak preferences is taken to mean indifference and interpreted to mean equally well off. In practice, however, a lack of expressed strong or weak preferences may simply reflect the fact that the DM presently is unable to make a comparison. Also at the criteria level, incomparabilities may be expected due to the imprecision and indeed conflicts lying in the definition and assessment of many performance measures.

Most readers probably know the feeling. One faces for example the choice between two very different housing alternatives. It is felt that one of them must be better than the other. Presently, however, one just does not know which house is "best". Later on and most probably after a painful process of arguing back and forth, one sees the light and makes the choice. At that point of time, one wonders how one could have hesitated to begin with. In general, the existence of incomparabilities should not surprise us. Indeed, the whole multiple criteria approach is motivated by the initial existence of multiple intentions that do not unanimously point to a single alternative. We have to seek into our basic values in order to determine the relative importance of the different intentions so as to generate or identify a final compromise. In the housing choice problem, things may clear up, for example, when one finally decides to place more emphasis on home-life at the possible expense of job, transportation, or economic consequences.

Thus, it seems natural to allow for some **incomparability relation** R in the above models. This should enable us to incorporate the practical perspective into the formal models. Extending the pseudo-order structure, for example, would require that for any pair of alternatives, y' and y", one and only one of the six relations

$$y'' >^* y',\quad y'' \geq^* y',\quad y'' \approx^* y',\quad y' \geq^* y'',\quad y' >^* y'',\quad y'Ry''$$

must hold. The later, y'Ry", simply means that the DM is unable to compare y' and y". Of course, these evaluations must have suitable properties and relations to each other. For example, one must naturally assume the incomparability relation R to be intransitive. We might well be unwilling to compare y' and y" or y" and y"' since they may differ in many respects. Even then, y' and y"' may be so similar as to allow a direct preference statement. Continuing our previous problem of locating terminals in a food distribution system, y' and y"' may be minor modifications of the centralized distribution plan, thereby permitting a direct comparison and preference statement, while y" may be a decentralized alternative making it difficult to compare y" and y' or y" and y"'.

There are, however, costs involved in allowing for incomparabilities. One of these is less forceful prescriptions. We cannot necessarily point to a best action in all choice contexts. Another is more ad hoc modelling due to the introduction of the threshold parameters. Still, as a first cut into the preference structure, it may be useful to allow some incomparabilities and ad hoc'ness. Our next example illustrates this.

7.13. An Example

Let us end this discussion of less demanding preference models by illustrating a specific methodology, **the ELECTRE methods** which allow for many of the possibilities sketched above.

To be concrete, let us consider the choice between 7 different cars described by 4 different criteria as given in figure 7.4 below[5]. The weight, indifference, preference and veto parameters of the scheme will be explained below.

		Car							Weight	Indif. thresh.	Pref. thresh.	Veto thresh.
		y^1	y^2	y^3	y^4	y^5	y^6	y^7	π_j	q_j	p_j	v_j
Criteria												
Price	y_1^i	-300	-260	-250	-210	-200	-190	-120	5/15	25	35	115
Comfort	y_2^i	3	3	2	2	2	1	1	4/15	0	0	1.5
Speed	y_3^i	210	150	200	190	140	200	160	3/15	15	15	100
Looks	y_4^i	2	2	2	1	2	2	0	3/15	0	0	3

Figure 7.4 The Car Choice Problem

To start developing the ranking of alternatives, let us consider two alternatives y' and y". In the outranking litterature, one says that **y' outranks y"**, which is written as **y'Sy"**, if there are sufficiently strong arguments in all the criteria together to consider the statement, y' is at least as good as y", to be true for the DM's preference structure. Now, the problem is to define and exploit the outranking relation.

---

[5] The example resembles one by Roy and Vincke, c.f. the bibliographic notes.

Initially, consider the set of criteria (weakly) in favor of the statement y'Sy". This defines the **concordance coalition**

$$C(y',y'') = \{j \mid y_j' \geq y_j''-q_j\}$$

In the example above, $C(y^1,y^2) = \{2,3,4\}$: Evaluated on the comfort, speed and looks criteria, y^1 is at least as good as y^2 because the criteria values for y^1 are to the right of the corresponding indifference thresholds for y^2. Evaluated according to the price criterion, y^1 is worse than y^2 because it falls to the left of the indifference threshold for price. Similarly, one may consider the set of criteria strongly in disfavor of the statement y'Sy", i.e. the **discordance coalition**

$$D(y',y'') = \{j \mid y_j'' > y_j'+p_j\}$$

For example, we have $D(y^1,y^2) = \{1\}$ since y_1^2 exceeds y_1^1 by more than the preference threshold $p_1=35$.

Now, to start aggregating the different points of view represented by the n criteria, one introduces weights π_j, $j=1, \ldots, n$ attached to the different criteria, and presumed to reflect the relative importance of the criteria in the preference model. Note that this is a rather strong assumption, cf. the discussion in chapter 6 as to the use of weights to generate efficient solutions as well as the discussion earlier in this chapter on independence and additivity.

We assume that the weights w_j sum to one. Using these weights, we may calculate a measure of the total importance of criteria in favor of the statement y'Sy". The criteria in C(y',y") are weakly in favor, the criteria in D(y',y") are in strong opposition while the remaining criteria $E(y',y'') = \{1, \ldots, n\} \setminus (C(y',y'') \cup D(y',y''))$ are intermediate, i.e. neither weakly in favor nor strongly opposed. To incorporate the criteria in E(y',y") we may observe that when y_j' is less than but close to $y_j''-q_j$, the j'th criterion is pretty much in favor of the statement y'Sy", but when y_j' is greater than but almost $y_j''-p_j$, the criterion is rather disfavorable. Using linear interpolation in this case suggests the following measure, the **concordance degree** of the importance of criteria which can be taken into account for validating the assertion y'Sy"

$$c(y',y'') = \sum_{j\in C(y',y'')} \pi_j + \sum_{j\in E(y',y'')} \pi_j(p_j+y_j'-y_j'')/(p_j-q_j)$$

In the present example, $c(y^1,y^2)$ is (4+3+3)/15 since $E(y^1,y^2)$ is empty. The concordance degree for any other pair of alternatives is given in figure 7.5 below.

i \ j	1	2	3	4	5	6	7
1	-	10	10	10	10	10	10
2	12	-	12	7	10	7	10
3	11	11	-	10	10	10	10
4	5	8	12	-	12	12	10
5	8	11	12	12	-	12	7
6	11	11	11	11	11	-	10
7	5	8	5	5	5	9	-

Figure 7.5 Concordance Degrees $(c(y^i,y^j)\cdot 15)$

Next, to measure the importance of criteria opposing the assertion y'Sy", we introduce the discordance degree. Each discordant criteria is in opposition, but the strength can be more or less invalidating. One possibility is to introduce **veto thresholds** v_j $(\geq p_j)$ to reflect the capacity that a discordant criterion has for rejecting the assertion y'Sy" without help from any other criterion. We might say that the j'th criterion is **incompatible** with the assertion y'Sy" if

$$y_j' < y_j''-v_j$$

i.e. if y' falls below y" by more than the veto-threshold value, we cannot reasonably accept that y' outranks y". The **discordance degree** of criterion j against the assertions y'Sy" may now be defined as

$$d_j(y',y'') = \begin{cases} 0 & \text{if } y_j' \geq y_j''-p_j \\ (y_j''-y_j'-p_j)/(v_j-p_j) & \text{if } y_j''-p_j > y_j' \geq y_j''-v_j \\ 1 & \text{if } y_j' < y_j''-v_j \end{cases}$$

So, as long as criterion j is not in discordance with the assertion y'Sy" since $y_j' > y_j''-p$, the discordance degree is 0. As the performance of y' with respect to the j'th criterion deteriorates from $y_j'=y_j''-p_j$ to $y_j'=y_j''-v_j$, the discordance degree increases linearly to 1, and for even worse values, it remains 1. In the ELECTRE I, IS, and II methods, one actually only uses the strict veto condition, $d_j=1$. However, in ELECTRE III's fuzzy outranking relation, d_j is fully used.

In the concrete example of figure 7.4, we might observe immediately that strict vetos occur in only seven cases. The cars y^1, y^2 and y^3 cannot outrank y^7 due to the price veto. The price is so different that it makes the alternatives incomparable. Also, y^6 and y^7 cannot outrank y^1 and y^2 due to a comfort veto.

Finally, to define y'Sy", i.e. to define when there are sufficiently strong arguments to regard the statement: y' is at least as good as y" to be true for the DM's preference structure, the ELECTRE methods use two conditions. First, for a sufficient majority of criteria, y' must do no worse than y". Secondly, for no criteria must y' do very much worse than y". This gives the following definition

$$y'Sy'' \Leftrightarrow c(y',y'') \geq \alpha \;\wedge\; d_j(y',y'') < 1 \;\; \forall j \in D(y',y'')$$

where α is some parameter usually close to 1. Using $\alpha = 12/15$ in the present example and recalling the occurrence of strict vetos in the seven cases, we might construct the outranking relation as depicted in figure 7.6 below. In this graph, a directed arc between y' and y" means that y'Sy", i.e. y' outranks y". For example, y^2Sy^1 since $c(y^2,y^1) = 12/15 \geq 12/15$ and $d_j(y^1,y^2) = (210\text{-}150\text{-}15)/(100\text{-}15) = 9/17 < 1$.

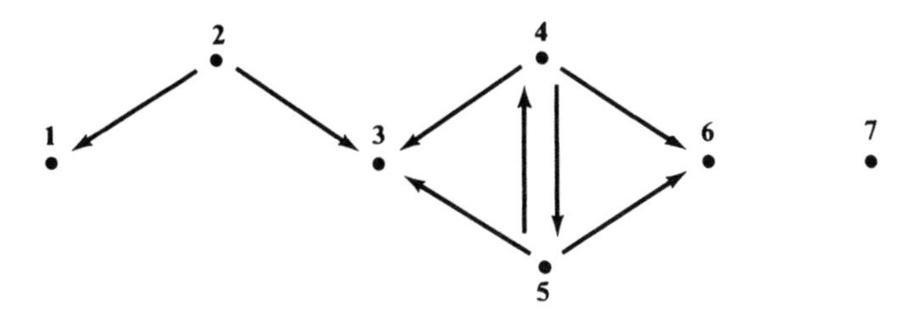

Figure 7.6 The Outranking Relation

We see that the kernels of the relation are {2,4,7} and {2,5,7}, i.e. it seems natural to restrict attention to either of these sets of alternatives in the subsequent attempt to make a good choice.

Outranking methods like the one just sketched have many virtues. Foremost among these are their allowance for different kinds of intransitivities and incomparabilities which occur in real world decision problems when a DM's evaluation capabilities are limited. On the other hand, the methods employ several more or less ad hoc parameters; the indifference thresholds q_j, the preference thresholds p_j, the veto thresholds v_j, the importance weights π_j and the concordance cut-off level α must be appropriately set. Also, even though the methods are structured around a few convincing ideas, the effect of combining things may seem unclear. An obvious idea in applications is therefore to perform extensive sensitivity analysis to insure that arbitrary parameter settings have no major impacts.

7.14. Summary

In this chapter we covered the "prior articulation of preferences" approach to decision making with multiple intentions. This planning mode involves two phases. First, the AN, by questioning the DM, constructs a model of the DM's preferences. Next, the AN exploits the constructed model to determine an optimal compromise solution or at least a reduced set of alternatives to be further investigated. The last phase is generally straightforward. Therefore, the focus in this section was on modelling the DM's preferences.

Initially we discussed how to establish a relevant set of criteria. The set of criteria should ideally be complete, operational, nonredundant, minimal and at least somewhat independent. The most natural way to generate and structure the multiple intentions is probably in terms of a hierarchy of values, objectives and criteria. The discussion is relevant for the rest of the exposition.

Then, we turned to the problem of aggregating these different desires, i.e. how to incorporate the relative importance of the different criteria to give a comprehensive preference structure. Typically, the aggregation has been assumed to be at least complete and transitive. This leads to the classical, ordinal preference model adopted throughout most of the economics and operational research literature. Additional properties like non-saturation and continuity allow for functional representations of the basic preferences in terms of a specialized utility function even when the set of alternatives is continuous and multiple dimensional. Finally, to get a really handy structure like the additive model, we need additional properties, most notably preferential independence. We emphasized the extensive need to make trade-offs, or, equivalently, to price out, in most of these models.

Finally, we discussed several newer attempts to preference modelling which permit consideration of a) intransitive indifferences via the semi-order model, b) hesitation between indifferences and preferences via the pseudo-order model, and c) incomparabilities via the incomplete models. These models introduce a degree of arbitrariness via their use of certain parameters. In addition, the assumptions underlying these models are less demanding than those underlying the classical preference models and consequently lead to less forceful prescriptions. In general, a whole set of promising alternatives, e.g. the kernel of an outranking relation, is identified.

7.15. Bibliographic Notes

Most of the preference models in this chapter have a long tradition in the literature on decision theory. Indeed, utility theory and the more inclusive socalled measurement theory have developed into subdisciplines of their own. Some useful general references are Fishburn(1964,70), Krantz, Luce, Suppes and Tversky(1971), Roberts(1979) and Roubens aand Vincke(1985). Additional references are provided in appendix 2. The most significant application oriented reference is Keeney and Raiffa(1976).

More specifically, we note here that the problem of using trade-off and pricing out procedures in cases with "significant changes" in some or all of the criteria is treated in some depth in Pruzan(1965,66a,66b) and Pruzan and Jackson(1963). An approach to multiple criteria decision making which is structured around criteria hierarchies and which has attracted considerable interest from theoreticians as well as practitioners is the socalled Analytical Hierarchy Process developed by T.L. Saaty and his collaborators, c.f. e.g. Saaty(1980,88a,88b) and Saaty and Alexander(1989). Finally, the socalled ELECTRE outranking methods have been developed by the French school surrounding B. Roy, c.f. e.g. Roy(1968,71,73,77,78,85) Roy and Bertier(1973) and Roy and Hugonnard(1982), c.f. also Ostanello(1985) and Roy and Vincke(1981) for good introductions.

Chapter 8

PROGRESSIVE ARTICULATION OF ALTERNATIVES

A third multiple criteria planning mode is characterized by the progressive articulation of alternatives. It involves several rounds of interaction between the DM and the AN. In each round, the DM poses a question about the set of alternatives and the AN provides an answer. Next, the DM evaluates the answer and decides whether or not to stop the search. If he feels reasonably comfortable with one of the alternatives identified so far, he may choose to use that as his compromise solution. If none of the proposals satisfies him, he can either give up this form of investigation or continue the search, in which case a new round of interaction is initiated.

Technically speaking, the multiple criteria procedures based on a progressive articulation of alternatives approach are basically iterative versions of the prior articulation of alternative methods discussed in chapter 6. Instead of the AN generating all efficient alternatives by parametric variations of constraints, weights or reference points, the DM now successively decides for which values of the constraints, weights or reference points he wants to see an efficient proposal. Also, the theoretical results underlining these methods are largely those presented in chapter 6. Therefore, to understand the present planning mode we primarily need some examples.

8.1. The Interactive Constraint Approach

Let us start by considering the interactive constraint approach. As in chapter 6, we assume for ease of presentation that in a given iteration, say the t'th, the DM sets constraints $\epsilon_2^t, \ldots, \epsilon_n^t$ on the last n-1 criteria. Next, the AN finds an efficient alternative y^t giving the best performance on the first criterion subject to those constraints on the other criteria[1]. The DM evaluates this proposal y^t together with those generated in previous iterations, $y^1, \ldots, y^{t-1}$. If one of these satisfies him, he stops. Otherwise, he sets new constraints and the search continues. This procedure may be summarized as in figure 8.1 below, where iteration number t is depicted

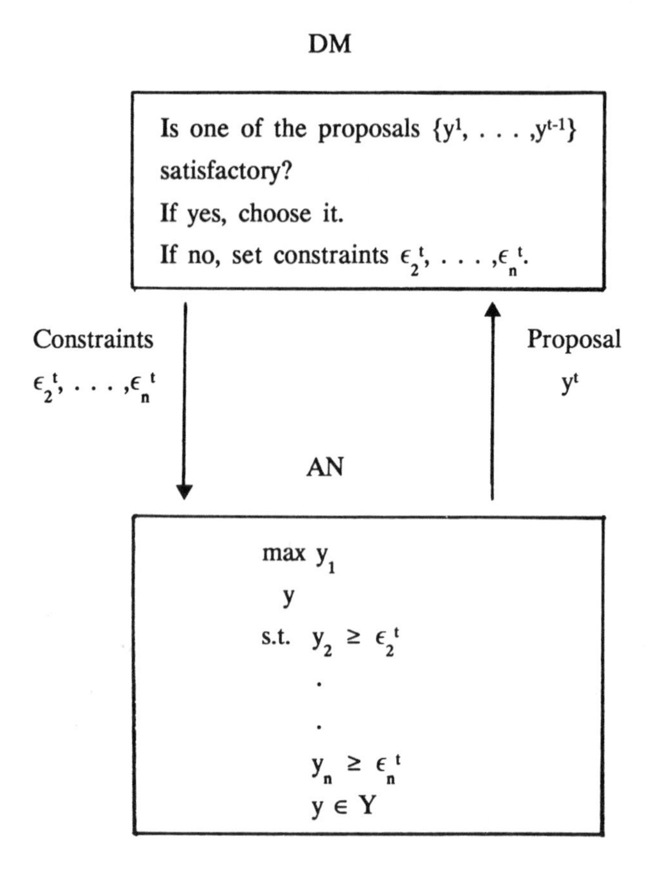

Figure 8.1 The Interactive Constraint Approach

The description of the DM's activities in figure 8.1 may seem somewhat loose. However, it simply reflects that the DM is in charge and that there are no restrictions

[1] We note that if there is more than one solution which maximizes the first criterion subject to the constraints on the remaining n-1 criteria, this procedure will have to be modified. For example, one could consider presenting the DM with the subset of these solutions which are efficient or, if it turns out that these are too numerous, than one could consider assigning apriori weights to the n-1 criteria which correspond to the constraints, in which case the best weighted alternative would be presented to the DM. Since it is not our purpose to present detailed algorithms but only to characterize the four major planning modes, we will not go into further detail here.

on the way he shall execute his authority and only little guidance as to how he can perform his tasks. The basic idea is, that by intelligently restricting the number of efficient proposals he is to evaluate, the DM will be able to steer the interactive process and to terminate it when he has a sufficient overview of his possibilities as well as the effort required to continue the search process in the hope that more attractive alternatives will be identified. This is the essence of the progressive articulation of alternatives planning mode.

The best way to get a feel for the procedure is probably through some small exercises. Take a simple choice problem that you feel is reasonably realistic. Then try to act as the DM in the procedure. Learn about your possibilities and make a choice. Let someone else or a computer act as the AN. Such an exercise is described below.

8.2. A Laboratory Experiment

In this example we illustrate what an application of the interactive constraint approach may look like. It describes a small experiment undertaken with students in managerial economics.

The context is the following. A student is eligible for a grant worth $12000. He contemplates how to allocate this amount between consumption and savings. Early on he decides that his planning horizon is rather short and that he only cares about the improvements in this year's consumption possibilities y_1, and in next year's consumption possibilities, y_2. He then contacts his financial adviser to seek assistance. The adviser is able to delineate the savings options depicted in figure 8.2. From a marginal-rate-of-return point of view, the most profitable of these options is to save up to $1000 out of the $12000 the first year with an annual real interest rate of 300%. If he reduces his consumption possibility in year 1 by $1000 - i.e. if he consumes $11000 and saves $1000 - he will be able to increase his consumption possibility in year 2 by $4000. This generates the line segment GF with slope $s=-4$ in figure 8.2. The second best option is a real interest rate of 200%, again with an upper bound of $1000 saved the first year. This generates the line segment FE. The remaining "frontier" options have real interest rates of 100%, 0%, -50%, -66 1/3% with upper bounds on first year's savings of $1000, $4000, $2000 and $3000 respectively. Finally, the student may chose neither to save nor to consume but to simply give some or all of the grant away, corrsponding to rejecting part or all of the grant. Thus, the set of alternatives is really the convex set delineated by OABCDEFG in figure 8.2 below. Of course, in the actual experiment, only the AN player and not the DM player can refer to this figure.

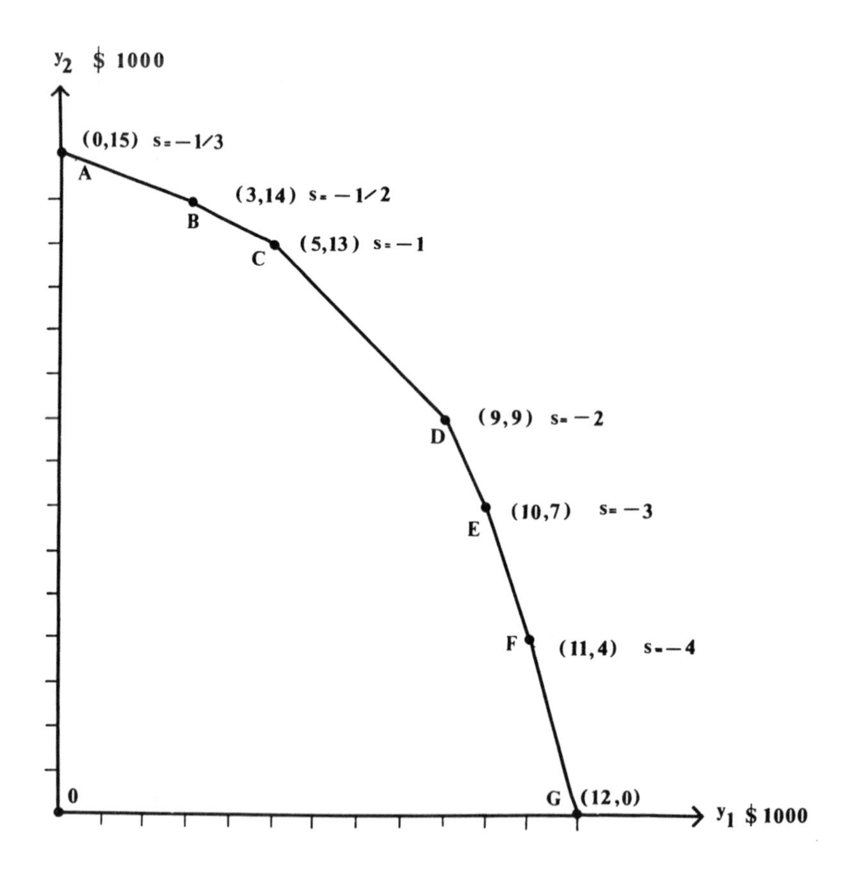

Figure 8.2 Liquidity Options

One example of the interaction between a DM and an AN using the interactive constraint approach is recorded in figure 8.3.

Iteration No. t	DM's min. requirement ϵ_2^t	AN's proposal y^t
0		Cross-effect matrix
1	3000	(11250, 3000)
2	10000	(8000, 10000)
3	12000	(6000, 12000)
4	8000	(9500, 8000)
5	7000	(10000, 7000)
6	Accepts y^4	

Figure 8.3 Communication Record

Based on the DM's comments during the process, we are able to give the following more lively description of the actual process behind this communication record. Initially, the AN submitted the cross-effect matrix

$$\begin{array}{c} \\ f_1 \\ f_2 \end{array} \begin{array}{cc} G & A \\ \left[\begin{array}{cc} 12000 & 0 \\ 0 & 15000 \end{array}\right] \end{array}$$

so as to give the DM a rough impression of his possibilities.

From this the DM sees that he can consume at most \$12000 (the grant) in period 1, or, if he desists from consuming in period 1, \$15000 in period 2. The DM, whose motto is "eat drink and be merry for tomorrow we may die", is primarily interested in consumption now. With this attitude, he finds the trade-off involved here rather disappointing. He feels that it is not satisfactory to only be able to increase his aggregate comsumption by \$3000 by postponing consumption a whole year. Therefore, in his first iteration, he sets his minimum requirements for period 2 as low as $\epsilon_2^1=\$3000$. The AN reports that in this case the DM is able to consume for \$11250 the first year. The DM is impressed. Getting \$3000 next year by only saving \$750 this year is something of a bargain, after all. So, substantially more optimistic, he wonders if it is possible to get this high interest rate for a large span of savings. In the next iteration, therefore, he sets ϵ_2^2=\$10000 and the AN replies by the consumption improvement plan (\$8000,\$10000). This is not completely crazy, the DM thinks. Getting \$10000 the second year by giving up \$4000 the first year corresponds, after all, to an interest rate of 150%. Now, before he can feel completely comfortable, he wants to learn a little bit more about the neighboring alternatives. He tries ϵ_2^3=\$120-00 and learns that this leaves \$6000 for the first year. Thus, compared to y^2, he has gained \$2000 more in the second year at the cost of a reduction in his consumption capability of \$2000 in the first year. That is not an acceptable change given that the student is primarily interested in increasing his consumption the first year. In the fourth iteration, therefore, he goes in the other direction, requiring only ϵ_2^4=\$8000. This leaves \$9500 for the first year. Thus, again compared to y^2, he sees that y^4 gives him \$1500 more the first year at the cost of \$2000 the second year. He thinks that this is a - relatively speaking - somewhat inexpensive way of improving his consumption in the first year and prefers y4 to y^2. He wonders then if he should decrease the second year's consumption still further. He tries ϵ_2^5=\$7000 and learns about the plan y^5=(\$10000,\$7000). But now he thinks that he is starting to pay too much for the first period consumption. Compared to y^4 it costs \$1000 in the second year to gain only \$500 in the first. So, he still likes y^4 the best and, having checked in the neighborhood, he decides at this point to accept y^4. He does not want to spend additional time and effort to fine-tune the plan since, after all, he does not feel completely certain about what he really wants and what may happen to him during the next years.

The exercise above is extremely simple. As a matter of fact, an interactive approach is probably less effective than a prior articulation of alternatives approach in simple two-criteria problems like this, where the whole set of alternatives might easily be exposed to the DM using a graphical presentation like the one in figure 8.2. Therefore, to better appreciate the interactive approach, one should really try to solve a problem of higher dimensions. Hopefully, however, the simplicity of the present example makes it easy to understand. In particular, it should be easy to follow the DM's search activities and to perform the AN's necessary calculations. Also, and despite its simplicity, the exercise does point to some more general characteristics of this planning mode.

First, observe that the DM does not need to conform to any specific preference model or to perform his search, learning and choice activities in any specific manner. In particular, there is room for some uncertainty, halfheld beliefs and indeed conflicts and contradictions. Also, he is allowed to change his wishes as he goes along; there are no explicit demands as to consistency since he can just continue the search using his new priorities. Furthermore, he is allowed to take a metaplanning perspective, as he did when he decided that it was not worth the trouble to continue the search.

Secondly, observe that all this freedom is not obtained for free. The DM has to develop on his own a strategy for thinking about his wishes and for posing new questions. The DM described above used a trial and error process, constantly seeking improvements of the best previous plan. He found several feasible trade-offs or interest rates, and he successively clarified whether or not he liked these trade-offs. Although his approach makes good sense, there is clearly nothing in the set-up that allows outside observers to evaluate the outcome. In particular, we cannot claim that the resulting compromise plan is optimal in any underlying, fully defined decision problem; it simply reflects the DM's subjective evaluation of the efficient alternatives he has indirectly chosen to look at, as well as of the potential "costs" and "benefits" of continuing the process.

Finally, let us note that the DM's choice of a search and solution strategy will depend on, among other characteristics, his background and the specific problem he faces. The strategy chosen above, i.e. the attempt to balance substitution possibilities against substitution wishes, is not entirely surprising, since the DM was a student in economics where this approach is a cornerstone. Furthermore, since both criteria are in monetary units and concern two periods, the trade-offs are naturally expressed in terms of interest rates, a widely used concept, in particular by economists. In the excercise, the DM had to calculate the interest rates himself, since this is not the central idea of the search technology provided by the interactive constraint approach. No serious harm was done here, since the whole exercise was very easy. Nevertheless, in view of the DM's background and the problem's nature, we might conjecture that he would have been better served by a procedure building more directly on the trade-off concept. In fact, he might be better off by using the procedure to which we now turn.

8.3. The Interactive Weighting Approach

As another illustration of the progressive articulation of alternatives planning mode, let us consider the interactive weighting approach. In a given iteration, say number t, the DM assigns weights or importance parameters $\alpha_1^t, \ldots, \alpha_n^t$ to the n different criteria. Next, the AN finds the efficient alternative y^t performing best as judged by the weighted objective $\alpha_1^t y_1 + \ldots + \alpha_n^t y_n$. The DM evaluates this proposal y^t together with those generated in previous cycles $y^1, \ldots, y^{t-1}$. If one of these satisfies him, he stops. Otherwise, he assigns new weights, and the search continues. Iteration no. t of this procedure is depicted in figure 8.4 below.

The weights $\alpha_1, \ldots, \alpha_n$ in this procedure may be interpreted in different ways.

First, and perhaps the interpretation most true to the whole philosophy underlying the present mode, one may think of the weights as simply a **steering instrument**. By increasing α_1, for example, one turns in the direction of the first axis, i.e. one gets a higher value of the first criteria. If the set of alternatives is nice and smooth, the effect of turning this steering wheel will be nice and smooth. If the set is less well-behaved, being discrete for example, it may take some turning on the steering wheel before a reaction occurs and the reaction will be somewhat abrupt, more or less like a jump.

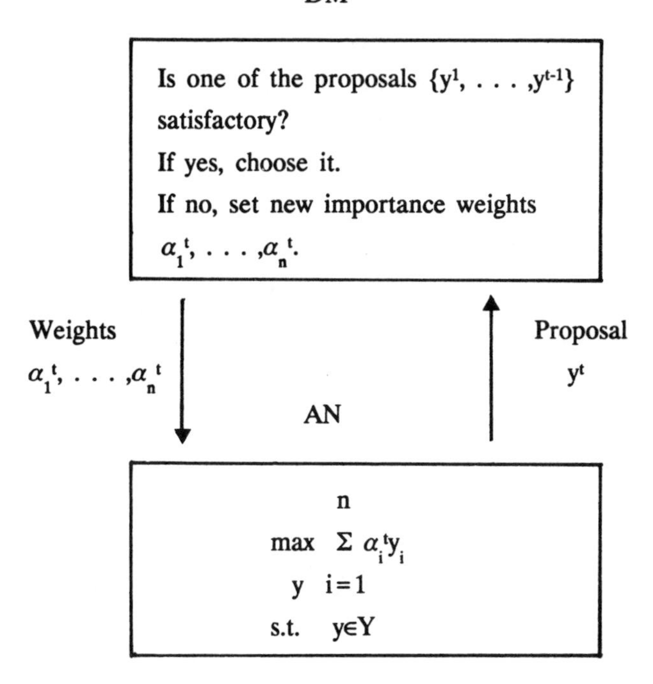

Figure 8.4 The Interactive Weighting Approach

Secondly, one may think of the weights as an indication of the DM's **substitution wishes.** In the 2-dimensional case for example, such information may be given in terms of the slope of the DM's indifference curves at a given point y. More generally, one may imagine that the DM sets α^t equal to his substitution (wishes) coefficients $\delta(y)$ as defined in section 7.7. Thus, by setting the weights as $\alpha_1, \ldots, \alpha_n$, the DM indicates his requirement of at least α_1/α_2 units of y_2 to give up 1 unit of y_1, α_1/α_3 units of y_3 to give up 1 unit of y_1 etc. As strongly emphasized in section 7.7, substitution wishes represent marginal evaluations and depend on the point around which the substitutions take place, i.e. $\delta(y)$ depends on the anchor point y. Some reasonable anchor points could for example be: the best plan generated so far, the possibly fictive plan tentatively believed to be optimal, or indeed some compromise between these plans. It must be underlined however, that the concept of substitution wishes employed here is nothing but a way of thinking or a strategy that may aid the DM in his utilization of the search technology defined by the procedure. It is simply an idea, just like the steering wheel interpretation, that may help the DM to make sense of the technology. The procedure does not demand that he uses this idea, and if he does, it does not demand that he uses a specific definition of the anchor point, nor that he states his substitution wishes with a particular degree of precision. The DM is in charge here and he can do whatever he likes.

A third interpretation of the weights is as an indication of the **substitution possibilities**. In the 2-dimensional case for example, such information may be given in terms of the slope of the boundry to Y at a given point y. More generally, when the weights $\alpha_1, \ldots, \alpha_n$ are used to generate a proposal y, we know that $(\alpha_1, \ldots, \alpha_n)$ may be interpreted as substitution (possibility) coefficients $\mu(y)$ at y, c.f section 6.7. This allows the DM to draw substantial inference about his possibilities from a given iteration. Not only can he conclude that y is an efficient alternative, i.e. that there is no alternative in the cube north-east of y, he can also infer that there is no alternative in the halfspace north-east of the hyperplane defined by the normal vector $(\alpha_1, \ldots, \alpha_n)$, at the point y, c.f. section 6.7 and figure 6.6 in particular.

As argued previously, the best way to get a feel for the progressive articulation of alternatives approach is probably through small exercises. It is straight forward to construct an exercise like the one in section 8.2. Presently, however, we will illustrate this planning mode by a more theoretical exercise. In the next section we assume that the DM's preference structure does not change during the course of the planning process. Rather, we assume that he has a certain fixed preference structure, and that he uses this together with a certain ad hoc search strategy to direct the investigations. This allows us, as theorists at this point, to envisage the development of the communication.

8.4. A Theoretical Exercise

Let us imagine a planning context where the set of alternatives in criteria space, known only to the AN, is the set delineated by OABCDEFG in figure 8.2 above. Indeed, we may assume that the story is the same, i.e. a student, the DM, is to choose between consumption-savings options. Presently, however, we will assume that the DM's implicit preference structure is defined by the preference function

$$F(y_1,y_2) = y_1y_2$$

i.e. when making a choice between y_1, consumption this year, and y_2, consumption next year, he in fact chooses so as to maximize y_1y_2. Note that with this preference structure all that counts is the product of the two consumptions, not their chronology; this is quite a different assumption than that underlying the analysis in section 8.2.

Also, we will assume that the DM uses the following search strategy. In the first iteration he chooses weights more or less arbitrarily. In subsequent iterations, however, he always chooses weights as a compromise between the substitution wishes he has and the substitution possibilities he thinks are available. In the present two-criteria example, characterized by figure 8.2 and by $F(y_1,y_2)=y_1y_2$, substitution conditions may simply be expressed as slopes of straight lines. Thus, more precisely, we assume that the DM chooses the slope in iteration t, $-\alpha_1^t/\alpha_2^t$, according to the following implicit procedure. He averages his substitution wishes slope in the last proposal, i.e. the marginal rate of substitution of y_2 for y_1 at y^{t-1}, $-\delta_1(y^{t-1})/\delta_2(y^{t-1})$, and the slope used to generate that proposal, $-\alpha_1^{t-1}/\alpha_2^{t-1}$, which expresses the substitution possibilities available at y^{t-1}. Now, as noted in section 7.7 the substitution wishes coefficients are defined from F by $\delta_1(y)=(\partial F/\partial y_1)=y_2$ and $\delta_2(y)=(\partial F/\partial y_2)=y_1$. Therefore, we get the following formal description of the search strategy

$$\text{Slope in iteration } t = -\frac{\alpha_1^t}{\alpha_2^t} = -\frac{1}{2}\left(\frac{y_2^{t-1}}{y_1^{t-1}} + \frac{\alpha_1^{t-1}}{\alpha_2^{t-1}}\right)$$

Of course, this is a somewhat naive and definitely a sterile description of the DM's behavior. Still, it makes some sense. In particular, it has at least some resemblances to the notion of satisficing decision makers discussed in section 2.4. A DM realizing that his intrinsic wishes, $-y_2^{t-1}/y_1^{t-1}$, are unattainable makes a certain regression in his aspirations. He partly adjusts towards what he tentatively believes to be realizable, $-\alpha_1^{t-1}/\alpha_2^{t-1}$.

In figure 8.5 we have summarized the communication resulting when the DM described above uses the interactive weighting approach on the present set of alternatives.

Iteration No. t	DM's importance weights (α_1^t, α_2^t)	AN's proposal y^t
0		Cross-effect matrix
1	(0.4, 1)	(3000, 14000)
2	(76/30, 1)	(10000, 7000)
3	(97/60, 1)	(9000, 9000)
4	(157/120, 1)	(9000, 9000)
5	Accepts y^4	

Figure 8.5 Communication Record

Initially, the AN submitted the cross-effect matrix

$$\begin{array}{c} \\ f_1 \\ f_2 \end{array} \begin{array}{cc} G & A \\ \left[\begin{array}{cc} 12000 & 0 \\ 0 & 15000 \end{array}\right] \end{array}$$

The DM, with implicit preference function $F(y_1y_2)=y_1y_2$, is equally motivated by consumption possibilities in both periods. Therefore he decided primarily to go for the larger period 2 opportunities that are available. He therefore decided, somewhat arbitrarily, to start the communication process by $(\alpha_1^1/\alpha_2^1) = (0.4, 1)$, i.e. $-\alpha_1^1/\alpha_2^1=-0.4$. The AN reports that the best alternative with these weights is B=(3000, 14000) as is easily seen from the slopes indicated in figure 8.2. At this point, the DM's marginal rate of substitution of y_2 for y_1 is $-\delta_1(y^1)/\delta_2(y^1)=-14/3$, i.e. he is willing to give up 14 units of y_2 to gain 3 units of y_1. Taking the average of his substitution wishes -14/3 and the substitution possibilities -0.4, the DM determines the new search weights as $-\alpha_1^2/\alpha_2^2=-76/30$. This leads the AN to generate y^2=E=(10000, 7000) and to present this as his new proposal to the AN. At this point, the DM's wishes are characterized by $-\delta_1(y^2)/\delta_2(y^2)=-7/10$. Hence the DM sets $-\alpha_1^3/\alpha_2^3=-97/60$ which is the average of -7/10 and -76/30. Now, facing these importance weights, the AN proposes D=(9000, 9000). At this point, the DM finds the two periods to be marginally equally important, i.e. $-\delta_1(y^3)/\delta_2(y^3)=-1/1$. In the next iteration, therefore, $-\alpha_1^4/\alpha_2^4$ is set as the average of -97/60 and -1, i.e. as -157/120. Again, the AN generates D. It is clear now that a continuation of the procedure would lead the DM to use slopes converging to -1 and the AN to keep on proposing D. We might therefore define D as the solution to this theoretical exercise.

A few clarifying remarks are called for. In the illustration above, we assumed that the DM had clearcut preferences described by an implicit preference function F. Of course, if in practice the dialogue between the AN and the DM indicated that the DM had such a clearcut and consistent preference structure, the DM might just as well attempt to articulate F explicitly, communicate it to the AN, and instruct the AN to solve the choice problem by simply optimizing F over Y. We would then once again be in a prior articulation of preferences mode.

The existence of the implicit preference function F may be thought of simply as a pedagogical device allowing us to illustrate what the interactive weighting approach may look like. It allows us to predict the outcome of the procedure and to illustrate the basic evaluations and calculations involved. This gives the reader a chance to check his understanding of the more abstract parts of the exposition.

Much more importantly, however, such exercises may be thought of as **theoretical experiments** allowing one to test the usefulness of different procedures. The idea is simply that a reasonably well-behaved DM must be able to use a procedure fruitfully. By describing the DM's search strategy and in particular by assuming that his preferences can be expressed by a specific preference function, we are able to logically deduce how the procedure evolves and to determine how well it performs. A natural benchmark is provided by the optimal solution to the underlying, now fully defined basic decision problem. If a hypothetical "clever" DM is not able to reach decisions, which are good with respect to the benchmark, this definitely speaks against the reasonableness of the procedure.

To clarify this point, we note that in the example above, the DM was well-behaved. He had firm beliefs and never hesitated nor changed his mind. On the other hand, his capacity for processing information and for directing the search was not excessive. We only assumed that at any iteration he was able to recall a) the weights, i.e. the slope, corresponding to the previous iteration, and b) the proposal generated during that iteration. Also, he used a somewhat stiff, naive and bureaucratic rule for setting new weights. As a matter of fact, it is easy to construct even regular convex cases where the procedure does not converge. Still, the fact that the DM with these clear limitations was able to exploit the data search technology, i.e. to generate the optimal proposal according to his basic decision problem, speaks in favor of the procedure.

Clearly, however, tests like the above are partial and definitely not sufficient. First, there is no serious attempt to model the DM as a human being. It is not clear how much one can reasonably assume about his desires being so well behaved, i.e. so clearcut and consistent as to be expressable by a simple preference structure like $F(y)=y_1y_2$. Furthermore no attempt is made to determine his capacity for information processing.

Secondly, there is no serious attempt to model the variety of costs and benefits associated with the procedures being tested. By focusing on the convergence of a procedure to the optimal solution to an underlying basic decision problem, this kind of logical experiment focuses entirely on the value of taking better actions. In so doing, one ignores important costs, like that of directing the search, and important benefits, like that of simply learning about the system, c.f. the discussion in section 1.5. Of course, one could most likely refine the methodology in these directions. It should be stressed, however, that no matter how well such theoretical experiments are designed, they can never substitute - but only complement - full scale, real world application characterized by ill-defined problems and contexts, less-than-perfect communication, time pressures and the like.

In spite of these limitations, we believe that the test methodology is of considerable utility. It may help discipline researchers who are designing multiple criteria planning technology by its demand that reasonably well-behaved and bright DMs must be able to exploit the technology succesfully. Also, attempts to demonstrate how a procedure could be used by a DM will force the researcher to think hard about the essential problem of directing the search. This may produce insight as well as rules of thumb to guide the DM in his use of a given search technology. Work along these lines has mainly focused on the usefulness of trade-off information when directing the search. See. e.g. section 6.7 for an illustration.

8.5. The Iterative Organization

One of the important characteristics of the progressive articulation of alternatives mode is that **the investigations of possibilities, Y, and wishes, F, are performed iteratively**, c.f. also the taxonomy in chapter 5. Now that we have a more concrete picture of such approaches, let us briefly reflect on this property.

The use of an iterative approach effects the kind of support available when investigating the set of alternatives and the preference structure. As illustrated in section 8.2 which treated the interactive constraint approach, wishes may be clarified in terms of desirable improvements of specific proposals, i.e. information about Y helps the DM produce information about F. Similarly, the exercise in section 8.4 where we considered the interactive weighting approach illustrates how information about the DM's wishes can support the search for alternatives by allowing us to derive interesting search directions, i.e. information about F helps the DM to direct the search in Y. Also, these examples illustrate how less than complete information will often be sufficient. In section 8.2, we did not have to develop a complete model of the DM's wishes, and in section 8.4, we only needed to determine four of the efficient alternatives to arrive at a decision.

In general, whenever we know something about Y, we may use this to clarify and reduce the information we need about F. In figures 8.6(a) and (b) below, we have assumed Y to be known precisely. We see how this allows us to distinguish between decision-irrelevant variations in preferences, as represented by variations within the classes $\{F^1,F^2,F^3\}$ and $\{F^4,F^5,F^6\}$ of indifference curves, and decision-relevant variations in preferences as represented by variations across these classes. Similarly, whenever we know something about F, we may use this to clarify and reduce the information we need about Y. In figures 8.6(c) and (d) we have assumed a fixed and known preference structure F. We then see how certain variations in the efficient frontier, namely those occuring within a class $\{Y_E^1, Y_E^2, Y_E^3\}$ or $\{Y_E^4, Y_E^5, Y_E^6\}$, are unimportant while others, as represented by variations across classes, are important.

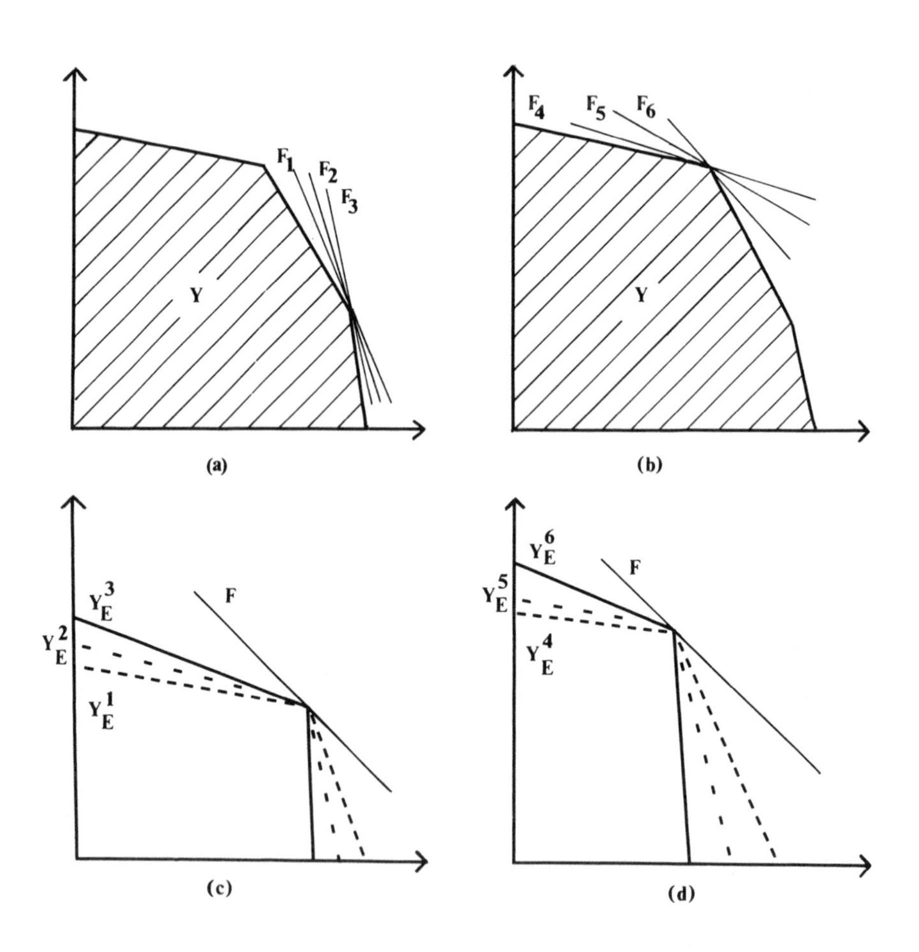

Figure 8.6 Relevant and Irrelevant Information

In essence, we see that it is often possible to make shortcuts in the planning procedure by using what we know about Y to clarify what we need to know about F and vice versa. The illustration in figure 8.6 was based on the assumption that the underlying aim is to find an optimal alternative. However, the arguments work equally well if one only seeks a satisficing alternative. It should be noted that the usefulness of these kinds of shortcuts is widely recognized in more practical, experience-based planning literature, where an iterative - or equivalently, cyclic - approach is usually recommended.

Still, the illustrations may exaggerate the practical value of such iterative approaches. First, observe that in general both F and Y must be clarified. Therefore, since we do not know F (Y) exactly, more details about Y (F) are relevant. Secondly, the possibilities of making shortcuts depend on the search technology. For example, a simple interactive constraint approach only allows us to exclude points in cubes while an interactive weighting approach allows us to exclude points in whole halfspaces, c.f. the illustrations in section 6.8. Thirdly, and most important, it requires considerable analytical skills and the ability to combine the information generated to take full advantage of the potential shortcuts. For example, to reduce the set of potential plans as much as possible in the weighting approach, the DM must at any stage of the process be able not only to recall and evaluate the proposals generated so far. In order to infer as much as possible about Y, he must also be able to utilize information as to the weights used to generate the proposals; he must be able, technically speaking, to determine the intersection of the halfspaces represented by the sets of weights so as to infer as much as possible about Y. Thus, substantial burdens are imposed on the DM, who directs the search. This is clearly illustrated when one tries to make more elaborate theoretical experiments along the lines of section 8.4. In essence, then, the idea of shortcuts simply allows the DM to replace some difficult preference investigations by additional, but also demanding analysis. From this perspective, the AN directive approaches discussed in the next section are much more attractive. In this planning mode it is the AN who has to perform the analyses and make the inferences, and this kind of work is presumably much more in tune with his capabilities and motivations.

8.6. The DM Directive Organization

The other distinct characteristic of the present planning mode is that the DM is in charge. Techniques within this class really give the DM the **authority and the responsibility to direct the search, to accumulate the information and to choose the final compromise solution.** There are, by and large, no restrictions on the way he can do this nor any guide as to how he should proceed. Of course, this **freedom** has its benefits and, at the least in the way it is accomplished, its costs. We have already noted some of these in sections 8.2 and 8.4 above. Now, however, let us try to be more systematic. We start by looking at the **benefits.**

The freedom means that the DM is allowed to let **non-modelled aspects** of the alternatives enter the choice considerations. He may, for example, make his own estimates of the problems associated with implementing different alternatives and let this contribute to his overall evaluation. Although this is a nice possibility, it should also be remembered that the omission of relevant criteria potentially may lead the AN to dominate away attractive alternatives. As emphasized earlier, it follows that all important criteria should be introduced explicitly.

Also, the great freedom allows the DM to take account of **meta-planning objectives.** He may, for example, choose to stop the search if he does not believe that the benefits from continuing in terms of an improved compromise solution and more general insight can justify the costs in terms of time, effort, and revelation of confidential matters, c.f. the discussion of different costs and benefits in section 1.5.

Let us emphasize, too, that the freedom - in contrast to what was presumed in the simple test example in section 8.4 - allows the DM to **change his tastes** as he proceeds. There is no assumption of some underlying, fixed preference structure. He is allowed to feel very devoted to some criteria and later on to change his mind and largely ignore some of them. He can simply continue the search focusing on some other attributes. If we believe that this kind of contradictory development is an intrinsic characteristic of the notion "learning about one's preferences", and it is certainly compelling to do so, the great freedom allowed here should definitely be appreciated.

Also, such procedures may **facilitate the generation or design of possibilities.** Since the two major components of the process - our preferences F and our possibilities Y - are interdependent, learning about F opens the door for the creative generation of new alternatives. Quite often it is just this identification of a new and better way of doing things which is the real outcome of the planning process, rather than the evaluation of and choice between already existing and well-known alternatives.

Finally, we note that iterative, DM directive approaches do not assume that the DM's **preference strucure** can be described by a classical preference model. His attitudes may be developed or formed in whichever way one can imagine. In particular, he may be bounded rational and think in terms of aspiration levels, influenced by both what he ideally would like and what he believes he can accomplish.

At first sight, all of this, the allowance for nontechnical aspects, for meta-planning considerations, and for real shifts in preferences or whatever we think characterizes the DM, seems very attractive. We probably all feel that these are important realities and that the usual decision theoretical paradigm, as illustrated by the basic decision model and the classical preference model, is much too restrictive to accommodate them.

But what about the **costs** of this freedom?

From a practical point of view, the extensive freedom given to the DM makes him highly **responsible** for his own success. It is largely his ability to search, learn and choose intelligently that determines the quality of the outcome. Naturally, this may not always be desirable considering for example the limited time a DM may be willing to offer on the search process. Also, a DM may well prefer to make decisions as to complex problems based on a concrete recommendation which the AN is able to support with at least seemingly scientific arguments, rather than by employing tools which allow him only to explore the possibilities. Our own experience suggests that some DMs prefer the AN to take over. They get disappointed by the limited help provided by the progressive articulation of alternatives approaches.

Again, from a normative perspective, this should not bother us per se. One should not pretend to be able to eliminate delicate preference issues without the DM having to undertake a possibly painful investigation into his priorities. Still, what remains is the legitimate requirement that the DM should have as much support as possible. And this is where the present planning mode may seem inadequate. It gives the DM the duties of directing, learning and choosing, but it **seldom provides much concrete guidance or help in performing these tasks**. The DM has to develop the following on his own: a) a way of thinking about his wishes, b) a search strategy, and c) a stopping rule. In contrast, for example, the AN directive procedures to be discussed in the following chapter largely give the AN the burdens of directing and learning.

Of course, the fact that the DM does not need to make explicit value statements makes him less amenable to criticism. Also, since he has **private** access to the information about the alternatives, it may be hard to infer whether he did well or not. In particular, it is hard to infer anything about his implicit values. Thus, not only does the progressive articulation of alternatives put the DM in control, it also makes it hard for the DM as well as for others to judge whether or not this control is excercised appropriately. This "cost", though, may also be considered to be a virtue in some contexts. In particular, as seen from the vantage point of many DMs, it has the advantage of not threatening established power structures.

Finally and from a more theoretical point of view, it is of course entirely legitimate to discard the classical paradigms. In particular, the incompleteness of any formal model, the relevance of meta-planning objectives and the restrictiveness of the classical decision theory are well established. However, to be really serious, some kind of new, more inclusive paradigm should be introduced. And it has not been. Presently known progressive articulation of alternatives approaches are not founded on serious models or theories of human choice behavior which encompass learning abilities, analytical capacities, changing wishes, and the costs of information processing. While the AN directive - progressive articulation of preferences - approaches to be considered in the following chapter may seem to build on too restrictive assumptions, the DM directive models seem to have gone to the other extreme. From a research-political point of view, this means that there are **no well-established virtues** which may discipline the researcher. Indeed, the ever expanding list of ad hoc procedures is presumably a result of the lack of a common, theoretical framework; there do not exist well-established benchmarks for the quality of the various planning modes.

8.7. Summary

In this chapter we have discussed the progressive articulation of alternatives approach to multiple criteria planning. This is an iterative arrangement directed by the DM. In each round, the DM asks the AN about the set of alternatives, the AN answers and the DM evaluates the answer. He then decides either to continue the search by posing new questions or to stop the search and choose one of the alternatives he has learned about so far.

In terms of theory, the approaches in this class are largely interactive versions of the prior articulation of alternatives approaches discussed in chapter 6. This partly explains the lack of new formal results here.

From a technical viewpoint, the progressive articulation of alternatives approaches are probably best thought of as ad hoc communication schemes or data search techniques.

From a more conceptual viewpoint, however, this new organization of the planning task raises many interesting perspectives.

We have emphasized how the iterative character of the mode influences the kind of support available to the DM and the AN when clarifying wishes and possibilities. The DM needs not investigate his preferences in a vacuum since concrete, real alternatives become successively available. That is, whatever we know about the alternatives can be used to clarify and reduce what we need to know about the preferences. Similarly, the AN needs not investigate the alternatives without guidance, as interesting search directions may be derived from the DM's wishes. That is, whatever we can infer about the DM's preferences can be used to clarify and reduce what we need to know about the possible alternatives.

We also emphasized the effects of the DM being in charge. He has great freedom, and can take into account non-modelled issues like implementation and his personal desires, meta-planning considerations including the costs of searching against the expected improvement of the final choice, and, most notably, he can form and change his wishes in whichever way he likes. However, it also imposes severe burdens on the DM as he is placed completely in charge of the investigation and choice processes. The multiple criteria techniques in this planning mode give the DM the duties of directing, learning and choosing, but they hardly give any guidance or help in performing these tasks. This unpleasant state of affairs is mainly due to a lack of a new paradigm to replace the classical decision theory; there exists a considerable theoretical vacuum.

For now, it seems fair, therefore, to look at the procedures simply as communication devices or data search technologies which hopefully allow the DM to take into account more of the innate complexities of real world planning problems than can be accommodated within the more classical theories of decision making.

8.8. Bibliographic Notes

Concrete progressive articulation of alternatives approaches can be designed in many ways. The DM can investigate the set of alternatives by imposing varying constraints, e.g. Benayoun, de Montgolfier, Tergny and Laritcher(1971), Nakayama and Sawaragi(1984), Nijkamp and Spronk(1980) and Rietveld(1980,ch.9). Alternatively, he may vary the importance weights assigned to the different criteria, e.g. Geoffrion(1967) and Soland(1979), his priority-goal structure, e.g. Charnes and Cooper(1977) and Lee(1972), his reference point, e.g. Korhonen and Laakso(1986), Wierzbicki(1979), and Lewandowski and Grauer(1982), or some combination, e.g. Kok and Lootsma(1984). Attempts to investigate how a DM could direct the search successfully have mainly focused on the use of trade-off information, c.f. Bogetoft(1985a,85b,86), Bogetoft, Hallefjord and Kok(1988) and Bogetoft and Tind(1990). Alternatively, these procedures on how to direct the search, can be thought of as multiple level, multiple criteria planning procedures describing how a headquarters with substantial capacity but a lack of information can find an optimal solution to some underlying decision problem.

Chapter 9

PROGRESSIVE ARTICULATION OF PREFERENCES

Finally, a fourth multiple criteria planning mode involves the progressive articulation of preferences. Once again, this is an iterative interactive approach. However, this time the AN is in charge. In each round, the AN poses a question to the decision maker about his preferences and the DM answers. If the AN now knows sufficiently about the DM's preferences he proposes a final choice from the concrete set of alternatives. Otherwise, the questioning continues.

In terms of theory, one should expect an intimate relationship with the theory underlying the prior articulation of preferences mode. Indeed, as was the case with that mode, the DM is once again assumed to behave in accordance with an underlying - and here implicit - preference function. However, although both the prior and progressive articulation approaches are founded on the implicit assumption that the DM has internally consistent preferences, their concepts of planning and their goals are quite distinct. The prior approach presumes that consistent preferences preexist the planning process and seeks to make these preferences explicit. In this way they can serve as context independent input data to an optimization algorithm which essentially functions as a surrogate decision maker. In the progressive approach, the underlying idea is that the DM's preferences do not preexist the planning process but that these develop and become manifest during the process. It is felt that the process will more realistically reflect the DM's preferences if the demands on explicitness and consistency which are so crucial to the development of a mathematical function are toned down and replaced by an emphasis on what the DM really wants in a given context.

It is characteristic therefore that approaches within the present planning mode are much less concerned about preference modelling as such. Historically, the point of departure has not been preference theory but rather ordinary single criterion optimization procedures. Since the DM's preference function is not explicitly available such optimization procedures are not immediately applicable. They may however suggest procedures that appear reasonable if we ask the DM to provide the information which otherwise would be extracted from the - nonavailable - preference function.

So although the present mode is interactive, once again emphasis is placed on the identification of a solution rather than on the DM's active participation in the planning process and the resulting insight as to his desires and possibilities. Hence the forementioned distinction between the prior and interactive modes with respect to concepts and goals is perhaps not so significant after all.

Another distinguishing characteristic of this mode as opposed to the DM directed ones, is that the existing techniques which can be classified as belonging to this mode usually make very strong assumptions about the DM's preference function and that a **convergence result** is usually provided. By this is meant that if the DM answers consistently according to some implicitly assumed and well behaved, e.g. linear, underlying utility function, the procedures converge to an optimal solution.

Since approaches within this mode are characterized by their point of departure in traditional single criterion optimization, they may appear somewhat technical. We have tried to keep the technical details to a minimum and we have generally referred such details to the last paragraphs of the presentations. Readers who find difficulty in following more technical details should therefore be able to grasp the main ideas by simply ignoring the paragraphs specifically indicated as containing more technical material.

There is a wide spectrum of procedures within this AN directed, interactive organization of multiple criteria planning. They differ by the computational duties of the AN and, more importantly here, by the kind of information requested from the DM. Usually, they either require direct information about the DM's **substitution wishes** at a given point or they require him to evaluate existing **substitution possibilities**. We commence by considering a substitution wishes procedure.

9.1. A Substitution Wishes Approach

One of the earliest progressive articulation of preferences procedures is the socalled Geoffrion-Dyer-Feinberg (GDF) procedure. Central to this procedure is that the DM can successively express his substitution wishes when confronted with different feasible alternatives. The GDF procedure is typical of the historical point of departure of many procedures within this mode. It builds directly on a classical, non-linear optimization routine, the Franke-Wolfe algorithm; the DM simply takes over those steps of the algorithm which require information about the preference function.

The GDF procedure implicitly assumes that the DM's multiple criteria planning problem can best be solved within a framework of the Rational Ideal Model. The **aim** of the GDF procedure may therefore be thought of as one of solving some implicit, underlying decision problem, i.e. to find an optimal solution to the basic decision problem

$$\begin{aligned} \max \quad & F(y) \\ \text{s.t.} \quad & y \in Y \end{aligned}$$

within a context of decentralized and not immediately available information.

To accomplish this, the procedure makes certain technical **assumptions** about the nature of the underlying decision problem, i.e. about F and Y. Loosely speaking, it is assumed that the preferences as well as the set of alternatives can be considered within a convex setting, an assumption which is very common in economics and operational research, c.f. section 6.5 and 7.8. We will return to these technical assumptions at the end of this section.

If these assumptions are fulfilled, then the procedure can be shown to converge rapidly towards an optimal solution. If these assumptions are not fulfilled in practice, e.g. because the DM does not answer in a manner which is consistent with the type of preference function assumed, then the procedure may break down and lead to confusing and unusable results. In this case the AN is placed in a rather awkward position, particularly because the DM is involved in the dialogue. How can the AN save the day - as well as respect for formalized planning procedures and perhaps one's reputation and job as well - if the iterative procedure performs poorly? On the other hand, the interactive setting can hopefully provide just the context which can lead to an even richer insight and dialogue in such cases. This will particularly be the case if the setting has contributed to an atmosphere of mutual respect and an understanding of the strengths - and limitations - of this approach to reducing some of the complexities associated with planning.

This possible mismatch between the underlying methodlogical assumptions and the actual real-world replies by the DM is not a specific weakness of this procedure. Rather the note of warning applies to any and all algorithmic approaches to planning, and cannot be repeated too often in a world which looks to economic planning models, decision support systems, expert systems and artificial intelligence as the means for taming and reducing complexity.

The **idea** of the GDF procedure is conceptually simple. It begins with a feasible alternative y' and makes the DM provide information about his substitution wishes around y'. These wishes indicate in which direction the DM would like to move, i.e. how he would like to modify y'. Now, the AN compares these wishes with the actual set of alternatives in an attempt to find a direction that takes into account the DM's wishes as well as the actual possibilities of substituting around y'. Next, the DM is asked to specify how large a step he would like to take in this direction. Hereby, a new and - if the assumptions of the procedure are fulfilled - better proposal has been identified. Using this as the point of departure, i.e. as the new y', the above steps may be reinitiated: the DM specifies in which direction he would now like to move, the AN presents him with the possibility of moving in a new direction which takes account of both his wishes and the actual possibilities of substituting around y', and the DM decides how large a step he would like to take in this direction. Proceeding like this a sequence of monotonically improving proposals are generated. The procedure stops when the DM finally does not want to move away from a given proposal, either because it cannot be improved upon or because he does not consider the possible improvements worth the effort.

We now turn to a more detailed but still technically simple outline of the procedure.

First of all, let us discuss **the DM's wishes to substitute** around a given proposal y', i.e. his desires to modify a given proposal. Consider a given proposal $y' \in Y$ in criteria space. The DM's exact willingness to substitute around y' is defined by the indifference curve I through y'. Figure 9.1 below illustrates this. We see that at y', the DM is willing to give up Δ_2 units of the second attribute y_2 to gain Δ_1 units of the first attribute y_1.

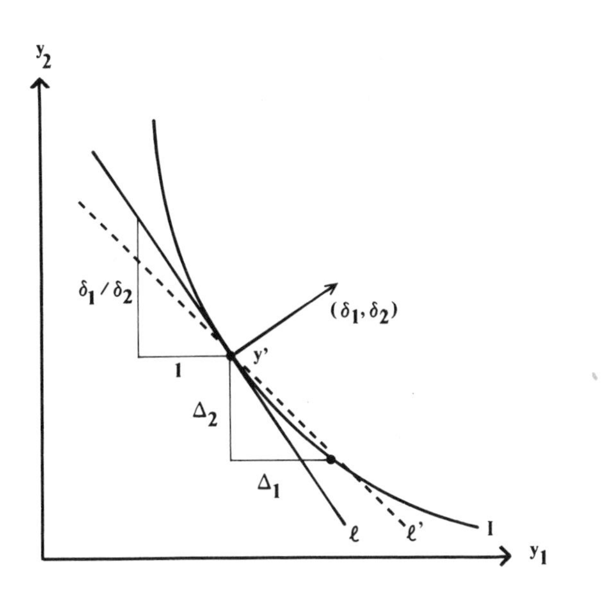

Figure 9.1 Articulation of Substitution Wishes

An approximate willingness is defined by ℓ, the linear approximation or support of I at y'. If the preference function is explicitly known, it is a simple mathematical exercise to determine this linear approximation. Indeed, this is how the Franke-Wolfe procedure proceeds. Presently, however, F is not explicitly known, so the DM must supply this information, i.e. the DM must **articulate substitution wishes**. This may be done, for example, by asking him to imagine a certain improvement Δ_1 of the first criterion, the reference criterion, and asking him for i=2, . . . ,n to state how much, say Δ_i, he is willing to decrease the i'the criterion to gain this improvement in the first criterion, given that the other criteria values remain unchanged. That is, the DM is requested to state decreases $\Delta_2, \ldots, \Delta_n$, such that he can subscribe to the statements

$$(y'_1, y'_2, \ldots, y'_n) \approx^* (y'_1 + \Delta_1, y'_2 - \Delta_2, y'_3, \ldots, y'_n)$$
$$(y'_1, y'_2, \ldots, y'_n) \approx^* (y'_1 + \Delta_1, y'_2, y'_3 - \Delta_3, \ldots, y'_n)$$
$$\cdot$$
$$(y'_1, y'_2, \ldots, y'_n) \approx^* (y'_1 + \Delta_1, y'_2, y'_3, \ldots, y'_n - \Delta_n)$$

To illustrate - in a provocative manner - let us assume that the choice problem concerns airport development and that the only criteria of relevance are capacity and safety. In that case, the DM must state how large a decrease in safety he is willing to accept, say by Δ_2 extra killed in an average accident, in order to increase the average capacity by some amount, e.g. $\Delta_1 = 1000$ extra passengers per day. Similarly, in a macro-economic planning problem, the DM may have to articulate how large a decrease in employment he is willing to accept, say by Δ_2 fulltime jobs, in order to improve the balance of trade by for example Δ_1 = one billion dollars per year. Needless to say, the articulation of such trade-offs may be extremely difficult in practice.

From figure 9.1 it is clear that we can use the expressed substitution wishes Δ_1 and Δ_2 to approximate the indifference curves. More precisely, we can use them to construct the linear approximation ℓ' of I, since the slope of this line must simply be $-\Delta_2/\Delta_1$. We might observe that this approximation depends on the reference variation Δ_1 and that as Δ_1 increases, we get a more horizontal line. To ensure that the procedure works well, i.e. converges, c.f. below, we would really like to construct the line ℓ with slope $-\delta_1/\delta_2$. This corresponds to the case where Δ_1 is arbitrarily small such that only marginal variations are considered. Fortunately, however, it can be shown that the difference between ℓ and ℓ' does not matter, provided it gets smaller and smaller as we proceed.

Before ending this discussion of the articulation of substitution wishes, let us emphasize that in applications one would want to give careful thought to the **experimental**

design used. Thus for example, it may be relevant to introduce a special interactive routine in which the AN may succesively present the DM with trial reductions of the different criteria, $\Delta_2, \ldots, \Delta_n$, until the DM feels comfortable with the indifference statements above. Also, it may be relevant to elicit more than the minimal n-1 trade-offs above so as to check the consistency of the DM's answers. Thus, for example, in the two criteria case of figure 9.1 one might want to ensure that the approximation ℓ' is not too dependent on the value and sign selected for Δ_1. More generally, one may for example ask the DM to supplement his statement of $\Delta_1, \ldots, \Delta_n$ above by stating improvements $\Delta_1^*, \ldots, \Delta_{n-1}^*$ of the first n-1 criteria, each of which exactly suffices to compensate for a certain decrease Δ_n^* in the n'th criterion. Now, if the DM answers consistently, we should have $\Delta_1/\Delta_i \simeq \Delta_1^*/\Delta_i^*$ for all $i = 2, \ldots, n$, i.e. it should not really matter whether we estimate the trade-offs one way or the other.

Based on the elicited substitution wishes at y', the AN may now initiate the search for a new and improved alternative.

Initially, it must be determined in which **direction** to search. One obvious idea is to move in the direction given by the vector of substitution wishes at y', i.e. in the direction $\delta(y)$ as given by (δ_1,δ_2) in figure 9.1. This is the direction the DM would like to move, since it gives the greatest marginal growth in the preference function implicitly assumed to underly the GDF approach. However, if y' is an efficient point, then it will not be possible to move in this direction as so doing would result in leaving the set Y of possible alternatives. Therefore in deciding upon the direction to search, the direction in which the DM would like to move must be compared with what is actually possible. In so doing, the procedure effectively compares the substitution wishes with the substitution possibilities. This is done by the AN who finds the feasible alternative y" that is best according to the substitution wishes articulated by the DM. The logic is as follows. Since, marginally speaking, the DM considered one unit of y_1 to be equally attractive as (Δ_2/Δ_1) units of y_2, one unit of y_1 to be equally attractive as (Δ_3/Δ_1) units of $y_3, \ldots$, and one unit of y_1 to be equally attractive as (Δ_n/Δ_1) units of y_n, his wishes may be approximated by the **uni-criterion** linear objective function

$$y_1 + (\Delta_1/\Delta_2)y_2 + \ldots + (\Delta_1/\Delta_n)y_n$$

To understand this approximation, note that in the two criteria case of figure 9.1, the level curves of this function are lines parallel to ℓ'. Therefore, the best alternative y" according to this expressed approximation to his substitution wishes is found by maximizing this approximate preference description over all points in Y, i.e. by the AN solving

$$\max_{y} \; y_1 + (\Delta_1/\Delta_2)y_2 + \ldots + (\Delta_1/\Delta_n)y_n$$
$$\text{s.t.} \quad y \in Y$$

In the two criteria case this means that the AN identifies the feasible alternative y" which belongs to the highest line parallel to ℓ'. In summary, we might say that the AN has found the best alternative y" under the hypothesis that the expressed substitution wishes are not only locally but also globally valid.

Of course, y" need not actually be better than y', since the substitution wishes can vary as we move away from y'; the local substitution wishes are probably not globally valid. However, it follows from the assumed regularity, i.e. convexity, of the whole problem that unless optimality has been reached, c.f. below, a new and improved alternative exists somewhere on the line between y' and y". Exactly where depends on the details of the DM's preferences. Hence, to find such a point, the DM must again be introduced into the procedure. This part of the procedure is often called the **step-size** problem since the DM must determine how large a step to take from y' in the direction of y". It is accomplished by simply asking him to choose his most preferred point, say y"', along the line between y' and y".

As a matter of notation, let us denote the set of points on the line between y' and y" by P, i.e. in formal terms

$$P = \{ \lambda y'' + (1-\lambda)y' \mid \lambda \in [0,1] \}$$

Thus P denotes the set of proposals from which the DM must select in the step-size problem. Again, to support the DM's choice from this concrete set of proposals, additional routines may be used. For example, since P is in fact a simple set, parametrized by a single parameter λ, graphics may be used to vizualize the choice possiblities, c.f. the example below.

By the preceding steps we have moved from one alternative y' to a new and better alternative y'''. Taking this latter alternative as the point of departure, i.e. as the new y', the above steps may be reinitiated. Hereby, the search for the best alternative proceeds until it is terminated by a socalled stopping rule. The procedure is summarized in figure 9.2, which depicts the steps of iteration number t.

Of course, different **stopping rules** may be used. In theory, the search for the DM's preferred compromise solution - which is formally translated here into his search for an optimal solution to his underlying basic decision problem - should continue until he does not want to move away from an alternative y'. Such a solution has been reached if y' is selected as the best proposal by the DM in two successive iterations. Referring to figure 9.2, this will be the case if the DM selects $\lambda=0$ in the expression for P or if a selected y' is also optimal in the AN's subsequent search for a new tentative proposal y''. In applications, less stringent rules may be useful. For example, the search may stop when the DM feels that the improvements generated do not justify the effort required to determine them.

Finally, let us comment on the **convergence** properties of this procedure. If the underlying basic decision problem has the assumed regularity properties and if the DM performs his tasks correctly, the above procedure is equivalent to the Frank-Wolfe algorithm which is known to converge. That is, a sequence of trial solutions $y'^1, y'^2, \ldots, y'^t, \ldots$ is generated which approaches the solution y^{opt} to the basic decision problem. In the present implementation of this procedure in a DM-AN environment, several factors may of course impede the convergence. In particular, one may expect the DM to supply only approximate estimates of his marginal substitution wishes and to select only an approximately best proposal from the set presented to him. Fortunately, however, it turns out that the procedure is rather robust when confronted with such approximations.

AN

1. Determine the best alternative y''^t according to the expressed substitution wishes, i.e. by solving

$$\max_{y} \; y_1 + (\Delta_1^{t-1}/\Delta_2^{t-1})y_2 + \ldots + (\Delta_1^{t-1}/\Delta_n^{t-1})y_n$$
$$\text{s.t.} \quad y \in Y$$

2. Present the set of alternatives P^t along the line between y'^{t-1} and y''^t, i.e.

$$P^t = \{\lambda y''^t + (1-\lambda)y'^{t-1} \mid \lambda \in [0,1]\}$$

to the DM

Set of Proposals P^t (AN → DM)

Selected Proposal y'^t, Substitution Wishes $\Delta_1^t, \Delta_2^t, \ldots, \Delta_n^t$ (DM → AN)

DM

1. Determine the preferred proposal y'^t in P^t

2. Articulate wishes $\Delta_1^t, \Delta_2^t, \ldots, \Delta_n^t$ to substitute around y'^t, i.e. articulate variations $\Delta_1^t, \ldots, \Delta_n^t$ in the different criteria such that with $y' = y'^t$ and $\Delta_1 = \Delta_1^t, \ldots, \Delta_n = \Delta_n^t$

$$(y'_1, y'_2, \ldots, y'_n) \approx^* (y'_1 + \Delta_1, y'_2 - \Delta_2, y'_3, \ldots, y'_n)$$
$$(y'_1, y'_2, \ldots, y'_n) \approx^* (y'_1 + \Delta_1, y'_2, y'_3 - \Delta_3, \ldots, y'_n)$$
$$\cdot$$
$$(y'_1, y'_2, \ldots, y'_n) \approx^* (y'_1 + \Delta_1, y'_2, y'_3, \ldots, y'_n - \Delta_n)$$

Figure 9.2 The GDF Procedure

Also, one might question the relevance of convergence since this is a long run property of the procedure. In applications, however, only a modest number of iterations can be carried out since the DM cannot be expected to participate in many question, evaluation and answer rounds. Therefore, it is probably more relevant to look at the socalled initial rate of convergence, i.e. the initial rate of improvements in the trial solutions $y'^1, y'^2, \ldots$ Again, however, it turns out that the present procedure is quite promising. Under certain additional assumptions it has been shown that the difference between the value of the basic decision problem, $F(y^{opt})$, and the actual value in a given iteration, $F(y'^t)$, is at least halved in each of the initial iterations.

In the next section, we illustrate what the GDF procedure may look like in a concrete application. Before we do so, however, let us briefly comment on the more **technical assumptions** and properties of the procedure. Readers with no technical interests may choose to ignore these remarks and proceed directly to section 9.2.

The GDF procedure presumes a convex multiple criteria setting, i.e. $Y=\{(f_1(x), \ldots, f_n(x)) \mid x \in X\}$ must be bounded, closed, and convex or X must be bounded, closed, and convex and $f_1, \ldots, f_n$ must be concave functions, c.f. chapter 6.4. Additionally, it is assumed that the preference function F is increasing, concave, and differentiable, c.f. chapter 7.8.

Now, in such an environment, information about the approximate trade-off wishes is provided by the substitution coefficients $\delta(y')=(\delta_1(y'), \ldots, \delta_n(y'))$ at y', c.f. section 7.7. The substitution wishes coefficients $\delta(y')$ constitute a normal vector to the linear approximation or support ℓ of the indifference curve I through y', see also figure 9.1. Hence, they define the direction in which the DM would like to move. If the preference function is explicitly know, it is a simple mathematical exercise to determine $\delta(y')$ since the i'th coordinate $\delta_i(y')$ is simply the marginal utility of the i'th attribute, i.e. the partial derivative $\partial F/\partial y_i$ of F with respect to y_i, c.f. section 7.7. Indeed, this is how the Franke-Wolfe procedure proceeds.

Also, note that except for possible estimation errors, the direction finding problem of the AN is equivalent to the problem of finding the best alternative y" according to the aggregate utility function $\delta_1 y_1 + \delta_2 y_2 + \ldots + \delta_n y_n$. This is once again precisely how the Frank-Wolfe procedure works.

Finally, let us note that if we had an explicit expression of the DM's preference function F, the step-size problem simply amounts to an ordinary, single criterion optimization problem, namely

$$\max_{\lambda} \quad F(\lambda y'' + (1-\lambda)y')$$
$$\text{s.t.} \quad \lambda \in [0,1]$$

Again, this is precisely how the Frank-Wolfe procedure proceeds. In summary, we may conclude that the GDF procedure builds directly on the Franke-Wolfe procedure.

9.2. Laboratory and Theoretical Experiments

To illustrate the GDF procedure, consider the two criteria problem studied in sections 8.2 and 8.4. Thus, we consider a student with a planning horizon of two years who has to choose a reasonable compromise between consumption this year, y_1, and savings this year corresponding to consumption next year, y_2. The set of alternatives is delineated by the set OABCDEFG in figure 9.3 below. In this figure we have also illustated how the procedure may develop by drawing a series of indifference curves and trial solutions.

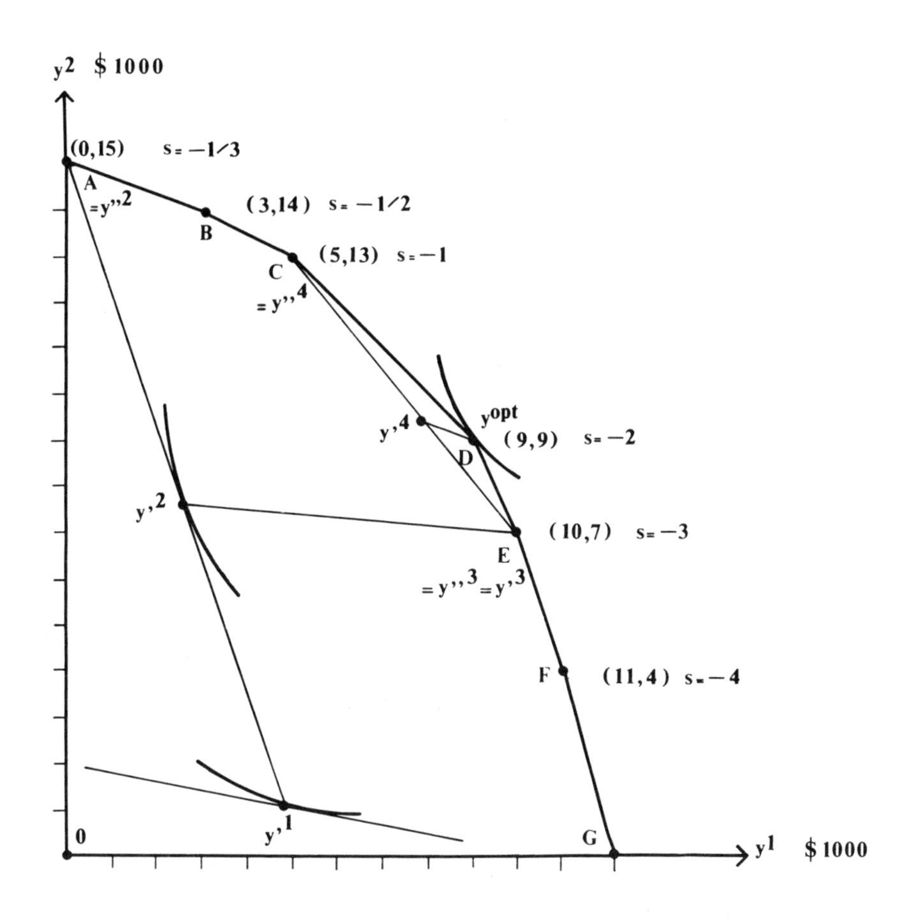

Figure 9.3 The Frank-Wolfe Algorithm in Trial Example

First of all, let us describe how a **laboratory experiment** may develop. In such an experiment no single individual would have all the information provided in figure 9.3. Rather, information about F and Y would be decentralized and not immediately available, i.e. the DM would have some information about the indifference curves and the AN would have some information about the set of alternatives OABCDEFG. Figures 9.4 and 9.5 illustrate how the communication would progress in such a case.

	AN		DM	
Iteration No. t	New Trial Proposal y''^t	Set of Proposals P^t	Best Proposal y'^t	Marginal Trades Δ_{2t}/Δ_1^t
1	(5, 1)	{(5,1)}	(5, 1)	0.2
2	(0,15)	Fig 9.5a	(75,210)/28	2.8
3	(10, 7)	Fig 9.5b	(10, 7)	0.7
4	(5,13)	Fig 9.5c	(95,114)/12	1.2
5	(9, 9)	Fig 9.5d	(9, 9)	1.0
6	(9, 9)			

Figure 9.4 Communication Record

To get started, the AN arbitrarily submits the feasible alternative $(y_1,y_2) = (5,1)$ to the DM and asks him to state his trade-off wishes. Let us assume that the DM expresses a willingness to give up approximately $\Delta_2=0.2$ units of y_2 to get an additional unit of y_1.

In iteration number 2 then, the AN uses this substitution wish to determine a new trial proposal y''^2. The best proposal that the AN can provide at this point is (0,15) since this is the feasible alternative which belongs to the highest straight line with slope -0.2. This is easily seen by comparing -0.2 with the slopes of the frontier line segments of Y depicted in figure 9.3 above. Hence, (0,15) is the best proposal if we tentatively believe the DM to have an overall preference function which is linear and has indifference curves with slope -0.2.

Now, the AN wants the DM to pick the best alternative on the line between (5,1) and (0,15), i.e. from the set

$$P^2 = \{\lambda(0,15) + (1-\lambda)(5,1) \mid \lambda \in [0,1]\}$$

To expose these possibilities to the DM, the AN presents the graphs in figure 9.5a. Here, the developments of y_1 and y_2 are depicted as functions of the step-size λ. For $\lambda=0$, this represents the original proposal (5,1) and as λ increases to 1 we gradually move towards (0,15).

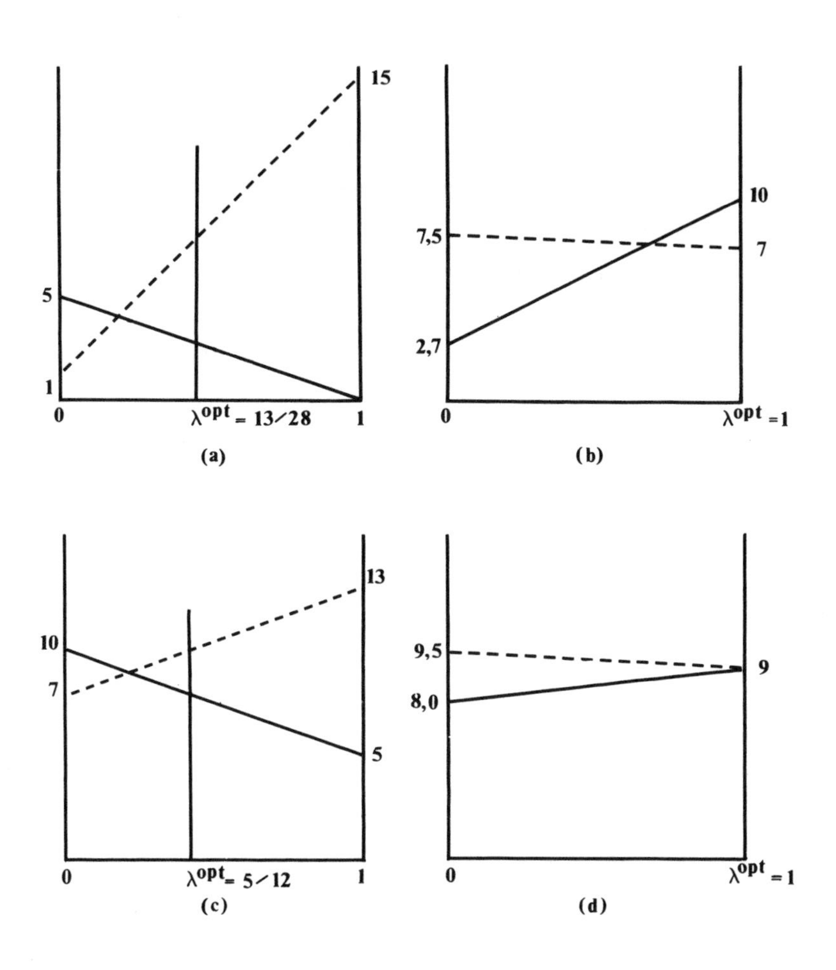

Figure 9.5 Sets P! of Proposals

The DM is now supposed to look at these graphs and pick the value of λ where the corresponding criteria values y_1 and y_2 make him most comfortable. Let us - somewhat hypothetically - assume that he picks a step-size $\lambda = 13/28$ corresponding to a best proposal y'^2 in P^2 equal to

$$(13/28)(0,15) + (15/28)(5,1) = (75,210)/28$$

i.e. $y'^2 = (75,210)/28$.

To complete iteration two, the DM must now articulate his substitution wishes given this new best proposal. Since consumption y_1 is quite low at this trial solution, he is most likely willing to trade off quite a bit of consumption next year, y_2, in order to increase consumption this year. Let us assume that the DM expresses a willingness to give up approximately $\Delta_2 = 2.8$ units of y_2 to get an additional y_1 unit.

Being informed about $y'^2 = (75,210)/28$ and $\Delta_2^2/\Delta_1^2 = 2.8$, the AN is now able to start iteration number 3. Since the subsequent iterations proceed in a similar manner, no detailed comments are necessary. Let us just note that the procedure stops in iteration number 6, since the AN cannot find a new tentative proposal which is potentially better than (9,9).

Up until now, we have considered a laboratory experiment where we assumed that information as to F and Y is decentralized and not immediately available. We will conclude this section by describing what a **theoretical experiment** might look like. In fact, due to the intimate relationship between the GDF procedure and the Frank-Wolfe algorithm, this is equivalent to a simple illustration of the latter algorithm. Since the details of this illustration are slightly more technical, some readers may want to turn directly to the next section.

The set of alternatives is again delineated by OABCDEFG above. Now, however, we also assume that the DM's implicit preference function is in fact

$$F(y_1,y_2)=y_1y_2$$

We assume too that the DM performs his tasks perfectly correctly, i.e. that he responds to the AN's querries in accordance with his preferences, which now are precisely determined by this implicit preference function.

Before proceeding, let us compare this context with the assumptions of the GDF procedure. Clearly, the set of alternatives in criteria space, Y, is convex. Also, the DM's assumed preference function $F(y_1,y_2) = y_1y_2$ is increasing for $y_1>0$ and $y_2>0$. However, it is not concave but only quasi-concave, c.f. section 7.8. By an increasing transformation like $\ln(F(y_1y_2))$ it does however become concave and it does not matter whether we use $F(y_1,y_2) = y_1y_2$ or $F^{\#}(y_1,y_2) = \ln(y_1y_2) = \ln(y_1)+\ln(y_2)$ below since this transformation does not affect the relative values of the marginal utilities, i.e. the marginal rates of substitution δ_1/δ_2. Finally, it is clearly differentiable.

Also, as a small mathematical exercise, let us determine how the DM behaves when he performs his tasks in accordance with his implicit preference function. First, observe that at (y'_1,y'_2) the marginal rate of substitution of criterion 2 for criterion 1 is

$$\delta_1/\delta_2 = (\partial F/\partial y_1)/(\partial F/\partial y_2) = y'_2/y'_1$$

Therefore, given (y'_1,y'_2), if the DM is asked to state the amount Δ_2 that he is willing to give up in y_2 to get Δ_1 more in y_1 he should for Δ_1 arbitrarily small state y'_2/y'_1. Secondly, note that the step-size problem becomes

$$\max_{\lambda\in[0,1]} (\lambda y''_1+(1-\lambda)y'_1)(\lambda y''_2+(1-\lambda)y'_2)$$

This is a second order polynomial in λ. By differentiation, it follows that the largest value obtains for

$$\lambda^{\#} = (1/2)[y'_1/(y'_1-y''_1) + y'_2/(y'_2-y''_2)]$$

Hence, the optimal step-size, λ^{opt}, is $\lambda^{\#}$ when $\lambda^{\#}\in[0,1]$, 0 when $\lambda^{\#}<0$, and 1 when $\lambda^{\#}>1$.

After these small exercises, let us return to an illustation of how the GDF procedure would develop in this theoretical exercise. That is how the GDF procedure develops for the case where the AN asks the right questions and makes the correct calculations, and where the DM understands the questions and replies in complete accordance with his preferences as determined by his implicit preference function $F(y_1,y_2) = y_1y_2$. This is easy since the answers in the "laboratory experiment" above were in fact chosen so as to conform with the implicit preference function $F(y_1,y_2) = y_1y_2$. Therefore, figures 9.3, 9.4 and 9.5 do in fact illustrate how the GDF procedure would develop if Y and F were explicitly known, i.e. they illustrate the development of the Frank-Wolfe algorithm.

To get started, the AN arbitrarily submits the feasible alternative $(y_1,y_2) = (5,1)$ to the DM and asks him to state his trade-off wishes. At this point, the (absolute value of the) slope of the DM's indifference curve is $\delta_1/\delta_2 = y_2/y_1 = 1/5 = 0.2$, i.e. the DM is willing to give up approximately $\Delta_2 = 0.2$ units of y_2 to get an additional y_1 unit. In fact, he is willing to give up exactly $1/6 \approx 0.167$ units of y_2 to get one additional unit of y_1 since $F(5+1,1-1/6) = 5 = F(5,1)$. At the margin however, i.e. when Δ_1 gets infinitesimally small, he his willing to pay $\Delta_2 = 0.2\Delta_1$ units of y_2 to gain Δ_1 units of y_1.

In iteration number 2 then, the AN uses these substitution wishes to determine a new trial proposal y''^2 as explained earlier. The best proposal is (0,15).

Now, the AN wants the DM to pick the best alternative on the line between (5,1) and (0,15), i.e. from the set

$$P^2 = \{\lambda(0,15) + (1-\lambda)(5,1) \mid \lambda \in [0,1]\}$$

We may predict his answer from the mathematical analysis above since λ^* becomes

$$\lambda^* = (1/2)[5/(5-0) + 1/(1-15)] = 13/28$$

such that the best proposal in P^2 is $y'^2 = (75,210)/28$ as previously.

Additionally, the DM must articulate his substitution wishes in this new best proposal. We may predict the answer here since $\delta_1/\delta_2 = y_2/y_1 = 210/75 = 2.8$, i.e. the DM should "at the margin" be willing to give up 2.8 units of y_2 to gain one unit of y_1. Being informed about $y'^2 = (75,210)/28$ and $\Delta_2^2/\Delta_1^2 = 2.8$, the AN is now able to start iteration number 3.

The subsequent iterations proceed similarly. Let us just note that the optimal step-sizes in iterations 3, 4, and 5 become 1, 5/12, and 1, and that the procedure stops in iteration number 6, since at this point the lower support ℓ' to the DM's indifference curve is an upper support to the set of alternatives, i.e. the AN cannot find a new proposal which is potentially better than (9,9).

As indicated earlier, this procedure appears to work well when all the underlying assumptions are reasonable. However, if this is not the case it may be difficult to characterize the performance. Consider for example the situation where the DM's preferences change after a statement of substitution wishes. Then he may not want to move in the direction subsequently proposed to him by the AN. Nevertheless, the present proposal need not be the best compromise solution, even though it would be classified as such according to the formal stopping rules given above. Also, one may imagine that halfheld beliefs, uncertainties, preference statement errors etc. cause the procedure to cycle or at least stall. For any of these reasons, the procedure may lead to a recommendation that the DM does not accept. In such a situation, quite a burden will be placed on the AN. He will have to determine where - and perhaps why - the basic assumptions do not appear to hold. It should of course be considered whether the apparent difficulties may be due to misunderstandings rather than the method and its underlying assumptions as to a convex setting and the like.

9.3. A Substitution Possibilities Approach

As mentioned in the introduction to this chapter, the procedures within this AN-directive, interactive organization of decision making differ by the kind of information requested from the DM. In the previous sections we considered a procedure based on direct information about the DM's **substitution wishes** at a given point. We proceed now to consider a well-known procedure based on the DM having to evaluate existing **substitution possibilities**, the socalled Zionts and Wallenius (ZW) procedure.

Once again, this procedure is inspired by a classical, single objective optimization routine, namely the simplex method for solving linear programming problems. Those familiar with the simplex algorithm will know that information about the preference function is used to iteratively evaluate which socalled "nonbasis variables" may be attractive to introduce into the "basis". This algorithm is therefore modified here; in the absence of an explicit preference function, the DM has to make these evaluations. Additionally, to avoid overloading the DM with such questions, the ZW procedure introduces an inference mechanism such that the AN successively builds up information about the preference function from previous answers. This allows him to reduce the set of alternatives and the associated trade-off possibilities that are potentially relevant. Hence the requirements as to the DM's participation are also reduced.

The **aim** of the ZW procedure may again be thought of as one of solving some implicit, underlying problem, i.e. to find an optimal solution to the basic decision problem

$$\begin{array}{ll} \max & F(y) \\ \text{s.t.} & y \in Y \end{array}$$

within a context of decentralized and not immediately available information.

To accomplish this, we must again make certain **assumptions** about the nature of the preference function F and the set of possible alternatives Y. In the (original) ZW procedure it is assumed that the DM's implicit preference function F is strictly increasing and linear, i.e. that

$$F(y_1, y_2, \ldots, y_n) = \lambda_1 y_1 + \lambda_2 y_2 + \ldots + \lambda_n y_n$$

for some unknown vector $\lambda=(\lambda_1,\lambda_2, \ldots ,\lambda_n)$ of positive weights. These weights, then, efficiently define the DM's substitution wishes, and it is implicitly assumed that these wishes do not depend on the point of departure, i.e. the "anchor" point $y=(y_1, \ldots ,y_n)$.

Referering to the discussion of additive preferences in section 7.9, we might observe that the present assumption is rather demanding. This will particularly be the case in planning contexts characterized by "significant decisions" which may lead to far more than marginal changes in the values of the criteria characterizing the system. Therefore, perhaps it is more appropriate to think of the linear preference function simply as an analytical convenience which hopefully allows for a reasonably good approximate description of reality.

It is difficult to generalize as to how well the procedure works if the DM's preferences cannot be reasonably modelled by a stationary, linear preference function. Therefore, as was the case with the GDF procedure, the present procedure can not be said to lead to optimal behavior in general. In particular, and as indicated above, difficulties may be expected in cases where a decision may result in a state of the system characterized by criteria values far removed from the present value of y'. In very different states one can hardly expect the DM to assign the same relative importance to the various attributes, i.e. the criteria weights would change. In other words, the implicit assumption of linear F becomes more and more tenuous the greater the changes in the values of the criteria.

Furthermore, it is assumed that Y is a socalled (bounded) polyhedral convex set. This is a technical assumption which may not be familiar to all readers. Therefore, we will return to it at the end of this section. Intuitively, however, the idea is simply that Y must be a convex set with a piecewise linear contour. An example of this is the set Y delineated by OABCDEFG in figure 9.3 above. One may of course wonder if real sets of alternatives possess this property. In many cases, they certainly do not. On the other hand, experience suggests that it may often generate resonable outcomes if reality is approximated this way. Thus, in many cases one may again look at this assumption as an analytical convenience which hopefully allows for a reasonably good description of the actual planning context.

The **idea** of the ZW procedure is to learn or draw inferences about the DM's substitution wishes as defined by the weights $\lambda_1, \lambda_2, \ldots, \lambda_n$ which he assigns to the different criteria. To begin with, it is only assumed that these weights are positive, i.e. the vector of weights belongs to the set Λ defined by

$$\lambda \in \Lambda = \{\lambda \in \Re^n \mid \Sigma_i \lambda_i = 1, \lambda_i > 0 \ \forall i\},$$

Now, learning means that portions of this weighting space Λ are eliminated. This learning or inference mechanism is operated by the AN who iteratively asks the DM questions about his attitudes towards various substitution possibilities. Thus, for example, the AN may ask the DM if he would like to go from one alternative $y' \in Y$ to some other alternative $y'' \in Y$. From the DM's response, inference can be made about the actual set of weights. If the DM prefers y' to y'', we must have $F(y') > F(y'')$. It follows then from the assumption that the DM's implicit preference function is linear and that the weighted sum of the y'-coordinates is larger than the weighted sum of the y''-coordinates. This information allows the AN to reduce the set of possible weights. The relevant weights are now those which generate a preference for y' over y''. Proceeding like this, the AN builds up information about the actual weights until he finally knows sufficiently to pick out the best - that is, the DM's most preferred - alternative in Y.

We now give a more detailed but still technically simple explanation of the ZW procedure.

An important effect of the special regularities imposed on F and Y here is that it suffices to look at a finite set of candidate solutions. This is the set **Z** of socalled **efficient, extreme points** of Y. We will return to this concept more formally towards the end of this section. For now, let us just think of the efficient extreme points as those efficient alternatives that are also corner points. Thus, in figure 9.3, the efficient extreme points are simply Z={A,B,C,D,E,F,G}. Also, given an efficient extreme point y', it is possible to define a subset of neighboring efficient extreme points **Z(y')**, the socalled **adjacent efficient extreme points**. In figure 9.3 we have for example Z(D)={C,E}, i.e. the efficient extreme points that are neighbors to D are C and E.

In more complex, higher dimensional problems, it does of course require a special effort to determine an efficient extreme point and its adjacent efficient extreme points and this is precisely where special algorithms like the simplex method may be useful.

A central step in the ZW procedure is to let the DM **evaluate substitution possibilities** corresponding to moves from an efficient extreme point to its adjacent, efficient extreme points. Consider as the trial solution an efficient extreme point $y' \in Z$. Now, (some of) the substitution possibilities around y' are given by the moves

$$y' \rightarrow y'' \ , \ y'' \in Z(y')$$

from y' to the adjacent efficient extreme points. The ZW procedure suggests that the DM should be asked to evaluate these substitution possibilities. This means that for every $y'' \in Z(y')$ the DM must make one - and only one - of the statements

$$y' >^* y'' \ , \ y' \ {}^*\!< y'' \ , \ y' \approx^* y''$$

i.e. for every y" he must express whether y' is preferred to y", y" is preferred to y', or y' is equally as good as y".

One way to present these possibilities to the DM is in terms of composite or total trade-offs. The DM is asked for example: Here is a trade. Are you willing to accept a combined change of criterion 1 by $\Delta_1 = y''_1 - y'_1$, of criterion 2 by $\Delta 2 = y''_2 - y'_2$, ... , and of criterion n by $\Delta_n = y''_n - y'_n$? Respond yes, no, or indifferent! Note that the trades considered here are composite in the sense that when comparing y' and y" most likely many or all of the criteria will vary at one time. This may be contrasted with the trades in the previous GDF procedure which were only partial in the sense that only two criteria were assumed to vary simultaneously.

We might note too, that, given the assumptions underlying the ZW procedure, it makes sense to present changes $\Delta_1, \ldots, \Delta_n$ without any reference to the point of departure y'; due to the assumed linearity of F, the DM's substitution wishes and hence his evaluation of substitution possibilities is presumed to be independent of the "anchor" point.

No matter how the questioning is actually designed, the DM's evaluations may be summarized in terms of a partition of Z(y') into three sets

$$\begin{aligned} YES &= \{y'' \in Z(y') \mid y'' >^* y'\} \\ NO &= \{y'' \in Z(y') \mid y'' \,^*\!< y'\} \\ INDIF &= \{y'' \in Z(y') \mid y'' \approx^* y'\} \end{aligned}$$

indicating the trades which are considered favorable, which are considered unfavorable and which leave the DM indifferent.

Based upon the DM's evaluation of the substitution possibilities around the trial solution y', the AN is now able to draw inferences about the DM's actual weighting of the criteria. The idea of the **inference mechanism** is very simple. If for example the DM prefers y' to y", i.e. he does not like the combined trade $\Delta_1, \ldots, \Delta_n$ and therefore his answer is "no", it follows that the weighted sum of the y'_i's must exceed that of the y''_i's, i.e.

$$y' >^* y'' \Leftrightarrow \text{"NO"} \Leftrightarrow \Sigma_i \lambda_i y'_i > \Sigma_i \lambda_i y''_i$$

Similarly, we get

$$y' <^* y'' \Leftrightarrow \text{"YES"} \Leftrightarrow \Sigma_i \lambda_i y'_i < \Sigma_i \lambda_i y''_i$$

and

$$y' \approx^* y'' \Leftrightarrow \text{"INDIF"} \Leftrightarrow \Sigma_i \lambda_i y'_i = \Sigma_i \lambda_i y''_i$$

Hence, assuming that the DM answers in accordance with his implicit preference function, we are able to reduce the set of possible weights Λ to a subset Λ' by introducing for each adjacent efficient extreme point y" one of the three types of constraints above. More precisely, let Λ(YES), Λ(NO), and Λ(INDIF) be the sets of weights that are consistent with the yes, no, and indifferent answers respectively. Thus for example

$$\Lambda(NO) \quad = \{\lambda \in \Lambda \mid \Sigma_i \lambda_i y'_i > \Sigma_i \lambda_i y''_i \quad \forall\, y'' \in NO\}$$

and similarly for Λ(YES) and Λ(INDIF). Then the inference process may be described as

$$\Lambda' = \Lambda \cap \Lambda(YES) \cap \Lambda(NO) \cap \Lambda(INDIF)$$

i.e. we reduce the sets of possible weights that may be relevant by assuming that the DM has answered in accordance with his actual, but unknown, set of constant weights λ.

Given this new knowledge about the DM's weights, it may be that the AN is now able to pick out the best proposal. This would be the case if all the remaining weight vectors point unanimiously towards the same proposal. That is, the AN may not know exactly how the DM weights the different criteria but he may still know enough to select from the concrete set of alternatives, c.f. also the discussion of figure 8.6 in section 8.5. We will show how to check for this case in a moment.

For now, let us assume that the AN finds a **new trial solution**. He picks a set of weights, say $\lambda=(\lambda'_1, \ldots, \lambda'_n)$, from the now reduced set of possible weights Λ'. Using these weights, he is able to find a new trial solution y" by solving

$$\max_y \; \Sigma_i \lambda'_i y_i$$
$$\text{s.t.} \quad y \in Z$$

That is, the AN behaves as if he tentatively assumes the selected weights to be the weights actually characterizing the DM's implicit preference function and he finds a new trial solution as the best proposal according to the corresponding preference function. It is a simple mathematical exercise to demonstrate that y" will be - or can be selected to be - an efficient extreme point. Thus we still restrict investigations to points in Z.

At this point, the AN could of course determine substitution possibilities around this new trial solution y" and present these to the DM. Now, however, the AN knows more about the potential weights and he may therefore in some cases be able to discard certain trade-off possibilities without having to introduce them to the DM. Apparently an adjacent efficient extreme point is **relevant** to consider only if there exists at least one possible version of the preference function which would lead the DM to prefer it to y". Other tests of relevance could be introduced as we will discuss in the more technical paragraphs below. For now, let us simply simply think of the **relevant adjacent efficient extreme points** around y" as those points in Z(y") which would be preferred to y" for at least one of the remaining weight vectors. Let us denote this set by **Z*(y")**.

The set of relevant adjacent efficient extreme points Z*(y") may be empty. This apparently means that given the AN's present knowledge, the proposal y" is potentially optimal and none of the neighboring efficient extreme points can be better. It follows from the assumed regularity of the problem that in this case no other alternative can be better than y". Hence, the optimal alternative has been identified. Hereby, the set Z*(y") provides the key to the **optimality check.**

If the set of relevant points in Z(y"), i.e. the set of points Z*(y"), is not empty, it means that there is still ambiguity as to which alternative is most preferred. For the vector λ' of weights used to generate y", that alternative is superior. However, for any other point in Z*(y"), say y"' we can also find weights which do not contradict any of the previous answers and which make y"' superior to y". In essence therefore - and presuming all along the existence of an implicit linear preference function - we see that AN still lacks information about the DM. Therefore the questioning continues. The AN presents y" and the corresponding relevant adjacent efficient extreme points Z*(y") to the DM and asks him to state his evaluation of the trade-offs. His answers allow new inferences about the set of potential weights. In particular, if the set YES is empty, then the present solution y" is the optimal alternative.

The procedure proceeds as described above and summarized in figure 9.6 below which depicts the t'th iteration.

AN

1. Draw inference about potential weights
   $\Lambda^t = \Lambda^{t-1} \cap \Lambda(YES^{t-1}) \cap \Lambda(NO^{t-1}) \cap \Lambda(INDIF^{t-1})$

2. For some possible weights $\lambda^t \in \Lambda^t$ choose
   a new trial solution y^t by solving
   $$\max_y \; \Sigma_i \lambda_i^t y_i$$
   $$\text{s.t.} \quad y \in Z$$

3. Determine the set $Z^*(y^t)$ of relevant, adjacent, efficient, extreme points to y^t.

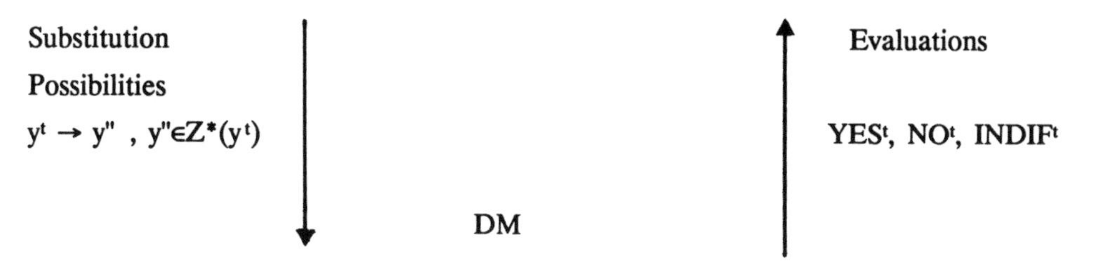

DM

1. Evaluate substitution possibilities
   $y^t \rightarrow y''$, $\forall \; y'' \in Z^*(y^t)$

2. Prepare answers
   $YES^t = \{y'' \in Z^*(y^t) \mid y'' >^* y^t\}$
   $NO^t = \{y'' \in Z^*(y^t) \mid y'' <^* y^t\}$
   $INDIF^t = \{y'' \in Z^*(y^t) \mid y'' \approx^* y^t\}$

Figure 9.6 The ZW Procedure

As usual, different **stopping rules** may be used. In theory, if we assume that the DM answers all questions perfectly correct, the procedure stops when the DM does not want to move from the present trial solution y^t to one of the relevant adjacent efficient extreme points. This is the case when $Z^*(y^t)$ is empty as explained above, or when $Z^*(y^t)$ is not empty, but when YES^t is empty. Also, using this rule, the procedure **converges** in a finite number of iterations. This follows since in each iteration the trial solution y^t is either classified as optimal or, if it is less desirable than one of the adjacent points, the trial solution is eliminated from further consideration by the inference mechanism. This inference mechanism, based on a "yes"-answer generates a constraint which prohibits that y^t can ever become the trial solution again. Thus, because there is a finite set of extreme points and at least one is eliminated in each question session, the solution process is finite.

In actual applications, there are of course numerous possible modifications of the procedure above. Let us just mention that it is recommended to ignore indifference statements in the inference process, since these require an unreasonably high precision of judgment by the DM. Also, the AN need not expose all relevant, adjacent, efficient extreme points to the DM in each iteration as long as he manages to identify at least one desirable trade-off in each iteration, c.f. the convergence argument above. Finally, we should mention that modifications of the procedure have been proposed to handle general concave preference structures and cases with discrete sets of alternatives.

In the next section, we illustrate what the ZW procedure may look like in a concrete application. Before we do so, we just want to explain the more **technical assumptions** of the procedure. Some readers may therefore chose to proceed directly to the illustrative example.

Readers familiar with convex sets will recall that polyhedral convex sets are simply intersections of half-spaces. This means that it must be possible to express Y in terms of linear inequalities, i.e. as $Y=\{(y_1, \ldots, y_n) \mid \Sigma_i\, a_{hi} y_i \leq b_h,\ h=1, \ldots, p\}$ for suitable choices of the constants a_{hi} and b_h. In particular, this is the case if X is a polyhedral convex set and all criteria f_i, $i=1, \ldots, n$ are linear.

Also, to understand - at least in theory - the details of the ZW procedure without going into the simplex algorithm, we need a few concepts from the theory of convex sets. Recall that a point y' in a convex set Y is an extreme point of Y if and only if there is no way to express y' as a convex combination $\alpha y'' + (1-\alpha)y'''$ of any two different points y'' and y''' in Y with $0<\alpha<1$. Thus, the extreme points are corner points, i.e. points which do not lie on any line between other points in the set. Now, an important property of a bounded, convex polyhedral set like Y is that there exists a finite set of extreme points, say $Q \subset Y$, which span the whole set Y in the sense that any point in Y can be written as a convex combination of extreme points. It easily follows that the optimal value of a linear composite objective function like F over Y is attained at an extreme point, i.e. it suffices to consider choices between the points in Q. Indeed, when F is increasing as we assume here, it suffices to consider the extreme points Q that are also efficient, i.e. the finite set $Z=Q \cap Y_E$ of efficient extreme points, c.f. also section 6.1. Finally, we need the idea of adjacent efficient extreme points. Let y' be an efficient extreme point. Then another efficient extreme point y'' is adjacent to y' if and only if the line between y' and y'' consists solely of efficient points, i.e. $\{\alpha y' + (1-\alpha)y'' \mid \alpha \in [0,1]\} \subseteq Y_E$.

Finally, let us comment briefly on the notion of relevant adjacent efficient extreme points $Z^*(y')$ around y'. Apparently a necessary condition for an adjacent efficient extreme point $y'' \in Z(y')$ to be relevant, i.e. to be in $Z^*(y')$, is that there exists at least one possible version of the preference function which would lead the DM to prefer y'' to the present solution y' i.e. in order for $y'' \in Z(y')$ to be relevant we must have at least

$$\exists\ \lambda \in \Lambda' : \lambda y'' > \lambda y'$$

Alternative tests of relevance are possible. The ZW procedure actually uses a somewhat stronger test.[1]

---

[1] It requires that $\exists\ \lambda \in \Lambda' : \lambda y'' > \lambda y' \geq \lambda y'''\ \forall\ y''' \in Z(y') \setminus \{y''\}$, i.e. the procedure requires that the substitution from y' to y'' must potentially be the only substitution that is strictly desirable. Although this test allows less inference than the first test - since less substitution possibilities will in general be presented to the DM under the latter test - it still allows the AN to eliminate y' when it is not optimal, and this is really what makes the communication progress, c.f. above. At the same time it may well require fewer answers from the DM. Thus, it is probably better than the first test.

9.4. A Numerical Illustration

To illustrate the ZW procedure, let us once again consider the two criteria problem studied in sections 8.2, 8.4 and 9.2, and let us assume that the DM performs his tasks in accordance with his preferences.

Thus, we assume that the set of feasible **alternatives** in criteria space Y is the set delineated by OABCDEFG as depicted in figure 9.3 above. This is indeed a socalled polyhedral, convex set as assumed by the ZW procedure. Also, the extreme points are precisely the corner points O, A, . . . ,G. Only one of these is inefficient, namely O, i.e. the set of efficient extreme points is Z = {A,B,C,D,E,F,G}. Also, adjacent efficient extreme points are easy to identify since they are simply the neighboring efficient extreme points. Thus, for example, given the efficient extreme point F, the adjacent, efficient extreme points are Z(F) = {E,G}.

Also, let us assume that the DM's true but unknown **preference function** is

$$F(y_1,y_2) = 0.4y_1 + 0.6y_2$$

i.e. his true but unknown weighting of the criteria is given by $\lambda^o = (0.4 , 0.6)$. In this simple two criteria problem, a weighting (λ_1,λ_2) is equivalent to a certain slope β of the linear indifference curves. Given the weights (λ_1,λ_2), the slope can be calculated as $\beta=-\lambda_1/\lambda_2$, and given the slope β, the weights can be calculated from the conditions $\beta=-\lambda_1/\lambda_2$ and $\lambda_1+\lambda_2=1$, $\lambda_1>0$, $\lambda_2>0$. To ease the exposition and graphical arguments here, it is most convenient to think of the weights as defined by the slopes. Thus, instead of the set of possible weights defined as $\Lambda=\{\lambda\in \Re^2 \mid \Sigma_i\lambda_i=1,\lambda_i>0\forall i\}$, we shall think of it in terms of the set of possible slopes $B = \{\beta \mid -\infty < \beta < 0\}$. In essence, therefore, the AN is searching for the best alternative according to a system of linear indifference curves, but he is unable to determine it immediately since he does not know the slope of these indifference lines.

Using the above assumptions, we are now able to illustrate how the ZW procedure works. Note that although the DM is assumed to behave in a manner consistent with his implicit preference function, the development is not entirely fixed apriori since the AN is left with some freedom in his choice of the initial and subsequent trial weights. The communication record of a possible development is given in figure 9.7 below.

	AN	DM
Iteration No.	Substitution Possibilities (Δ_1,Δ_2)	Substitutions Attractive?
1	(-1,3) and (1,-4)	Yes and No
2	(3,-1)	Yes
3	(-1,2)	Yes
4	(-4,4)	Yes
5	(-2,1)	No
6	Best Alternative is (y_1,y_2)=(5,13)	

Figure 9.7 Communication Record

Note that since the DM's implicit preference function is assumed to be linear, whereby the weights and substitution wishes are constant, i.e. independent of the alternatives, no assumption is required here as to a start solution. In the first iteration, the AN therefore simply asks the DM how he feels about giving up one unit of y_1 to gain 3 units of y_2. The DM answers, that he likes this trade. Similarly, the DM is asked to evaluate a gain of 1 unit of y_1 against a loss of 4 units of y_2. The DM answers that he does not consider this to be an attractive trade. Using these answers, the AN makes certain calculations and comes up with a new proposal for a trade. How about increasing y_1 by 3 and decreasing y_2 by 1? Again, the DM finds it attrative and the questioning proceeds as depicted. After 5 iterations and a total of 6 evaluations, the AN concludes that the best point is (5,13). This is how the communication would look to the DM or an outside observer.

The following is a more complete account of the calculations and evaluations underlying this development of the communication. A summary is provided in figure 9.8 below; the entries in the B^t column are open intervals, e.g. (-3,0) is short hand for $\{\beta \mid -3<\beta<0\}$.

	AN				DM	
Iteration No.	Inference	Trial Solution		Substitution Possibilities	Evaluate	Answers
t	B^t	β^t	$y^{\prime t}$	$Z^*(y^t)$	>* *< ≈*	YES^t NO^t
1	$(-\infty,0)$	-4	F	{E,G}	F*<E,F>*G	{E} {G}
2	(-3,0)	-0.2	A	{B}	A*<B	{B} Ø
3	(-3,-1/3)	-2.5	E	{D}	E*<D	{D} Ø
4	(-2,-1/3)	-1.5	D	{C}	D*<C	{C} Ø
5	(-1,-1/3)	-0.7	C	{B}	C*>B	Ø {B}

Figure 9.8 The ZW Procedure in the Example Problem

Initially, to get started the AN somewhat arbitrarily selects a trial slope β=-4. He then determines a best alternative according to the corresponding composite objective function. Since all points between F and G lie on the highest indifference line with slope -4, he arbitrarily selects one of the two extreme points F and G as the new trial solution, say y^1 = F = (11,4). Next, he determines the adjacent, efficient extreme points, i.e. E = (10,7) and G = (12,0). He then presents these substitution possibilities to the DM, either directly as the possibilities F → E and F → G, c.f. figure 9.8, or indirectly in terms of the two possible trades E-F = (-1,3) and G-F = (1,-4), c.f. figure 9.7.

Next, the DM inspects these substitution possibilities and decides how he feels. Graphically, we see from figure 9.3 that since the slope of the DM's actual indifference curves is -0.4/0.6 = -2/3, he prefers E to F and F to G, i.e. F *< E and F >*

G. Analytically, we - who have access to his implicit preference function F(.) - can arrive at these rankings by calculating the values of F(.) at E, F and G:

$$F(F)=F(11,4)=6.8,\quad F(E)=F(10,7)=8.2,\text{ and } F(G)=F(12,0)= 4.8.$$

Alternatively, since the DM's substitution wishes do not depend on the "anchor" point, we can also get the rankings by calculating and then aggregating the gains and losses accompanying a substitution. Thus for example the trade $(\Delta_1,\Delta_2) = (-1,3)$ corresponding to the move from F to E is evaluated as F(E-F)=F(-1,3)=1.4 and since this is positive it is a desirable trade and we get F $^*<$ E.

Either way, the AN is now able to draw inferences about the DM's possible weights. Graphically, we see from figure 9.3 that since he prefers E to F, the slope of his indifference lines must be more than -3, the slope of the line segment from E to F, and since he prefers F to G the slope must be more than -4, the slope of the line segment from F to G. Furthermore, since all the - unknown - weights are assumed positive, the slope in any iteration must be less than 0. Thus, assuming that the DM has answered correctly, the AN now knows that the possible set of slopes for the next iteration is

$$B^2 = B^1 \cap \{\beta|\beta>-3\} = \{\beta|-3<\beta<0\}$$

Alternatively, he could have made this inference in terms of linear inequalities on the weights. Thus, from (11,4)=F $^*<$ (10,7)=E we get

$$\lambda_1 11 + \lambda_2 4 < \lambda_1 10 + \lambda_2 7$$

which is equivalent to $\beta = -\lambda_1/\lambda_2 > -3$ and from (11,4)=F $>^*$ G=(12,0) we get

$$\lambda_1 11 + \lambda_2 4 > \lambda_1 12 + \lambda_2 0$$

which is equivalent to $\beta = -\lambda_1/\lambda_2 > -4$.

In the second iteration, the AN therefore picks one of the remaining relevant slopes, say β=-0.2. He determines the best efficient extreme point for this trial type, i.e. y^2=A=(0,15), since this point lies on the highest line with slope -0.2, c.f. figure 9.3. There is only one efficient extreme point adjacent to A, namely B, since the other adjacent extreme point O is not efficient. Also, B is relevant since it may well be better than A for one of the relevant slopes, i.e. slopes in the interval (-3,0). Thus, for example, if β=-0.4, B would be better than A, and therefore B passes the test of relevancy. Hence, the set of relevant adjacent efficient extreme points becomes $Z^*(A)=\{B\}$. The DM now has to evaluate the substitution possibility A → B. If he acts in accordance with the assumed preference function F(.), he prefers B to A. Again, this follows as the slope of his indifference curve is -2/3 which is less than the slope of line segment between A and B, which is -1/3, or it follows by direct calculations as above. The AN can now infer that the possible set of slopes in round 3 is $B^3=B^2 \cap \{\beta | \beta<-1/3\}=\{\beta | -3<\beta<-1/3\}$.

The next steps proceeds similarly. By simple inspections of the graph in figure 9.3 it should be easy to reconstruct and understand the remaining iterations. It suffices, therefore, to comment here on the determination of relevant substitution possibilities. In iteration number 3, the trial solution is E. There are two adjacent, efficient extreme points, namely D and F. However, at this point in the procedure, we know that the slope of the DM's indifference lines is strictly between -3 and -1/3. We therefore see that F can never be attractive, as the slope of the line segment from E to F is -3. Hence, F is not relevant and only the possibility of substituting to D is presented to the DM. In iteration number 4(5) where the trial solution is D(C) and the adjacent, efficient extreme points are C and E (B and D), we similarly exclude E (D) since it is irrelevant for a DM with a slope larger than -2 (-1).

Finally, let us observe that we stop after iteration number 5; the DM does not want to move from the corresponding trial solution y^5=C to any of the relevant adjacent efficient extreme points around C, i.e. to B. In other words, the set YES^5 is empty which is a condition for stopping the procedure. Indeed, we see that if we introduce the answer from iteration 5 into the inference mechanism we can conclude that $\beta \in B^5 \cap \{\beta | \beta<-1/2\} = (-1,-1/2)$. We see that this knowledge of the DM's preferences suffices to conclude that C is optimal. In fact, C is optimal if and only if β belongs to [-1,-1/2], c.f. figure 9.3. Hence, we see that the AN has learned enough but not much more than enough about the DM's preferences to pick out the best alternative.

It should be emphasized however that the above development of the procedure presumes that the DM responds in accordance with his true but unknown preference function and that that function is linear. If in fact it took on the form $F(y_1,y_2)=y_1y_2$ as was assumed in the example presented in section 9.2, then the procedure would lead to different results dependent upon the initial point chosen by the AN to instigate the procedure, clearly an undesirable result. In other words, we once again must warn the reader that simply applying such a procedure without checking as to the reasonableness of the underlying assumptions may lead to incorrect, even incomprehensible results. But once again we also note that this criticism is not specific for the ZW procedure; it applies as well to all algorithms designed to support planning and decision making.

9.5. The Iterative Organization

One of the important characteristics of the present planning mode is its iterative nature. This has two major implications.

First, it influences the kind of information available when wishes have to be clarified. In the present mode the DM has concrete real alternatives and trade-off possibilities to focus on. It can be argued that this makes the DM more comfortable than the fictive alternatives and trades used in the prior articulation of preferences mode.

On the other hand, it is clear that the increased realism may be gained at the cost of complexity. Thus, for example, the ZW procedure requires the DM to evaluate composite trades, i.e. simultaneous variations in all criteria, rather than partial trades, where only two criteria vary at a time. Requiring such composite evaluations may lead to "incorrect" answers as the DM may not be able to consistently provide the responses required. The chance of such inconsistent evaluations increases as the variations in the criteria become larger. Similar remarks hold for the GDF-procedure.

Although only partial trades are involved in the articulation of substitution wishes, composite trades must certainly be evaluated in the step-size subproblems.

Secondly, the iterative organization influences the amount of information needed to make a choice. Whatever we know about the set of possibilities Y can be used to delineate more precisely what we need to know about the preference function F and vice versa, c.f. section 8.5. The ZW procedure illustrates this. We need only learn about the DM's attitudes towards trade-offs corresponding to relevant adjacent, efficient, extreme points. Indeed, in the example in section 9.4, we ended up acquiring almost exactly the minimal amount of information about F needed to pick out the optimal alternative. Also, it is relevant to observe that the burden of making such short-cuts, which may be quite demanding, is placed on the AN in the present mode. It is the AN who has to draw inferences and to foresee which pieces of information are still missing.

A drawback of reducing the information need via the tight coupling of possibilities and wishes used in the present mode is of course that less general preference information is generated. Such information might for example be useful in related or future decision problems. In the GDF procedure considered earlier in this chapter, the established preference information is highly partial and problem specific. One learns about the DM's trade-off wishes for certain problem-specific proposals and one learns about his most preferred points in certain problem-specific simplified sets of proposals. In the ZW-procedure, more information is generated via the inference mechanism but it does in general stop well before a concrete preference function has been established.

9.6. The AN Directive Organization

The other distinct characteristic of the present planning mode is that the AN is in charge. He has to direct the search, accumulate the information, and make the final proposal. Still, the AN's task is in general well-defined in these methods, i.e. it is described how he should define the questions, when to stop and how to make the final proposal. The computations needed to follow the prescriptions may of course be very demanding. However, since our prime concern is the limited time and analytical orientation of the DM, this should not worry us too much. The AN has presumably both the required analytical talents and computational facilities to perform the analyses. He may however have to demonstrate considerable tact and intuitive talent, particularly if the procedures do not appear to perform as expected, e.g. due to difficulties in communication, inconsistencies in the DM's responses - or a mismatch between the assumptions underlying the procedure and the DM's actual preference structure.

The DM's role and duties are also well-defined. He simply has to answer the questions posed to him. Assume for example that he has an explicit utility function but that for various reasons it is not submitted to the AN, who would be able to use it to directly solve the basic decision problem. We can in this case give the DM exact mathematical instructions to follow. In reality, this is hardly ever the case and answering the AN's questions may be hard and painful by requiring a journey into the unexplored territory of the DM's basic personal and organizational desires in the context of a specific planning problem. Still, compared to the DM-directive arrangements, he is facing a much more well structured activity, since he does not have to direct the AN and systematically accumulate information about the actual alternatives.

As a final virtue of the present mode, let us emphasize that the aim of these methods is usually rather well-defined. At least, it seems that a prime concern is to approximate the solution of the underlying but unknown basic decision problem. It follows that convergence or perhaps better the initial rate of convergence becomes a natural yardstick. This means that there exists at least a screening device to discipline research.

Now, these virtues of the present mode do of course come at a cost. Since the methods within this mode are extremely well-structured, there is not much room for non-modelled aspects to enter the process, nor for meta-planning perspectives to guide the use of the procedures. This means that the DM is sometimes reduced to what may resemble a simple answering machine. He has to produce answers without being able to influence either the nature of the questions or the type of answers that are acceptable.

Most important, perhaps, is that the methods in this class assume a fixed preference structure of a rather simple nature. The preference structure must for example be linear or at least concave. Also, the convergence depends on the DM being able to answer all questions consistently based on his presumed fixed preference function. In reality, one may well question the validity of these assumptions.

There are however some easily available modifications to the latter assumptions. In the GDF procedure for example, the AN does not accumulate information about the DM's preferences. In principle, therefore, if the DM changes his preferences, the procedure simply proceeds. Also, in the ZW procedure the "oldest" answers in the inference mechanism could succesively be discarded so as to allow for changing wishes. Note however that by introducing such freedoms, we also eliminates the convergence properties of the procedures.

A related criticism could be that the procedures do not explicitly allow for uncertainties and inaccuracies in the answers provided by the DM. It should be noted though that these issues are not unique to the present procedures. Such imperfections of the DM are basically ignored or at least treated in an ad hoc fashion throughout the mathematically and computationally oriented literature on planning with multiple objectives. To illustrate, consider again the ZW procedure. Indifference answers are often eliminated in the inference process since the DM is not believed to be able to judge indifference with the accuracy required. It is not modelled, however, how precisely he may judge, nor do such inaccuracies affect the inference process. This lack of explicit modelling of uncertainty and imprecision is probably due to the historical connection of multiple criteria analysis with mathematical programming and its traditional implicit assumption of a deterministic world.

As a final effect of the AN directive organization let us note that the DM not only gives up control of the process. His intentions become much more visible, not only for himself, but for others as well. He has to state specific trade-off wishes either directly as in the GDF procedure or indirectly as in the ZW procedure. Needless to say, the DM may find this to be unsatisfactory as he may consider his particular reactions to be confidential.

9.7. Summary

In this chapter we have explored what we have christened the progressive articulation of preferences approach to multiple criteria planning. This is an iterative arrangement directed by the AN. In each round, the AN poses a question to the DM about his preferences and the DM answers. If the AN now knows enough about the preferences to make a choice from the concrete set of alternatives, he makes a final proposal. Otherwise, the questioning continues.

Within this general organization we distinguished between two prototypes depending on the kind of information requested from the DM. In one class the AN requests direct information about the DM's substitution wishes while in the other class the AN asks the DM to evaluate existing substitution possibilities. These classes do not constitute a genuine partition of all the existing techniques which can be categorized within this mode. In particular, a combination of such questioning is often proposed. Still, we believe that these prototype questions cover the basic approaches suggested in the literature. We also note that the different techniques differ in the way in which information about substitution wishes is requested and in which substitution possibilities are presented.

To illustrate the use of substitution wishes we discussed the socalled GDF procedure. This procedure begins with a feasible alternative y' and interrogates the DM about his substitution wishes. Then tentatively assuming the local substitution wishes to be globally true, a new trial solution y'' is obtained. A single dimensional search is carried out by the DM to determine the best feasible solution on the line segment connecting y' and y''. The new solution replaces y' and the process is repeated until a solution is generated which does not change from one iteration to the next.

Similarly, to illustrate the use of substitution possibilities, we discussed the socalled ZW procedure. This procedure presumes a linear preference function such that the only unknown aspect is the weights assigned to the different criteria. It operates by iteratively asking the DM questions about his attitudes towards substitutions from some point to some adjacent points. From the responses, inference is made about the actual set of weights, i.e portions of the weighting space are eliminated. The process continues until the set of possible weights has been reduced to so sufficiently small a region that the AN can identify a solution to the DM's basic decision problem.

Finally, we turned to some more general implications of using an iterative, AN directive organization.

The iterative organization means that attention can be focused on concrete, real alternatives or trade-offs when preferences have to be clarified. The drawback of this is of course that realistic questions may be very complex. Also, the iterative arrangement allows for short-cuts between preference and alternative information which means that the informational requirements may be reduced. Again, this advantage is gained at the expense of the information being rather problem-specific. It cannot so easily be employed to solve other problems, as was the case with the prior articulation of preference mode considered in chapter 7.

The AN directive organization means first of all that the burdens of accumulating information, directing the search and making the final proposal are placed on the AN. This is accomplished at the cost though of rather stiff methods which leave almost no leverage for nonmodelled aspects and meta-planning perspectives, and which require that the DM has an underlying preference structure that is fixed, well-behaved and reasonably simple.

Since the applicability of an iterative procedure depends upon its convergence, and in particular its initial rate of convergence, we briefly discussed these attributes of the procedures. From a practical point of view, this focus is due to the fact that DMs cannot be expected to have the patience - or consistency - necessary to participate in prolonged dialogues as to substitution wishes and possibilities. From an algorithmic point of view, this focus is due to the origin of many of the present techniques in ordinary, single objective optimization. Although convergence can neither be considered a necessary nor a sufficient test of multiple criteria planning methods, it does constitute a filtering device that may help discipline research in this area. It should be emphasized, however, that convergence results presume that the DM is able to behave in a rather ideal manner; he must behave consistently, i.e. as if his preferences were defined by a stationary implicit preference function.

9.8. Bibliographic Notes

Concrete progressive articulation of preferences approaches can be designed in many ways. The AN may collect relevant preference information by asking the DM to state substitution wishes based on given feasible alternatives, e.g. Geoffrion, Dyer and Feinberg(1972), Musselman and Talavage(1980), and Oppenheimer(1978). Alternatively, the AN may ask the DM to evaluate given substitution possibilities, e.g. Chankong and Haimes(1983a,ch.8), Korhonen, Wallenius and Ziont(1984), Steuer and Choo(1983), Steuer and Schuler(1978), White(1980), Zionts(1981), Zionts and Wallenius(1976,83). Rather general substitution wishes and substitution possibilities approaches are discussed in Bogetoft(1986).

Chapter 10

CHOOSING BETWEEN PLANNING MODES

In the preceding chapters we have described different organizations of multiple criteria planning and theories and techniques that may support such planning.

It is time now to take more of a **meta-planning perspective** and to consider **the planning of planning**. That is, to examine whether or not, in a given context, to introduce multiple criteria planning and if so, which particular mode to choose.

We will consider which "meta-criteria" are relevant for choosing between alternative planning modes in general and between the multiple criteria planning modes described in chapters 6-9 in particular. Also, we will consider how specific contexts may affect the relative importance of these meta-criteria. Combining information on a) the alternative planning modes, and b) the criteria chosen to characterize them, with c) information on the relative importance of these criteria in a given context will provide a rational basis for the choice of mode in a given context.

For example, an approach which appears to be appropriate in a context characterized by a very important, one-shot choice to be made between only a few alternatives and where the outcome may have significant and wide-reaching long range implications, may be quite inappropriate in a context characterized by routine choices between a large number of alternatives, where the individual choices as such do not have any significant impact.

We emphasize that the choice level we shall primarily operate at now is at the top of the three-tiered choice hierarchy whose levels are: 1) choice of an overall organization of multiple criteria planning activities, i.e. a multiple criteria planning mode, 2) choice of an MCDM technique within the mode chosen, and 3) application of the

MCDM technique to the decision problem at hand to make a choice of alternative. Initially, however, we shall address the even higher order problem of choosing whether to use a mutiple criteria planning mode in the first place.

10.1. Whether to Use Multiple Criteria Planning

We have throughout this book argued the relevance of multiple perspectives in planning. We have emphasized some fundamental complexities in real world planning, and in particular we have focused upon the incomplete information about possibilities and wishes and the multiplicity of criteria required to characterize choice contexts. And we have tried to demonstrate how multiple criteria planning offers a way to reconcile these complexities with rationality.

In the spirit of the multiple criteria planning we have advocated so eagerly, however, we must also realize that planning itself has multiple effects and is not simply an objective, invisible instrument for improving choices and their successful implementation. Therefore we cannot expect that multiple criteria planning will always be the best approach to organizing the investigation, communication and choice activities. Indeed, there are many cases where and many reasons why such an approach may not be succesful.

An important factor is **the type of planning problem**. While multiple criteria planning may be natural in connection with major strategic and tactical issues, like the choice of an overall energy strategy for a nation, or the selection of a new computer system in a firm, it may not be relevant for daily routines like the shopping in food stores. Despite its familiarity, the latter problem could be considered to be a rather complex planning problem involving a multiplicity of criteria, like costs, quality and time. Yet, most shoppers would probably feel that it would be like attempting to kill sparrows with a cannon to tackle these problems with the apparatus of this book. Also, one may wonder if shopping could really be improved this way. The more formalized and therefore more stylized approach may well lead to poor decisions which are avoided by a more traditional approach based on the shopper's intuition, his experience based on many years of actual shopping and his capacity to handle very conflicting pieces of information from a diversity of sources. And, after all, it can be fun to brouse and to follow one's impulses, i.e. shopping may have value not just because of the purchases made, but also as a more-or-less pleasurable activity of its own.

Also, the relevance and likely success of multiple criteria planning depend intimately on **the type of decision maker**. While the approach may appeal to an idealistic, participative manager, it may not appeal to a manipulative and dictatorial manager who may feel that such methods leave him naked for criticism and indeed for manipulations by the analyst involved. Also, a bureaucratic manager functioning in a political environment may be attracted by the apparent possibility to introduce structure and rationality into complex issues, while a charismatic manager able to sell his ideas without apparent scientific backing may consider such methods a waste of time and even a threat to his authority.

Similarly, the viability of multiple criteria planning most likely will depend on **the type of organization and its culture**. In an organization based on a hierarchical distribution of power and a traditional emphasis on the bottom line, the introduction of multiple criteria planning may well be out of tune. It may be mistrusted as yet another cynical PR number introduced by the leadership as a refined and disguised way of pursuing classical goals of shareholder wealth and managerial power. In a flatter organization with a history of cooperation and trust, the multiple criteria approach may be seen as a natural extension of the established procedures - or perhaps simply as a "scientific" confirmation of established behavioral norms, rules and programs.

We shall henceforth restrain from additional commentary on this basic issue of why and when to apply multiple criteria planning in the first place. We have already commented quite extensively on the merits of multiple criteria planning as opposed to the more traditional, rational OR approach; this has been weaved into the presentation so far. In addition, we cannot thoroughly expand on this perspective without introducing more explicit alternatives to multiple criteria planning and thus developing an intellectual and operational framework for choosing between these meta-alternatives; this is not possible within the confines of this book. Instead, in the following sections we shall give a more systematical coverage of the relationships between contextual characteristics and the choice of an appropriate multiple criteria planning mode.

We emphasize, however, that most of the discussions below are equally relevant for the problem of whether to introduce multiple criteria planning per se. In particular, we delineate a series of costs and benefits of planning which are generally relevant. Also, we suggest a way of thinking about the meta-planning problem which is generally useful. Indeed, our procedure for tackling meta-planning problems provides greater insight than the specific results we derive for the choice between the different multiple criteria planning modes. Most of these specific results are simply illustrative.

Our presentation will closely follow that of earlier chapters. In particular, we once again emphasize that the whole train of thought underlying the analyses implicitly assumes a single decision maker - or, equivivalently a collectivity willing to behave as an individual. Thus, in the present chapter we ignore more complex contexts characterized by: a) multiple decision makers, each facing both their own multiple criteria planning problem and the problem of arriving at a joint decision, and b) multiple decision makers and multiple decision receivers. These far more complex settings will first be explicitly considered in chapter 11.

10.2. A Review of the Taxonomy

Since the bulk of this chapter concerns the choice between the modes defined by the taxonomy developed in chapter 5, let us commence with a brief review of that taxonomy.

The basic conceptual setting is one where each alternative action in decision space is characterized by the vector of criteria it generates, y, and where a decision maker is to make a choice from the set of feasible alternatives in criteria space, Y. His preferred compromise solution is presumed to be characterized by a vector in criteria space that results in the highest value of his implicit preference function F(y).

In general, however, information as to F and Y is decentralized and not-immediately-available; we do not have clear cut and exhaustive expressions of preferences, F, and alternatives, Y, to begin with - if ever. In order to analyze this situation, we have to investigate what F and Y look like. We imagine therefore, that a decision maker (DM) is able to investigate his values and preferences, to communicate the results of his investigations when appropriate to the analyst, and to behave, i.e. choose, in accord with these preferences. We imagine too that an analyst (AN) is able to investigate the set of alternatives in criteria space, Y, to communicate the results of his investigations when appropriate to the decision maker, and to recommend, when appropriate, which choice best satisfies the decision makers preferences. In other words, we assume that the DM and the AN are able to perform certain investigative and communicative tasks on their own and that they are also able to synergetically combine the results of these tasks so that new insights are gained as to Y and F and so that the final choice is in fact the DM's most preferred alternative. Therefore we consider the planning process in terms of its investigation, communication and choice activities as they are performed by the two agents, the decision maker and the analyst.

In particular, we focus upon two major characteristics of this process: the **timing of the investigations** of F and Y, and **who directs the search**. This leads us to the taxonomy reviewed in figure 10.1 below.

	DM directed	AN directed
Phased	Prior articulation of alternatives	Prior articulation of preferences
Iterative	Progressive articulation of alternatives	Progressive articulation of preferences

Figure 10.1 The Taxonomy of Multiple Criteria Planning Modes

Considering the timing first, we have worked with two arrangements: a **phased** or linear arrangement, where the inquiries as to F and Y are performed in two distinct phases, and an **iterative** or cyclical arrangement which involves a sequence of investigations of F and Y.

Considering next the question of who directs the search, i.e. who leads the search, keeps track of the information collected on F and Y and makes the final choice proposal, we have once again assumed only two possible arrangements: a **DM-directed** approach, where the decision maker is in charge of these tasks, and an **AN-directed** approach, where the analyst is in charge.

Clearly, in any actual setting, this taxonomy may prove to be an overly simplified description. Nevertheless, as argued in some depth in chapter 5, we feel that this classification scheme represents the best compromise between descriptive realism and pedagogical demands.

The reader is referred to chapter 5 for a more detailed presentation of the taxonomy and its rationale.

10.3. Criteria for the Choice of Multiple Criteria Planning Modes

In principle, we face a problem of infinite regress: if we are to select criteria to evaluate multiple criteria planning modes, then we can also ask how these criteria are to be chosen. I.e. which multiple criteria mode and technique and which criteria should be employed to select the criteria. And this then leads to the question as to which multiple criteria mode and technique and which criteria are relevant for answering that new, higher level question and so on ad infinitum. We certainly do not want to embark upon such a fruitless excursion; our approach here is pragmatic. We aspire to provide a rational and logical background for the choice of a multiple criteria planning mode. This whole area is virgin territory. What really counts here is not our particular choice of criteria or the evaluations they lead to, but the overall theme of employing a multiple criteria approach to evaluate multiple criteria planning modes.

We should emphasize that although we focus on the choice of the overall planning mode here, the methodology presented could be further refined so as to be applicable not only to the first level problem of choosing a planning mode, but also to the integration of the the first two levels, the problem of choosing both a planning mode from the taxonomy as well as a particular MCDM technique within this mode. However, given the nature of the present book, we only consider here the "top of the hierarchy" problem of choosing between alternative planning modes.

We will consider first the criteria which can be employed to characterize the three major attributes which we employ to characterize a multiple criteria planning mode: a) the investigations it employs, b) the communication that it presumes, and c) the choices it leads to[1]. In so doing, our point of reference will primarily be that of the decision maker, and not that of the analyst or of others who might be affected by the decisions made - this latter problematique will be considered in the next chapter.

We will employ these criteria in two ways. First, on a rather abstract level, we will directly characterize the multiple criteria planning modes as such, independent of the specific planning context. The results of this analysis are summarized in figure 10.5. Secondly, using illustrative hypothetical problems, we will demonstrate how the context-independent characterization of the four planning modes can be utilized to make a choice of a particular mode within a given context. The results of such an exercise are summarized in figure 10.6.

As will be evident from the analyses of the hypothetical cases, valid recommendations as to the choice of a multiple criteria planning mode can only be achieved by considering an actual problem in an actual context. We emphasize therefore that the main purpose of our presentation is not to provide results which are valid for the prototype problems considered, but to suggest a process, a way of thinking about the question of how to choose among alternative multiple criteria planning modes.

---

[1]We should recall that in general two or more of the criteria chosen to reflect a decision maker's preferences will at times provide more-or-less alternative measures of the same, underlying value. A result can be an overemphasis on such a value and the concomitant lack of consideration of other criteria and values. Unfortunately, as will be evident here, it can be very difficult to develop measures of performance which are completely independent of each other.

10.4. Investigation Criteria

We suggest that the following criteria should be utilized to evaluate the investigation activities characterizing alternative planning modes:

1. Is the information generated as to F and Y context specific or can it be employed as well to analyze other (classes of) problems?

2. Which risks are involved for the DM and the organization? In particular as regards: a) misuse of information on the DM's preferences, b) misuse of information on alternatives, and c) opportunity costs of not choosing the best compromise solution due to inappropriate investigation.

3. What are the direct costs (demands on the DM and the AN) involved in performing the investigations of F and Y?

The following are brief evaluations of the four planning modes with respect to these crtieria; we underscore that these evaluations are context-independent and therefore abstract and quite often of a "on the one hand, on the other hand" nature. In practical application the evaluations will be sharpened as problem-specific information is obtained.

Criterion 1: Can the Information as to F and Y be Applied to Future Investigations?

The DM-directed, prior articulation of alternatives approach provides explicit information as to Y while the AN-directed, prior articulation of preferences approach provides explicit information as to F. Thus, in principle, both these modes provide information for future investigations. In many specific cases however, the information on the alternatives will only be relevant for the specific problem being considered. For example, if we are considering problems dealing with investment in new production capacity, each particular problem will be characterized by its own specific alternative decisions. Furthermore, even though the same decision alternatives may be considered for several investment decisions, the information from one specific analysis may not be relevant for another such analysis; the criteria may be context-dependent and the mapping of a given decision alternative from decision space to criteria space may vary with the problem situation.

The situation is not quite so context specific as regards information on preferences. Although preference information will most likely be related to the particular class of problems being considered, e.g. decisions as to investment in production capacity, the DM's preferences may be independent of the particular setting. That is, information as to a decision maker's preference function F as evaluated on a set of relevant criteria may be employed by the AN to rank alternative decisions without - initially at least - involving the DM and requesting new preference information from him. Furthermore, if a grandioise attempt has been made to elicit the DM's preferences independent of any given setting, than certainly this information may be relevant for future investigations.

As regards the two iterative approaches, neither of these approaches provides explicit information which can be relied upon in future decision situations. The investigation processes do not result in explicit deliniations of F or Y. Furthermore, whatever information is collected is only partial and depends upon when the investigations terminate.

Criterion 2: Risks Involved

We consider three potential risks related to the multiple criteria planning modes. The first of these is the risk of misuse of the information as to a DM's preferences. The second is the risk of competitors obtaining detailed information as to the set of alternatives being considered. Finally, there is the risk that the investigation leads to decisions which are not as good as they could otherwise have been due to inappropriate investigations. We consider these three risks in turn.

Criterion 2A: Risk of Misuse of Information on DM Preferences

In particular the prior articulation of preferences can be said to entail risk for the DM. If the investigation process leads to a disclosure of his preferences as expressed via a preference function, F, he can then be criticized if he behaves in a way which does not optimize F. This can lead to a stifling of his creative behavior and to an unhealthy focus upon formalistic consistency rather than on innovative leadership. In other words, knowing that others can peak over his shoulder and criticize his behavior based upon previously obtained preference information can tend to transform decision making into a computational task rather than a creative and rational search process.

Of course, in those cases where such preference information is collected with respect to specific types of problems, i.e. in the progressive as opposed to the prior articulation of preferences mode, the risks of it being misused in other situations is much less.

Another risk is that such detailed, explicit information as to a DM's preferences can lead to his manipulation. For example, knowledge of the preference function may be of value to those who want to persuade him to make particular choices. If they are able - in advance of the decision making process - to predetermine the choice which utilizing F would lead to, they may be tempted to tinker with the way the alternatives are presented, i.e. with the representation of the actual alternative in criteria space. On the other hand, what may be considered to be a risk here, will also be considered to be a benefit in relation to the communication criterion to be considered later on: "Information serves as a guide for behavior elsewhere in the organization". Information on F may for example provide those who are to screen or even to design the alternatives, with an excellent frame of reference for their tasks.

Aside from the prior articulation of preferences, and to a far lesser extent the progressive articulation of preferences mode, none of the other approaches are considered to be risky here.

Criterion 2B: Risk of Misue of Information on Alternatives

The more the set of alternatives is described and characterized (e.g. by its efficient members), the more information is potentially available to competitors. This may lead to demands that the planning process be confidential. And this may be damaging to the organizational culture. Seen from this perspective, the prior articulation of alternatives approach may be unattractive to an organization which emphasizes openess, participative planning and ethical behavior.

None of the three other major approaches is considered to be characterized by risk here.

Criterion 2C: Risk of Inappropriate Investigations

Finally, there is the risk that the investigation process may not provide relevant and/or correct information and therefore may lead to poorer decisions than would otherwise have been the case. The more the DM is decoupled from the process and therefore unable to introduce his subjective, intuitive and creative insights, the greater is the risk that the decisions made will be inconsistent with the DM's true, unarticulated (and perhaps unstable) preferences. This risk will be the greatest for those modes where the DM is least involved.

First and foremost here is the prior articulation of preferences mode since once F is developed by the AN, the DM is essentially decoupled from future decision making with respect to similar problems. Next most risky here is the prior articulation of alternatives mode, where the DM is essentially left to himself to choose among the (efficient) alternatives presented to him by the AN. Here he is strongly involved in the choice activity - but is more or less on his own. If the subset of alternatives presented to him is extensive and/or if the criteria are many and overlapping, the complexity of the choice situation may lead to decisions which are inconsistent with this underlying preferences. On the other hand, the more restricted the subset of alternatives is, the lesser is the risk for opportunity loss here. Indeed, in this case the planning mode may be quite suitable since the DM will be able to balance his more personal and perhaps confidential values with the explicit values employed to determine the efficient set.

The iterative approaches, which provide for an on-going communication between the DM and the AN as to alternatives and preferences are therefore once again considered to be the least risky. The DM is involved in the process and can introduce his personal, intuitive and creative insights.

Criterion 3: Direct Costs of Investigations

Two perspectives are applicable here: the first is the time and effort expended by the decision maker, the second is the demands as to analyst time, computer capacity, data availability and the like.

Criterion 3A: DM Time and Effort

We have on occasion introduced certain "parameters" to make the evaluations of the planning modes more precise. For example, when considering the criterion "inappropriate investigations" above, we rather casually introduced the idea that an approach may be more or less attractive depending upon the number of alternatives presented to the DM. To indicate how the method of analysis presented can be made more selective for specific contexts, we will analyze the crierion "DM time and effort" by explicitly introducing the parameter: "repetitive versus one-shot decisions".

We consider first the case of **repetitive decisions.** In this case, both the prior articulation approaches tend to be less demanding with respect to DM time and effort than the iterative approaches, and the prior articulation of preferences appears to be the least demanding of all.

Under a prior articulation of alternatives approach the analyst does essentially all the preliminary work of collecting and analyzing data as to the alternatives, delimiting the set, for example by determining an efficient subset, and then presenting this subset to the DM. In this context of repetitive decision, the DM on the other hand repeatedly has the burden of making a choice from among the set of efficient alternatives, with little or no support from the AN. He is though able to utilize his experience with the particular class of problems being analyzed.

Under a prior articulation of preferences approach, considerable trade-off information may be requested from the DM during the development of F. On the other hand, the demands on the DM can presumably be concentrated to a few interview sessions and the results may be available for future analyses whereby the whole burden can be given to the AN. If the AN has an analytical expression for F and if he gathers information about the alternatives in a new context, and **if** the expression for F is still presumed to hold, then the decision making process can, at least preliminarily, be placed in the hands of the AN.

In contrast, the two iterative procedures can be said to make the greatest demands on DM time and effort in the case of repetitive decisions. Each time a decision is to be made, the DM must actively engage in an exploration of his substitution wishes or possibilities in view of the alternatives characterizing the specific context.

The demands on the DM tend to shift when we move from the case of repetitive decisions to **significant, one-shot decisions**. We consider first the prior articulation of preferences mode. If the DM is more or less removed from the actual decision making process, then a very detailed prior mapping of F will be required. And if such a mapping does not already exist, this will require the DM - and the AN as well - to spend considerable time and effort in the prior analysis of his preferences. Furthermore, it is almost certain that the DM will become deeply involved in the process and will not leave the decision making to the AN; after all, we are speaking about significant, one-shot decisions.

The demands may also be considerable in the case of a prior articulation of alternatives approach. Although the AN will be responsible for performing the analysis of the alternatives, the DM's burdens could be considerable here, given the significant nature of the decision to be made. These burdens would most likely appear not in the form of time required but as doubt: "Am I making the best choice? Can I rely upon the information provided by the AN? Might there not be attractive alternatives among the set of non-efficient alternatives, particularly as the criteria may not explicitly include some of my personal values?"

Due to the significance of the decision, the demands on the DM could also be rather heavy in the case of the iterative approaches. It is likely that rather thorough analyses will be carried out in order to both avoid the opportunity costs of terminating the analyses too early as well as to check the consistency of the analyses. On the other hand, much of the burden here will be placed on the AN. In addition, since the number of alternatives to be considered by the DM may be quite limited in such significant one-shot situations, the iterative investigations will tend to place more limited demands on the DM.

It appears from the above analyses that the evaluation of DM time and effort could be more precise if we were to distinguish between repetitive and one-shot decisions. Nevertheless, we have abstained from distinguishing between these two cases in figures

10.2 and 10.5 which summarize the results. Paramatizing the rough analyses could lead to an apparent accurarcy which we do not feel is justified at present and we have introduced the parametrization simply to indicate how the present analyses may be made more precise in their application to specific contexts. Therefore, and since all four approaches are rather demanding in the case of one-shot decisions, we have chosen to distinguish between the approaches assuming the case of repetitive rather than one-shot decisions. This leads to the conclusion that the prior articulation approaches will be better suited than the progressive articulation approaches, and that the prior articulation of preferences mode will place the least demands on DM time and effort.

Criterion 3B: AN Related Costs

As regards the direct costs due to AN support, computer time, data acquisition and the like, it is argued that the prior articulation of alternatives mode is by far the most demanding approach. This is particularly the case in situations where repetitive decisions are to be made in new contexts, i.e. where the alternatives, criteria and criteria-values change. Each time a decision is to be made this approach requires a preliminary investigation as to which criteria are relevant for the DM as well as extensive data collection and analysis in order to delineate the efficient set.

Also the prior articulation of preferences mode may be rather demanding. This will in particular be the case for non-repetitive decisions in new contexts where previous information on F may be misleading. In such cases there may be large "sunk" costs involved in developing F; F will have to be up-dated, or, alternatively, it will have to be developed from scratch.

If we assume that in most cases the iterative approaches do not require a large number of iterations before terminating in a choice, then, seen from an AN prespective, they should be less costly than the phased approaches. It is true that they require the application of interactive search algorithms and that the AN must use some time communicating with the DM. However, the algorithms most likely will be available as standard software packages. Furthermore, it is anticpated that the reduction in AN and computer time which results from not having to examine all of Y will, in general, compensate for the possible extra demands as to communication in the iterative approaches.

Figure 10.2 below provides a rough synthesis of the subjective evaluations of the four multiple criteria planning modes with respect to the investigation criteria.

	Prior art. alternat.	Prog. art. alternat.	Prior art. prefer.	Prog. art prefer.
Contrib. to future inves.	1	0	2	0
Risks involved:				
A) prefer. info.	0	0	-2	-1
B) altern. info.	-2	0	0	0
C) inapp. inves.	-1	0	-2	0
Direct costs:				
A) DM time etc.	-1	-2	0	-2
B) AN time etc.	-2	0	-1	0

Figure 10.2 Evaluation of Modes w.r.t. Investigation Criteria

The numerical entries reflect apriori evaluations without reference to an organization's present way of planning or any other such specific contextual information. Their interpretation in this and the following figures is as follows: A **"0"** signifies that the evaluation of the approach with respect to the given criterion is neither positive nor negative; for example, considering the criterion-mode combination: "contributes to future investigation-progressive articulation of alternatives", our conclusion is that the approach neither contributes to future investigations nor does it detract from them. A **"1"** signifies that the approach receives a positive evaluation while a **"-1"** signifies a negative evaluation. A **"2"** represents a rather positive evaluation, while a **"-2"** signifies a rather negative evaluation of the approach with respect to the given criterion. Therefore, as regards the first criterion, only the values **0**, **1** or **2** may appear in the figure as this criterion is "positive", i.e. refers to a contribution. Similarly, the entries corresponding to the last five criteria in figure 10.2 only may take on the values **0**, **-1** or **-2** as these criteria are "negative" ones, i.e. refer to risks and costs.

10.5. Communication Criteria

Four communication criteria are selected to evaluate the multiple criteria planning modes in the taxonomy. These are:

1) Does the mode provide information which can serve as a guide to behavior elsewhere in the organization?
2) Does the mode contribute to the integration of analysis and decision making?
3) Does the mode contribute to the DM's learning process in connection with planning?
4) What are the direct costs (demands on the DM and the AN) of communication?

The following are brief, context independent evaluations of the four multiple criteria planning modes with respect to these criteria.

Criterion 1: Provides Information to the Organization

The prior articulation of preferences mode is the only approach which, in general, can be said to generate information which is directly relevant to guiding behavior in other parts of the organization. By providing a mapping of the DM's preferences for any relevant vector of criteria values, it can in principle be employed without requiring the participation of the DM. For example, it can serve as the basis for decision rules in other parts of the organization where the DM's authority is sufficiently respected and where the decisions to be made are of a more routine and repetitive type. Thus, this approach can contribute to an organization's ability to decentralize decision making, particularly with respect to repetitive decisions. We note that we previously considered the potential negative aspects of this approach under the heading: "risks of misuse of information on DM preferences".

The prior articulation of alternatives approach produces information about Y. However, this information is only relevant for similar problems with the same alternatives and criteria. Usually, other parts of the organization face different problems characterized by different alternatives and different criteria. Therefore, it cannot be said to provide information which can support the organization.

Neither of the interactive approaches are able to generate information which is sufficiently general and valid that it can be employed elsewhere in the organiation. The progressive articulation of preferences mode stops short of providing a complete mapping of the DM's preferences and the mapping provided is very context dependent, i.e. depends on the set of alternatives being considered. Similar remarks apply to the progressive articulation of alternatives mode.

Criterion 2: Integration of AN and DM

The two interactive approaches presume that the DM and AN work closely together. The "give and take" characterizing these iterative methods, with their gradual eliciting and expression of information, can lead not only to significantly increased awareness by the DM as to his choices and his preferences in a given context. It can also lead to an integration of the analytical and decision making processes and to a synergetic teamwork between the DM and AN.

It is one of our tenets that a major barrier to a planning process which truly reflects a DM's preferences is the separation of the analytical and political aspects. Roughly speaking, there are two possible results of that separation. Either bureaucratic planning, where the DM has to react to detailed proposals he has little intrinsic knowledge of since he has not actively participated in generating and analyzing the proposals. Or ad hoc, charismatic decision making, where power, charm and intuition may appear convincing, but are very risky as they are not sufficiently supported by rational analysis.

Thus, the two interactive approaches can provide both participants with insights into their own values and roles as well as their mutual dependency. When well performed, this should also result in increased commitment to the planning approach, to each other and to the organization as a whole.

In general we do not expect these benefits to arise in the two phased modes. In these, the DM and AN work rather independently of each other and have but limited communication.

Criterion 3: Contributes to the DM's Learning Process

The iterative methods provide the DM with the opportunity to gain insight, self-understanding and improved capacity to participate in the planning process. This is particularly characteristic of the progressive articulation of preferences approach. By essentially compelling the DM to make trade offs between his various criteria it promotes introspection and reflection as to what he wants and what he can do.

The progressive articulation of alternatives may be regarded as a communication device or data search technology. By permiting the DM to take non-modelled issues into account, it provides a laboratory for the balancing of softer issues and more innate complexities of real-world planning on the one hand, and more traditional, quantitative and objective measures of performance on the other hand. Therefore, this approach too may stimulate reflection, insight and learning.

The two phased modes will not in general contribute to learning; the prior articulation of alternatives approach demands simply that the DM makes an (unaided) choice among a subset of the possible alternatives, while the prior articulation of preferences approach simply subjects the DM to a series of hypothetical questions, with but little direct relation to the planning process. This is not to say that the methods based on the prior articulation of alternatives or preferences do not provide information which may be of value with respect to future analyses; as discussed earlier, having analytical descriptions of F and Y can certainly lessen the burden of future decision making, particularly in the case of more-or-less repetitive decisions. However, they do not contribute to the DM's insight. He is not at all involved in the generation of Y, and has very little to do with the generation of F, where he essentially answers hypothetical querries as to trade-offs.

Criterion 4: Direct Costs of Communication

The evaluation of the four modes with respect to the time and effort needed to communicate is quite obvious. The prior articulation of alternatives requires least communication; the DM simply receives a list of efficient alternatives and, in principle, aside from the preliminary identification of his relevant criteria, there is no need for communication between the DM and the AN. The total amount of communication in the prior articulation of preferences mode may also be quite limited, especially in repeated problems, where already established preference information can be utilized by the AN to determine which course of action is to be taken. Still, some amount of questioning is necessary in order to determine F, and therefore some time and effort must be spent by the DM and the AN on communication activities. Finally, a major part of the time and effort spent in the interactive modes is related to communication.

	Prior art. alternat.	Prog. art. alternat.	Prior art. prefer.	Prog. art prefer.
Provides info. to the org.	0	0	2	0
Integration of AN and DM	0	1	0	1
Contrib. to learning	0	1	0	2
Direct costs of commun.	0	-2	-1	-2

Figure 10.3 Evaluation Modes w.r.t. Communication Criteria

Once again, we summarize these observations by assigning subjective scores indicating the degree with which a mode satisfies a criterion. The procedure is identical to that employed above with respect to the investigation criteria.

10.6. Choice Criteria

The problem of characterizing the four multiple criteria planning modes with respect to their choice attributes is closely related to our proceeding analyses of investigation and communication. Here we want to characterize the four planning modes by some additional potential contributions to the DM's capability for actually making choices which are in accord with his preferences.

We propose the following choice criteria:

1) Does the mode support the integration and balancing of organizational and personal values?

2) Does the mode facilitate the implementation process? In particular, does it a) lead to well defined choices, and b) contribute to insight as to possible reactions by "stakeholders", i.e. those affected by a decision and whose reactions affect the success of the decision?[2]

Context-independent discussions of the four planning modes with respect to these criteria are given below.

Criterion 1: Integration of Organizational and Personal Values
This criterion concerns how best to balance the more organization-oriented aspects of planning (e.g. will the decision lead to improved profits and market share?), with the more personal aspects (e.g. will the decision improve my personal development, job security, prestige, power, position and income? and will it be in harmony with my moral, political and aesthetical values?).

---

[2] This concept is treated in some depth in chapter 11.

We note that the literature on planning in general, and in particular on multiple criteria decision making, is quite silent as to this important aspect of planning. It is almost as though discussing it "isn't done". There is considerable need for increased attention to this rather tabu subject, both on a theoretical and empirical level as well as with respect to the design of systems supporting decision making.

Neither of the phased modes directly motivates the DM to harmonize personal and organizational values. Nevertheless, the prior articulation of alternatives certainly permits the DM to consider how to balance his personal values and those of the organization. This approach essentially filters the alternatives and provides the DM with a subset of efficient solutions to be evaluated. Thus, if the subset of alternatives he is to consider is relatively small so that he can mentally perform such evaluations, the mode may be well suited. Note, however, that the likely omission of explicit, personal criteria may imply that the best compromise between personal and organizational values may not be attainable in this mode. The "efficient" solutions presented to the DM may omit alternatives which are in fact efficient with respect to the more inclusive set of criteria.

This is also true for the progressive articulation of alternatives mode, where it is the DM who leads the process and formulates questions to the AN, until he is satisfied and willing to make a decision. The DM steers this iterative approach in accord with his, at no time explicitly expressed, values. Therefore, he does not have to explicitly express and treat the conflicts which could arise due to possible mismatches between choices which can forward his own values at the expense of the organization's values and vice versa. Expressed in another way, a DM's behavior will always reflect a balance between his desires to forward the organization's expressed goals and his individual, personal goals and this balancing will be implicitly manifest in the way he arrives at his best compromise solution.

Neither the prior nor the iterative articulation of preferences mode contribute to the integration of organizational and personal values. Perhaps just the opposite is the case; both these approaches focus exclusively on the explicit criteria chosen to represent the relevant values, and these will in general belong to the category of organizational values.

Criterion 2: Facilitates the Implementation Process

This criterion is somewhat related to the communication criteria treated earlier. It is relevant, in that "good" decisions which are not carried out according to the DM's wishes and expectations, may turn out to be "poor" decisions in practice. We distinguish between two major aspects of the implementation process:

A. Do the investigation, communication and choice processes characterizing the planning mode result in a well defined choice? This is necessary if the implementation process is to result in tasks, plans, budgets and a delegation of responsibilities which further the DM's values.

B. Does the approach contribute to the decision maker's insight as to the aspirations and values of the stakeholders who will be affected by the action taken and whose reactions can affect the implementation of the decision? Just as the DM balances his views as to "what is good for the organization with what is good for himself", so too do the other parties who participate in, and/or are affected by the decision. The results of these, often subconcious, evaluations may be crucial for their enthusiasm in supporting the implementation.

Before using these two implementation criteria to evaluate the four multiple criteria planning modes we should note that some of the problems to be discussed below can also explicitly be treated in a particular planning context via the explicit introduction of **implementation criteria**. I.e., the alternatives will not only be described by such attributes as refer to their substantive characteristics, but also by attributes which refer to their procedural characteristics. Included here could be the consideration of such factors as the demands on the organization, availability of motivated and capable employees, attitudes of major customers, competitors, activists etc.

Criterion 2A: Contributes to Well-Defined Choice

Approaches which directly involve the DM in the delineation and evaluation of alternatives will presumably lead to more precise definitions of the alternatives - and therefore to more operational plans for implementing the ensuing decisions. From this perspective, the least attractive mode is that based on the prior articulation of preferences as it completely removes the DM from contact with the alternatives to be considered. Next poorest is the prior articulation of alternatives. The preliminary search amongst the set of alternatives and the identification of the efficient subset is performed by the AN, and when the DM gets involved, he is essentially on his own with only limited possibility to really probe into the definition of the alternatives. However, if both the original set of alternatives as well as the subset presented to the DM for evaluation are "small", he may have reasonable opportunity to perform investigations of the alternatives which can lead to successful implementation.

The progressive articulation of alternatives mode can contribute to well-defined choice since it directly involves the DM in the examination of the set of alternatives; the DM is essentially involved in "designing" the set of efficient solutions. The other iterative approach, the progressive articulation of preferences mode, only provides the DM with a rather limited ability to analyze the alternatives; his role in delineating the alternatives is reduced to participation in the trade-off dialogues as to substitution wishes.

Criterion 2B: Contributes to Insight as to Stakeholder Preferences

The progressive articulation of preferences mode can contribute to the decision maker's insight as to stakeholder preferences. This is due to the fact that the DM is compelled to evaluate his trade-offs between the various attributes characterizing the alternatives and in so doing he must reflect, even if only indirectly, upon the stakeholders and their possible reactions. Such reflection goes on "internally" and the DM requires no explicit definition of the stakeholders, their values, criteria and preferences. Similarly, the progressive articulation of alternatives may stimulate reflection as to stakeholder motivations and reactions. For example, procedures where weights or restrictions are modified may invite the DM to reevaluate demands as to product quality, customer service and the like.

Neither of the phased approaches can be said to stimulate the DM to consider stakeholder preferences; the prior articulation of alternatives does not in any way induce the DM to consider stakeholder values, criteria, preferences and possible reactions, while the prior articulation of preferences can only illuminate such matters in a very abstract way; the hypothetical questions employed to elucidate the DM's preferences cannot be expected to be able to meaningfully tackle the very complex issues involved here.

The discussion of the choice criteria may be summarized as in figure 10.4 below.

	Prior art. alternat.	Prog. art. alternat.	Prior art. prefer.	Prog. art. prefer.
Integrates org. & personal values	1	2	0	0
Contrib. to well defined choice	1	2	0	1
Contrib. to insight as to stakeholder values	0	1	0	1

Figure 10.4 Evaluation of Modes w.r.t. Choice Criteria

10.7. Context Independent Evaluations of the Modes

In summary, we arrive at the overall, context-independent evaluation of the four multiple criteria planning modes depicted in figure 10.5 below. We will make frequent reference to this figure in the following sections where we attempt to introduce contextual characteristics in the form of hypothetical (prototype) decision problems.

Before concluding the context-free evaluation of the multiple criteria planning modes, two reservations are called for.

First, the entries in this figure cannot meaningfully be added or in any other simple way aggregated; they simply provide the raw material for characterizing the four planning modes within a given context. In a specific context one or more of the criteria listed may be important, while others may be insignificant. Also, the evaluation of the different modes with respect to the different criteria may have to be modified in a given context. Furthermore, other criteria not considered here may turn out to be important in a given setting.

	Prior art. alternat.	Prog. art. alternat.	Prior art. prefer.	Prog. art prefer.
Contrib. to future inves.	1	0	2	0
Risks involved:				
A) prefer. info.	0	0	-2	-1
B) altern. info.	-2	0	0	0
C) inapp. inves.	-1	0	-2	0
Dir. inves. costs:				
A) DM time etc.	-1	-2	0	-2
B) AN time etc.	-2	0	-1	0
Provides info. to the org.	0	0	2	0
Integration of AN and DM	0	1	0	1
Contrib. to learning	0	1	0	2
Direct costs of communication	0	-2	-1	-2
Integrates org. & personal values	1	2	0	0
Contrib. to well defined choice	1	2	0	1
Contrib. to insight as to stakeholder preferences	0	1	0	1

Figure 10.5 Evaluation of Modes w.r.t. Investigation, Communication and Choice Criteria

Secondly, the characterizations of the taxonomy's four modes have many times been predicated by conditional statements such as: "however, in the case of one-shot decisions...", and "if the set of efficient alternatives is relatively small...". This highlights the point that attempting to evaluate alternative multiple criteria planning modes independently of a particular setting may lead to rather unprecise characterizations. We therefore considered parametizing the presentation. For example, we could have developed tables such as Figure 10.5 above for the case of repetitive/one-shot decisions, a large/small number of alternatives, etc. We have introduced the idea but have not explicitly parametized the analysis. We felt that the extra insights would not sufficiently compensate for the resultant extra complexity - and would perhaps lend an air of precision to the analyses which is not justified. On the other hand, such a more detailed approach may be justified in a given setting; our intent has simply been to suggest and demonstrate a meta-analysis as to the choice of planning approach rather than to provide an in-depth template.

10.8. Choosing a Multiple Criteria Planning Mode within a Specific Context

In order to be be more specific as to how the analysis so far can contribute to the evaluation of the four taxanomical classes of multiple criteria approaches in practice, we now introduce a series of four "case studies" in the form of hypothetical planning problems. The first three of these are rather brief and simply indicate the nature of context-dependent analyses of alternative multiple criteria planning modes. The fourth and concluding case provides a much more thorough analysis of the methodology; readers with only a limited interest here are advised to skip this final case and proceed to chapter 11.

We are in all these cases at the highest level of the "choice hierarchy", i.e. the choice we face is the choice of a multiple criteria planning mode. We proceed as follows. First, we will subjectively determine which of the criteria defined in the preceeding section are of significance for the case considered. For each of these criteria we will then refer to figure 10.5 to assist us in determining the suitability of the alternative planning modes. Finally, we will consider the "scores" given to each of the modes and draw our very tentative and rough conclusions. We underline that the analysis is illustrative, highly subjective and only intends to provide suggestions as to how to structure the meta-planning problem of choosing between alternative multiple criteria planning modes.

The problem formulations are of course arbitrary, very broad and only roughly defined. In a specific setting on the other hand, not only the particular problem being faced but also the relevant setting - the organization and its traditions, customers, competitors, suppliers and community - can be characterized far more precisely than has been done here. Furthermore, the AN will be aware of which particular MCDM **techniques** - as distinguished from multiple criteria planning **modes** - could be relevant; certainly this will influence the choice of mode. We suggest therefore that an analysis as to which mode/technique combination will be most appropriate can be specifically designed, following the procedural guidelines developed here.

Example 1: Establishing Guidelines for Wage Increases.

The problem to be considered here exemplifies a class of problems characterized by repetitive choices among many alternatives where it is felt that decision rules alone cannot be relied on. In particular, we will consider the problem of choosing between a limited number of procedures to support decisions as to annual wage adjustments. These decisions are to be made by a DM who is the manager of personnel in a department of a large, decentralized corporation. The manager wants to establish a set of guidelines as to how, once the total budget for the department's wage increases is roughly decided upon, the budget is to be divided among the employees in the department. These allocation decisions are considered to have such important "political" aspects, that the DM is not inclined to relinquish his decision making authority to automated decision rules - as is the case in the concluding, more detailed example dealing with automatic purchase orders.

An example of such guidelines could be the following: For each employee generate a graphical profile of how well he does according to a series of criteria like position, current wage, seniority, number of days absent in past year, educational level and immediate supervior's evaluation of productivity and social talents. Based upon this profile, calculate an aggregated weighted score. The profile and the score constitute a starting point for interviews and for the decision as to the employee's wage increase.

Another example of such guidelines could be the following: Based on a set of objective criteria, a decision rule is used to assign each employee to one of a number of wage-increase categories like e.g.: high wage increase, moderate wage increase, no wage increase and wage decrease. A score is subjectively assigned to each category, for example 4 to the category "high wage increase", 3 to "moderate wage increase", etc. Based upon the number of employees assigned to each category and category score, the total weighted score is calculated by summing the number of employees times their category score. This total is then divided into the total budget so as to determine the parameter, "wage increase per score point". This is then used to calculate a preliminary wage increase for each employee as the product of his score points and the wage increase per score point. A list of the results is given to the DM and serves as a basis for his subjective evaluation. If the DM's personal evaluation deviates from the proposal, e.g. if he considers the employee to be a "trouble maker" and would like him to quit, if the employee is a key figure in his group, or if the employee is being considered for a managerial position, then he will deviate from the proposed increase.

The problem at hand is to determine which of the four planning modes the DM should employ in order to choose the "best" guidelines in the given context. In other words, we are at the highest level of the three-level decision hierarchy: we are to choose an overall organization of the multiple criteria planning activities, i.e. a planning mode. At the second level a choice is to be made of a specific MCDM technique within the approach chosen at the first level. At the third and final level the MCDM technique is to be employed to support the choice of the actual guidelines for wage increases. A final, operational level which is outside our frame of reference, consists of actually using the guidelines as a decision support in making wage decisions. We suggest again that the methodology employed here to choose a planning mode could also be used to choose a specific MCDM technique within a planning mode or - via a composite analysis - to simultaneously choose both a planning mode and an MCDM technique.

We note too that the actual choice of the guidelines - level 3 - cannot be based on "objective criteria" alone. The choice of criteria to characterize alternative guidelines will most likely require subjective evaluations of criteria such as "is in accord with company policy", "fair", "can be understood by the employees", "will meet union approval", and "easy to administer".

We commence by considering which of the criteria developed in sections 10.1 - 10.6 and summarized in figure 10.5 are most relevant.

There are few risks involved as to preference information. The DM does not want to hide the criteria he will employ to determine wage increases. Just the opposite is true, he wants the employees to know which qualities the firm emphasizes. Therefore this criteria is not of importance with respect to choosing between the four planning modes. Similarly, there is only limited risk involved if others should obtain information as to the alternative guidelines the DM is considering. Also the risks in the form of inappropriate investigations of guidelines and the resulting opportunity costs of choosing a "wrong" guideline are considered to be negligible; the DM's guidelines will be just that, he will have considerable leeway in making the actual decisions, and will, for example, be able to take special matters into account - at the risk of course, of creating unrest if he deviates too greatly from the previously established norms - particularly if these are public knowledge.

The direct DM and AN costs of evaluating the alternative guidelines are considered to be insignificant with respect to the total wage budget, so also this criteria will be neglected.

We note however, that if the task at hand was not one of choosing a multiple criteria planning approach (level 1) or of choosing an MCDM technique within that approach (level 2) but was instead the actual choice of the guidelines using the specific MCDM technique selected (level 3), then such costs could certainly play an important role. The guidelines will be applied a great number of times, at least once a year for all the employees, and there could be significant costs differences depending upon which guidelines are chosen. For example, as indicated earlier, some guidelines might require considerable managerial evaluation and communication, while others might minimize the DM's participation in the wage evaluation process.

Neither is it anticpated that the choice of a multiple criteria planning mode would be significantly affected by the criteria: "Information to the organization". Since the DM has rejected the possibility of using decision rules, it is anticipated that no matter what actual guidelines are selected (level 3), they will be communicated to the organization. This will indirectly provide far more information on the DM's preferences than can be deduced from the investigation of the DM's preferences during the planning analyses. Similar conclusions can be drawn with respect to the criterion: "Integration of decision making and analysis". The increased insights which potentially can be gained by the DM and the AN should they work together in evaluating the alternative planning modes will be insignificant compared to the insights both parties can gain by working together at level 3 to actually choose the guidelines - and by applying the guidelines in practice.

This is also the case as regards the ability of the alternative approaches to contribute to well defined choice; the DM himself will be the user of the guidelines and will most certainly see to it that he understands their workings. Furthermore, it is likely that at the very early stages of the planning process he will be involved in the design of the alternative guidelines themselves. Therefore, this criterion cannot be used to distinguish between the alternative planning modes.

On the other hand, the following criteria for the choice of the guidelines are considered to be important.

Contribution to future investigations: The multiple criteria planning approach to choosing the guidelines can contribute to future investigations. For example, a prior articulation of preferences approach could certainly provide valuable information should the DM decide to design guidelines with regard to promotions.

Contribution to learning: Depending upon the choice of approach, the DM may be stimulated to reflect upon very basic questions as to what the firm expects of its employees, how policy as to wage increases will affect effectiveness, the firm's reputation as an employer, etc. It is not likely that this will be the case if a prior articulation of preferences approach is employed due to the hypothetical nature of the questions typically employed. On the other hand, it is felt that the trade-off information requested during a progressive articulation of preferences mode will contribute to such reflection.

Integrates organizational and personal values: Following up on the above remarks, it is likely that, depending upon the approach chosen, the DM will not only consider broad company criteria; he is responsible for the operations of his department, wants to be respected and admired by the employees as a fair and understanding leader, has his own style and values, and wants to balance company values with his own outlook. Therefore, as can be seen from figure 10.5, since there is quite a difference between the capabilities of the four approaches to contribute to the integration of organizational and personal values, this criterion is quite relevant here. In particular, it indicates that the choice of a progressive articulation of alternatives approach may lead to increased DM insight as to which criteria, both organizational and personal, are important to him and how best to balance them.

Contributes to insight as to stakeholder values: This is certainly an important criterion here. The choice of which planning approach should be used to evaluate alternative guidelines can lead to significant differences in the DM's insight as to employee values and their possible reactions to the guidelines. Similarly, the choice of approach can be of importance with respect to the insight which can be obtained as to the reactions by other departmental managers, by corporate top management and by the unions. As can be seen from figure 10.5 and from the section preceeding it, this points in the direction of a progressive articulation of preferences approach.

Considering now this list of criteria, it appears from figure 10.5 that the two progressive articulation approaches are the most attractive while the two prior articulation approaches are less attractive. In particular, it is felt that insight as to stakeholder values is so important here that a progressive articulation of preferences approach is the most attractive choice. Once again however, we underline that the procedure followed here is simply suggestive and that an actual application would need to take many other matters into account, including the DM's style, the possible MCDM techniques being considered, the organizational design and culture, the possible AN support, and many other factors.

Example 2: Choice of Location for A Major New Facility.
The prototype problem to be considered here is representative for a class of problems with the following charcteristics: seldom but significant choices among few alternatives. Indeed, choices as where to locate a major facility, e.g. a factory, warehouse, airport, hospital, or oil platform, are often made between a fairly small number of sites which, based on strategic considerations, have been singled out for more detailed analysis from a larger number of possible sites. Such decisions typically lead to large investments in site, plant and distribution facilities, as well as to logistical and organizational problems. The task at hand is to determine which broad class of multiple criteria planning modes should be employed as a "top of the hierarchy" approach to the locational planning.

We argue briefly that the following criteria should be taken into account:

Contribution to future investigation: The locational decisions considered here are assumed to be made infrequently, but each time are of considerable significance. If a sufficiently extensive set of alternatives is considered, developing a planning approach which is based on the prior articulation of alternatives might provide a powerful database for future analyses. Similarly, a mapping of the DM's preferences as to locational decisions can provide at a minimum a screning device to remove undesirable alternatives in connection with future locational decisions. This points in the direction of the phased approaches.

Risks of misuse of information on efficient alternatives: Since the decisions involved are of considerable significance, the actual MCDM analysis may have considerable value for competitors. This will especially be the case for techniques belonging to the prior articulation of alternatives approach. Knowledge for example as to where a supermarket chain considers locating new supermarkets can be of considerable strategic importance to a competitor.

Direct costs due to DM time and effort required: The MCDM analyses employed (level 3) can be quite complex and involve many qualitative and quantitative criteria such as investments in site and plant, distribution costs, quality of the local housing, cultural facilities and schools, supply of skilled labor, proximity to highways, airports and railroads, union strength, and effect on competitors, local politicians and special interest groups. Thus, it is likely that if iterative approaches are employed, they will place considerable demands on DM time and effort. This will not be the case with a prior articulation of alternatives approach where the major demands on time and effort will be placed on the AN. On the other hand, the DM will be faced with the burden of choosing from amongst the presumably relatively few efficient alternative sites. While the prior articulation of preferences will remove this burden from the DM, this approach will essentially be ruled out as such complex and strategic decisions cannot be left to the AN. This tends to point in the direction of a prior articulation of alternatives approach. However, in this case with very important choices to be made at level 3, the DM's evaluation and choice activities will presumably necessitate more extensive dialogues with the AN then the stereotyped characterization of the approach suggests.

Contributes to learning: No matter which approach is employed, the significance of the decisions and their strategic complexity will necessitate considerable reflection as to values, objectives, criteria and prefences and to the relationships between key variables. Approaches which contribute to the meaningful structuring of such information and which make it explicitly available will certainly contribute to the learning process and to the DM's planning capability. We would expect that the progressive articulation of alternatives approach would be best suited here. It is felt that such a structuring can best be achieved by presenting the DM with new efficient alternatives and having him direct the search for possible improvements. On the other hand, if the set of alternatives has been sufficiently filtered via a preliminary analysis, then the prior articulation of alternatives approach could also be appropriate. This would in particular be the case if the delineation of the original set of alternatives and the smaller set resulting from the preliminary analyses, are based upon extensive communication between the DM and the AN as to which values are of importance and which criteria are suited to expressing and measuring these values.

Contributes to insight as to stakeholder values: Locational decisions are not only important for top management. They can affect for example the following stakeholders: employees to be relocated to a new site, the local community of the new site, customers to be served from the new site, and suppliers to serve the new site.

Therefore DM insight into stakeholder preferences and possible reactions can be of great importance in locational decisions, and perhaps be more important then the more common cost criteria. A close, investigative dialogue will contribute to this insight, and this points in the direction of an iterative approach, perhaps in particular the progressive articulation of alternatives.

Based upon the analysis leading up to figure 10.5, and assuming a small number of possible sites to be investigated by the DM, it would appear that the prior articulation of alternatives could be well suited while the prior articulation of preferences is essentially ruled out due to the significance of the problem. If, on the other hand, the set of alternative sites is large, say due to the fact that the DM will not leave it to the AN to perform the initial screening, then the progressive articulation of alternatives approach could be best. Clearly, which approach a DM would select in a given context would to a great extent also depend on the planning environment, the particular MCDM techniques available and the personalities of the AN and DM.

Example 3: Choice of Market to Enter.
As a final brief example before the concluding detailed case, let us consider the problem of deciding upon whether to enter a new market. Such a strategic problem is representative of the class of problems that involve unique, significant choices. The example we consider here deals with the decision of whether or not to diversify by going into any one of four possible new fields. These fields have been thoroughly analyzed by the company staff and outside consultants. If the company decides to enter one of the markets, this will be a very significant and risky decision and place great demands on the organization. But the problem is more complicated than just choosing between one of five alternative plans, i.e. four possible new markets as well as status quo. There are several significantly different ways of entering each of the markets, and several alternative plans if the new market strategy is rejected. Therefore, although at first glance it appears as though the number of alternatives is limited, the number is in fact quite large. It is by no means clear at the start as to whether a phased or an iterative approach will be most appropriate.

The task at hand is to recommend to the managing director which of the four multiple criteria planning modes should be employed as an overall framework for structuring the firm's planning process here. We note that the final approval of the decision will most likely be made by the firm's board of directors. Therefore the DM will not only have to consider his own preferences, but also those of the board members as well as his ability to argue for his position. At present, however, he wants to carry out an analysis which will make it clear for himself, what he feels is the best decision.

We consider in turn only those criteria considered to be relevant.

Contributes to future investigations: Only the prior articulation of preferences is felt to be able to make a serious contribution here as it alone can provide the DM with a strong background for making future analyses of the same type of investment activity. This will however only be the case if his preferences can be expected to be stable over time. This reservation is not to be slighted; such strategic decisions are presumably rather infrequent. The prior articulation of alternatives is not relevant, partly because the characteristics of the alternatives are likely to change over time, partly because such future investment decisions very likely might include other markets than those presently under consideration.

Risk of inappropriate investigations: The potential opportunity costs due to inappropriate investigations are very large. If the investigations of the possibilities at level 3 are deficient, considerable damage can be done to the firm - and the DM could find his prestige and position threatened. This rules against the prior articulation of preferences approach, as the techniques employed under this approach essentially remove the DM from the actual decision making process; it is only via communicating with the AN during the mapping of his preference relation that the DM is involved in the planning at all. Given the nature of the decisions to be made, criticism can also be made as to the other phased approach, the prior articulation of alternatives. By leaving the choice burden to the DM and by only supplying him with a more-or-less attractive subset of the (efficient) alternatives, the DM has now complete resonsibility - but may feel a considerable need for interactive support not typically provided by this phased planning mode.

DM time and effort: Depending upon which type of approach is employed, the demands on DM time and effort can be considerable. As there are in fact many alternatives, the prior articulation of alternatives approach may have distinct advantages here, particularly if the set of efficient alternatives is reasonably small. The prior articulation of preferences approach can at first glance also appear attractive here. However, it is just for this reason that the DM could very well be wary of this approach. It leads to analyses which leave the responsibility for making a recommendation to the AN. There may be many attributes not really expressed by the set of criteria chosen to characterize the DM's preferences, including of course his non-articulated personal values. Furthermore, such an analysis will not stimulate his learning and insight and therefore make it difficult for him to discuss the recommended alternative with the board of directors. For these reasons, and taking into account the related strong criticisms earlier, the prior articulation of preferences approach can be eliminated from further consideration.

Integration of analysis and decision making: The significance of the decision to be made is such that it is reasonable to expect that the closer the DM and the AN are able to work together, the better the choice of strategy. This would tend to point in the direction of the interactive approaches.

Contributes to learning: This is considered to be an important criterion here, where new activities are being considered and where the DM's final choice of market strategy must be discussed with the board. In particular, the insights which might be gained as to important, qualitative and non-modelled issues via participating in a progressive articulation of alternatives approach could be of great importance here. Similarly, a progressive articulation of preferences approach with its focus on trade-off information could contribute to the DM's insight as to his preferences and possibilities.

As mentioned earlier, we can reject the prior articulation of preferences approach. The importance of the choice combined with the great pressure on the DM to be able to argue for his choice and place it within the context of the other choices, would suggest that the progressive articulation of alternatives is the most appropriate choice.

10.9. Example 4: Detailed Analysis of an Automatic Ordering System

We now proceed to a final example which presents a far more detailed hypothetical application of the methodology for choosing a planning mode within a specific context.

To delineate the planning **context**, consider the problem of establishing **decision rules** to be used to expedite **purchasing decisions**. More precisely, consider the problem faced by a wholesaler of office supplies. In connection with a reorganization of the firm and the implementation of new PC-oriented edp systems the manager is considering how to choose decision rules for generating purchase orders to replenish inventories. The firm supplies retailers of office supplies with roughly 50,000 different items. Based upon present knowledge as to the characteristics of alternative purchasing rules, 20 different decision rules are being considered.

Instead of analyzing each of the 50,000 items individually so as to select which decision rule should be used to determine when it should be ordered and in which quantity, we assume that the items can be apriori classified as belonging to a reasonable number, say 50, of item-groupings which are more or less homogeneous with respect to their purchasing and inventory characteristics. The underlying idea is that all items in a grouping are to be covered by the same purchasing rule. Placement in such an item-grouping is to be based upon such factors as: item size, supplier, rebate rules, item cost, demand, and special requirements as to storage.

Each of these groupings can then be analyzed and a purchasing decision rule assigned to it. For example, the decision rule chosen to generate purchase orders for items which are inexpensive, easy to store and in frequent demand would quite likely differ from the rule chosen for items which are expensive, difficult to store and where the demand is small and eratic.

Examples of such possible groupings could be: a) items which have a demand of at least α_1 units per year, cost less than $\$\beta_1$ per unit, are standard items not affected by style, can be ordered on short notice in case of stock-outs, and require minimal space per unit, and b) items which have an average demand of at least α_2 units per week, cost more than $\$\beta_1$ but less than $\$\beta_2$ per unit and where the time from order to receipt is roughly γ days unless special premiums are paid.

Examples of alternative rules could be: a) order an economic lot size when the inventory level is lower than $\delta\%$ of the expected demand over a lead time which corresponds to the expected time from order placement to order receipt, b) at equally spaced intervals of time order an amount corresponding to economic lot size minus stock on hand plus expected demand over lead time, and c) do not order to stock and place orders only when there is demand from a customer.

Summarizing, the DM's overall planning problem is to design an ordering system based upon a set of decision rules and item-groupings. For each of the 50 apriori groupings, the 20 alternative decision rules are to be analyzed and a decision rule is to be chosen for each grouping. The task at hand is to determine which of the taxonomy's four multiple criteria planning modes should be employed to match each grouping with a decision rule. We are thus at the top of the three-tiered choice hierarchy. The top level is the choice of multiple criteria planning mode which is well suited to the decision problem at hand. Once this overall approach has been decided upon, the second level is the choice of a specific MCDM technique within the framework of the approach chosen. The third and final level is the application of the MCDM technique to make the specific assignment of a decision rule to each of the 50 groupings. An additional level, which lies outside the scope of the book, is the actual application of the ordering rules in the firm's daily operations.

We will first consider which of the criteria listed in figure 10.5 are most relevant for the problem of selecting a planning mode. For each of the relevant criteria we will then, based upon figure 10.5 and the analyses leading up to it, evaluate the alternative approaches. Finally, we will subjectively consider these evaluations in their totality and conclude as to which of the four planning approaches appears to provide the best compromise solution to the meta-planning problem at hand. We commence by considering the relevance of the 12 criteria listed in figure 10.5.

The information generated as to the set of alternatives - the 20 possible decision rules for each of the 50 item-groupings - will be rather context specific and therefore will not contribute to future planning investigations in contexts other than those related to purchasing, inventory control and the like. Similarly, knowledge as to the decision maker's preferences will most likely be specifically related to the design of the purchase order system and therefore of little value in other planning contexts. Furthermore, such knowledge will be of limited value in situations where for example purchasing rules are to be determined for new items. Once the group-rule decisions have been made, purchase rules for the new items can immediately be determined via the determination of which grouping the item best belongs to. Thus, the first criterion in figure 10.5, "contributes to future investigations", is not considered to be relevant here. We consider next the risk criteria.

There is considerable evidence from operations research and industrial engineering that in contexts similar to the case considered here the consequences of rules as to when to order and in which quantities are not particularly sensitive to the parameters employed. The costs of purchasing and storing goods such as office items appear in many cases to be quite insensitive to the specific cost parameters, lead-times etc. employed. Therefore there are few risks involved should there be leakage of information regarding preferences or alternatives as a result of the analyses. Furthermore, we are dealing with well defined problems with readily obtainable statistical information as to demand, cost parameters etc, whereby the risk of not choosing the "best" multiple criteria approach for designing the ordering system will most likely be rather insignificant. All in all then, we conclude that the three risk criteria - as to preference information, alternatives information and opportunity costs - are not relevant here. They do not appear to be of significance for distinguishing between the four planning modes with respect to the design of the purchasing system.

We consider next the criterion: "Direct costs due to AN time etc." No matter which mode is actually chosen, the ensuing MCDM analyses as to which particular decision rules to choose will place considerable demands on data collection and analysis. In fact, these demands will far exceed the demands resulting from the analyses of which mode should be chosen. Furthermore, compared to the costs which directly and indirectly will result from actually running the purchasing system, the costs of analysis here will most likely be insignificant. Therefore, from an overall perspective, the costs of analysis here will not play a significant role in distinguishing between the four approaches, and we will disregard this criterion as well.

Using similar arguments we will disregard the criterion: "Provides information to the organization". The actual MCDM analyses of the groupings-rules combinations to make the choice of decision rules, what we earlier referred to as the third and final level of the decision hierarchy, will be rather context specific. Therefore, it is not anticipated that these analyses will provide any significant information to the organization regarding the DM's values and preferences.

On the other hand, it appears that the following criteria could be important in connection with the choice of which planning approach to employ when determining which of the 20 decision rules is best for each of the 50 item groupings:

DM time and effort
Integration of analysis and decision making
Contribution to learning
Integration of organizational and personal values
Contribution to well defined choice
Contribution to insight as to stakeholder values.

We start by considering the criterion: "DM time and effort". There can be a significant difference in the demands on DM time and effort due to employing alternative approaches for choosing the most appropriate grouping-rule combinations. If an interactive approach is employed, so that the DM is directly involved in the evaluation of the alternative grouping-rule combinations, it may require a significant amount of his time. There will be a large number of grouping-rule combinations, here 50 x 20 = 1,000. In addition, each grouping may be characterized by a relatively large number of efficient alternatives, i.e. decision rules. Finally, there most likely will be a reasonably large number of criteria for the DM to consider when performing his evaluations; these criteria will presumably reflect costs, service, demands on the organization etc. It may therefore be difficult for the DM to make the precise kinds of judgements, distinctions and trade-offs which the iterative methods presume. This difficulty may be compounded if, as is not unlikely, there are rather small differences between the individual criteria values characterizing the grouping-rule combinations.

We consider now the two phased approaches with respect to demands on DM time and effort. The prior articulation of alternatives appears to be very demanding. First of all, for each grouping the DM will have to choose between the efficient decision rules (more or less on his own). Secondly, since he will have to do this for each of the 50 item groupings, this task may be very tedious and abstract whereby there will be good chances that the DM's evaluations turn out to be more or less arbitrary and do not really represent his underlying preferences. In addition, if the prior articulation of alternatives approach is employed, the DM will of course have to spend some time with the AN prior to the AN's analyses; the AN will require information on the DM's values and objectives in order to determine which criteria to employ when characterizing the alternatvies, i.e. the grouping-rule combinations.

On the other hand, as it removes such tedious, repetitive and demanding burdens from the DM, the prior articulation of preferences may be particularly well suited for just such situations. Furthermore, given the well defined context where the DM is quite accustomed to thinking about ordering rules, it appears to be reasonable to assume that the AN will be able to solicit the DM for information on his preferences and that the DM will be able to consistently provide such information to the AN. This should permit the AN to generate an approximation to F without placing considerable burdens on the DM.

We conclude therefore that the prior articulation of preferences appears to be by far the most attractive approach as evalutated from the perspective of DM time and effort; the three other approaches all place considerable demands on the DM's participation.

We consider next the criterion: "Integration of analysis and decision making". There is an excellent opportunity here for such an integration; the problem is well defined and it is reasonable to anticipate that the AN has access to considerable experience as to this class of problems. Thus, the criteria of AN and DM integration points in the direction of an interactive approach to the evaluation of the decision rules for each item grouping. This result is in close accord with the results presented in figure 10.5. However, without more detailed attention to the specific MCDM techniques which could be employed, it is not reasonable here to attempt to distinguish between the two iterative approaches.

The next criterion to be considered is: "Contribution to leaning". This criterion is closely related to the criterion: "Integration of analysis and decision making" just considered. The 50,000 items are assumed to be rather inhomogeneous and therefore the grouping of these into roughly 50 homogeneous groups can be a rather important task. It is therefore also likely that rather different decision rules will be appropriate for the different groupings of the items. It follows that were the DM to participate with the AN in analyzing both how to group the individual items as well as which decision rule should be chosen for each of the 50 groupings, he could learn quite a bit about the purchasing system. In particular, he could gain insight as to the sensitivity of the ordering rules - and of the whole ordering system - with respect to the characteristics of the items. This information could be important for the DM's ability to structure the purchasing system, to supervise the implementation of the ordering rules chosen, and to provide information to sales management as to which groupings appear to be costly to administer and which appear to be attractive, seen from the ordering and inventory point of view.

The iterative approaches appear to be most attractive here. They presume an active dialogue between the DM and AN, while just the opposite is true for the two phased approaches. It is once again however difficult to distinguish between the two iterative approaches without going into far greater detail, e.g. as to the characteristcs of the specific MCDM techniques which could be employed.

The next criterion we will consider is "Integration of organizational and personal values". The overall performance of the purchasing system will depend upon many factors over and above the direct costs. These might include for example the system's potential integration with other systems, the reactions of customers and suppliers as well as of the existing organization, and the system's ability to handle emergency situations if experienced purchasers are replaced due to automatization. It is therefore anticipated that participating in the multiple criteria analyses could contribute to the DM's ability to integrate and balance organizational values, such as those mentioned above, and his own personal values. These personal values might include such factors as how reliant will he be on edb specialists?, how subject will he be to criticism by top management if he does not have the backup support of an experienced purchasing staff?, what will it mean for his prestige and job opportunities if he successfully introduces and operates an automated system?. Consideration of the integration of organizational and personal values points in the direction of choosing a multiple criteria planning mode where the DM deals with a limited number of alternatives and has the freedom to consider criteria other than those explicitly included in the analyses. If we assume that the DM can perform the evaluations by concentrating on a limited number of efficient decision rules for each of the 50 item groupings, then the prior articulation of alternatives would be quite attractive. If this is not the case, or if the demand that such subjective analyses have to be performed 50 times can be expected to lead to a serious reduction in the DM's ability or desire to perform the evaluations, then the progressive articulation of alternatives may be preferred. Once again it is the DM who directs the analysis and is able to balance his personal values with those of the organization. Only now the burdens on the DM are reduced and he no longer works in splendid isolation. On the other hand, neither the prior nor the progressive articulation of preferences modes will permit such an integration of personal and organizational values, as most likely only the organizational criteria will be considered since the process is AN directed.

The context of the problem indicates that a prior or a progressive articulation of alternatives approach would do well according to the criterion: "Contributes to well defined choice". The rules selected under such modes would be understood and approved of by the DM. He would clearly require detailed descriptions of the rules if he is to lead the investigations, perhaps supplemented by computer simulations of how the decision rules work for the various groupings under varying assumptions as to demand. Thus both of the DM directed approaches should contribute to his ability to supervise the implementation of the system so that its operations reflect his preferences - and not just those of for example the specialists involved. In contrast, neither the prior nor the progressive articulation of preferences approaches can be expected to contribute to the DM's ability to supervise the implementation of the ordering system; both these AN directed approaches essentially place all responsibility for the analysis of the grouping-rule alternatives in the hands of the AN.

Finally, we consider the criterion: "Contribution to insight as to stakeholder values". We assume that customer reactions to the service they receive and supplier reactions to the new ordering patterns and procedures are of major importance in determining the appropriateness of a new purchasing system. Therefore the AN and DM should consider how the alternative approaches could contribute to the DM's insights as to customer and supplier values. It is argued that such insight cannot be obtained via a prior articulation of preferences approach, where the DM has to respond to hypothetical questions posed by the AN. Neither will the prior articulation of alternatives approach contribute to such insight in the present context. With this approach, the DM is left to himself to select among the effecient decision rules. This would normally permit reflection as to stakeholder values. However, given that such reflection is to take place for each of the 50 item groupings and that there may for example be a great number of different categories of customers, it is felt that there is a rather strong chance that the DM would give up in desperation.

On the other hand, it is felt that such insight can best be stimulated by the DM participating in the investigation process via the progressive approaches. It is argued for example that when he responds to queeries by the AN as to trade-offs regarding substitution wishes or possibilities, he will have reasonable chances for considering stakeholder reactions and values.

We note that it is likely that the explicit consideration of such insight as to stakeholder values will be ignored if multiple criteria planning is not employed in connection with the design of such purchasing systems. In fact, as typical analyses of ordering and inventory systems tend to focus on the costs, such explicit criteria as customer service are essentially removed by determining a "cost of stockout per unit per day". In this way, the design problem of choosing a rule which best corresponds to the DM's preferences is reduced to a cost minimization problem in one dimensional space - with all the concommitant planning deficiencies referred to in earlier chapters.

To summarize. The context is a purchasing system with 50,000 items, 50 item groupings and 20 decision rules. For each apriori defined item grouping, the leader of the purchasing department faces the problem of choosing the "best" decision rule from the 20 alternative decision rules. The planning problem he faces now is to determine which of the four major approaches to multiple criteria planning is best suited as the framework for carrying out the MCDM analyses and for then making the choices as to decision rules. Our starting point is the context-free analysis summarized in figure 10.5.

We commenced by identifying those criteria which were considered as being most relevant for the given context. For each of these criteria we discussed the advantages and disadvantages of the four alternative planning modes. These analyses led on occasion to different results than those which we would have obtained if we had simply identified the relevant criteria and then directly employed the results from the context-independent analysis summarized in figure 10.5, i.e. without performing independent analyses of the case at hand. Figure 10.6 below summarizes our evaluation. We feel that the progressive articulation of alternatives is the most appropriate planning mode, closely followed by the progressive articulation of preferences.

	Prior art. alternat.	Prog. art. alternat.	Prior art. prefer.	Prog. art prefer.
Direct costs of DM time etc.	-2	-2	0	-2
Integration of AN and DM	0	1	0	1
Contrib. to learning	0	1	0	1
Integrates org. & personal values	1	1	0	0
Contrib. to well defined choice	1	1	0	0
Contrib. to insight as to stakeholder values	0	1	0	1

Figure 10.6 Evaluation of Modes in Relation to the Design of a Puchasing System

10.10. Summary

We have now been through quite a bit of mental gymnastics in an attempt to suggest a methodology for choosing between alternative multiple criteria planning modes. In summary, however, the message is simple: To choose a multiple criteria planning mode - as well as a specific MCDM technique - one must use a multiple perspective on planning and decision processes.

To emphasize the message, we have developed a series of criteria that we consider to be relevant in attempts to evaluate the performance of the alternative multiple criteria planning modes. Also, we have illustrated how the relative importance of these criteria depends on the specific planning context. Combining the methodological and contextual characteristics provides a systematical and rational basis for the choice of mode in a given context.

Without such a methodology - and to the best of our knowledge, serious treatment of this important meta-planning problem has not previously been available in the literature - the choice of planning mode, and thereby of MCDM techniques as well, is implicitly left to the AN as a "technical" matter. We have argued strongly that such choices can be decisive for the actual choice of an alternative at level 3 of the choice hierarchy. Therefore the choice of planning approach for significant planning problems must be considered from a managerial perspective rather than from a technical vantage point. Which is why we have taken the vantage point from the "top of the hierarchy".

However, in planning situations where the problems to be faced are not significant in nature, it may be reasonable for the DM to leave the initiative as to the investigation process to the AN. But also in this case the methodology is relevant. While in the first case, the DM and AN are able to work together from the very start, assuring consistency between choice of planning approach, MCDM technique and alternative, here the AN will have primary responsibility for carrying out the first two levels: the choice of approach and MCDM technique.

Since a manager cannot be expected to be versed in multiple criteria planning, the methodology presented here - as well as the whole idea of planning with multiple criteria - can only be practical if the analyst actively engages himself in the manager's problems. He must be able to generate a setting where the decision maker not only "feels at home" but where he is able to experience how important his participation in the process is and how greatly improved his chances will be for making decisions which are more in harmony with both the organization's values and his own, personal values. Here is a major challenge to all those who feel that they work in the fields of planning, MCDM and decision support!

10.11. Bibliographic Notes

As emphasized previously, c.f. for example chapter 1 and 5, there exist to the best of our knowledge no well developed theories about how to choose between different multiple criteria planning modes and techniques. The literature only appears to offer limited analyses as to the technical characteristics of particular techniques - e.g. as to the computational effort required - and not at all as to choice between approaches In this chapter we have attempted to indicate how this methodological issue may be addressed. In so doing, we have drawn extensively upon Bogetoft and Pruzan(1990).

Chapter 11

PLANNING WITH MULTIPLE DECISION MAKERS AND DECISION RECEIVERS

Until now, our inquiry into multiple criteria as a fundamental concept for planning has mainly been concerned with contexts involving a single decision maker.

Most significant planning situations involve multiple persons, each having their own more or less private and more or less conflicting values, their own more or less private possibilities to act, and their own more or less private perceptions of the planning context and the decision problem to be tackled. These characteristics are often sufficiently important to necessitate explicit considerations in planning.

Our aim in this chapter is two-fold. First of all, we want to provide a framework for considering such multiple criteria - multiple person planning contexts. Secondly, we want to argue and illustrate how multiple criteria thinking - if not specific multiple criteria techniques - may be useful in such settings. More specifically, we will now significantly extend the individual-oriented setting of the previous chapters and consider in turn the role of multiple criteria analysis within the context of a) decision making in a group, and b) stakeholder view of the organization.[1]

11.1. Intra-personal, Inter-personal and Systemic Conflicts

We start by presenting three notions of conflict which characterize three different frameworks for conceptualizing the planning process.

---

[1] Stakeholders are those parties who are affected by the decisions made - and whose behavior determines how successfully the decisions are implemented.

First, we have the conflict within an individual involved in a planning process. Such conflicts arise due to the fact that he must consider a multiple of noncommensurable and conflicting criteria. It is the exception rather than the rule here that a choice will be best according to all the criteria, i.e. that it will be optimal. This is the notion of conflict which we have referred to as **intrapersonal conflict** in chapter 3. Until now this has been our primary focus.

Secondly, we have the conflict **between the members of a planning group**. We referred to such conflict as **interpersonal conflict** in chapter 3. Such conflict may arise due to one or more of a variety of factors including:

a. the individuals have different values and objectives,
b. they employ different criteria when representing their objectives,
c. they have different preference relations; i.e., even if they are in agreement as to values and which criteria to employ, they are not in agreement as to which alternative is best,
d. even if they have the same underlying values, objectives and preferences they may disagree as to the likely outcomes of an action and therefore as to which action is best, and
e. they have difficulty in communicating with each other as to their values, objectives, criteria, preferences and expectations.

To illustrate, one may for example think of a group of employees who are to provide recommendations as to a new compensation scheme for their firm. The members of the group may have different values. For example, some may primarily consider their jobs as a way of earning money while others, who are more committed to the firm, care not only about compensation but also about "work-quality", their individual and professional development and the success of the firm. Also, even those focusing primarily on compensation may differ on the choice of the objectives to be followed and the criteria which are chosen to represent these objectives. Some may advocate the short run and therefore focus on present salaries and bonuses while others may advocate longer term perspectives and may focus more on the salary structure and the firm's policies as to salary in relation to experience and seniority. Thirdly, even those who focuse entirely on existing salaries and bonuses may disagree on how to "weight" or synthesize these criteria and therefore have different preferences. Some may want performance-dependent bonuses to constitute a large share of the compensation plan, while others may be more attracted by fixed salaries. Fourthly, they may have different beliefs as to how various actions, e.g. the installment of new machinery or the change of working hours, will influence the criteria. Some may expect the introduction of the new technology to lead to significantly increased productivity and bonuses. On the other hand, som may feel that management will attempt to change the bonus rules in order to take account of the productivity increases which can be attributed to the new technology. They may also argue that introducing the new technology may result in lay-offs, particularly amongst the less skilled members of the work force, and this may lead them to consider modifying the criteria already agreed upon. Finally, even though they may have largely the same values, objectives, criteria, preference relations and beliefs, they may not "speak the same language" and may therefore find it difficult to agree upon which decision to implement; all too often people who are fundamentally in agreement end up fighting each other due to cultural barriers, misinterpretation of the spoken word, or suspicion.

For any or all of the above reasons, the members of a group may experience difficulty in achieving consensus. Our contention is that **multiple criteria thinking** - if not formal multiple criteria analysis - may be a useful tool in coping with such interpersonal conflicts. We will expand on this in sections 11.2 and 11.3.

Finally, we have the conflict **between the decision makers and the decision receivers.** We will refer to such conflict as **systemic conflict.**

Such conflict is seldom considered in the traditional literature on managerial economics and operations research, as well as in the newer literature on decision support, artificial intelligence and the like. The focus is almost exclusively on the decision makers and the quality of decisions is therefore characterized solely from their point of view. For example, the literature on managerial economics rests on a notion of the "goals of the firm". But what is meant by this terminology? We argue, based upon our experience with a large number of managers as well as with students aspiring to be business leaders, that implicitly underlying this notion is the goals of the top management and/or the owners. Via the use of "carrots" such as fringe benefits and promises of promotion, as well as implicit threats as to the reduced quality of working life, employees have considerable motivation to accept the aspirations of top management/the owners as valid expressions of the "goals of the firm".

On the other hand, newer conceptions of "the firm" provided by organizational theory, systems science and applied philosophy indirectly extend this implicit notion to include not only the decision makers but the decision receivers - those affected by the decisions - as well.

In particular, we will introduce the concept of "**management by values**" to indicate that a fruitful way of interpreting and designing an organization is to regard it as a system which has as its fundamental goal the satisfaction of the goals of its subsystems, e.g. its employees, and its environment or suprasystems, e.g. its customers, suppliers, local community, and even nature, which can express its preferences without speaking. This concept can be visualized as in figure 11.1 below.

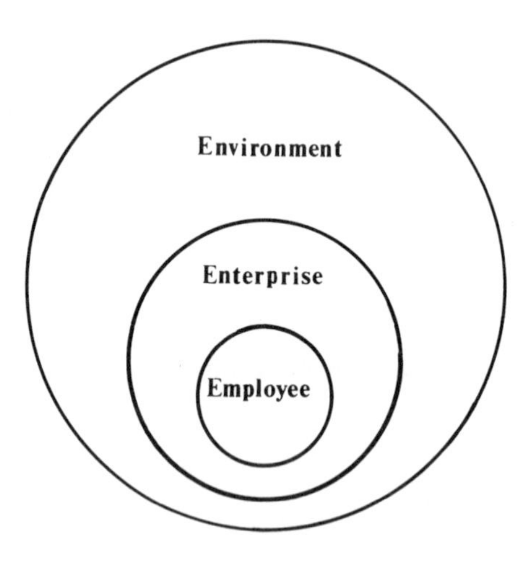

Figure 11.1 The Stakeholder Perspective

Management by values is an ongoing process where the organization identifies its stakeholders, investigates their values, and then formulates and communicates its own goals so as to also enhance these stakeholder values. Fundamtental to this concept is the postulate that in the modern pluralistic and specialized society, the best way for an organization to promote its own goals is to promote those values which are shared by the organization and its stakeholders. As is elaborated on in section 11.6, such values are basic motivations for both the organization and a stakeholder and underly their goals. For example, the values which were identified as being shared by a major Danish bank and its employees included amongst others: "Personal development", "Integration of family, leisure time and work" and "Commitment", while values identified as shared with the customers included "Mutual trust", "Human respect", "Competence" and "Quality".

Seen from the multiple criteria vantage point of management by values, shared values represent the primary links between the stakeholders and the organization and the foci of their mutual evaluations. From this point of view, promoting shared values is "good business" - economically speaking as well as from an ethical point of view.

This concept of the firm and its goals represents a radical departure from the shareholder view implicitly underlying most economic theories of the firm and has significant implications for its organization, management and planning. The focus is lifted from the bottom line to the ethical line to be followed. Such broader views of the "goals of the firm" can be traced to the notion of **autopoiesis** developed in biology, in the metaphorical translation of this notion to that of **self-organization** employed in organization theory, as well as to the notion of **stakeholders** which has become a central theme in the newer field of business ethics. We expand on these themes in sections 11.4 to 11.6.

11.2. Inter-personal Conflict: Game Theory and Social Choice Theory

Roughly speaking, two major theoretical frameworks are employed in the economics and operations research literature to analyze decision making where more than one individual is involved. These are game theory and social choice theory. We will very briefly consider these two theoretical frameworks for interpersonal conflict before presenting our own major theses.

Game theory is a discipline which models conflicts and their resolution via mathematical analysis. It essentially assumes that each participant in a conflict is only interested in his own results and that these results depend upon both his own choices and the choices made by those with whom he is in conflict, i.e. the other "players". The theory is both descriptive and normative; it focuses upon the ability to predict how such conflicts will be solved, i.e. which choices the players will make as well as which choices or strategies "rational" players should make.

Game theoretical models of conflict are highly stylized and simplified. This may be acceptable, even necessary, in theoretical studies aiming to provide partial insights into basic micro-economic phenomena. From a practical perspective, however, many of the simplifications are rather severe. The following are some of the basic assumptions underlying the theory.

Each player is assumed to know his own preferences with respect to any possible outcome as well as his alternative actions. Also, he must know the preferences and possibilities of his opponents, or at least have clearcut expectations in case he does not exactly know about these preferences and alternative actions. Futhermore, the communication among the players is usually assumed to be very restricted so as to enable the theorist to predict the outcome. From this point of view, game theory has quite a different focus than the perspective to be presented below, where we consider individuals **investigating and communicating** so as to arrive at a joint decision; the emphasis will be on a consensus-promoting process rather than on the specific implications of any particular decision.

Another major difference between the game theoretical approach to interpersonal conflict and that to be presented here is the complete neglect by the former of a significant criterion characterizing most group efforts - the **desire to jointly arrive at a decision.** As we will see, this limitation of game theory also characterizes social choice theory; both frameworks are based on a narrow conception of humans as selfish, ego-centered and willing to act in opposition to broadly accepted behavioral norms.

A third major difference between game theory and the approach to be advocated here is that game theory usually assumes that there is only one criterion to be employed to measure the preferences of the participants. In line with the **multiple criteria** approach, we would argue that this assumption is very delimiting from a practical point of view. By ignoring the inherent multiple criteria framework for the individuals' evaluations of decision making it provides a gross over-simplification of reality. Again, this simplification may be acceptable in theoretical studies. Indeed, it turns out that extensions of existing game models to allow for multiple criteria do not in general produce significantly new insights. It is, however, an unacceptable assumption when we take a more practical perspective - and in particular when we do not want to delimit ourselves to static models of conflict resolution but focus instead on the dynamic investigation-communication-choice process.

Social choice theory considers the properties of alternative voting rules and other formal procedures used to make collective choices. It assumes that when a decision is to be made, all the members of a group are presented with the same set of alternatives from which one is to be chosen. It furthermore assumes that each individual is able to rank these alternatives according to his preferences. Starting with these assumptions, the theory provides a series of theoretical results and a framework for the analysis of the performance of alternative voting rules.

An example of such a voting rule is "the alternative receiving the most votes wins". Another example is "the alternative receiving a majority of votes wins, and if no alternative receives a majority in the first round of voting, the two top scorers participate in a run-off vote".

Evaluating the performance of alternative voting rules may include consideration of such factors as anonymity (it makes no difference who you are, a vote is a vote), neutrality (it makes no difference what an alternative is named, it is only its characteristics which count), and independence of irrelevant alternatives (the relative ranking of any two alternatives is not affected by the introduction of any other alternative). In principle, the individuals participating in the voting can arrive at their individual rankings of the alternatives by performing some sort of multiple criteria analysis. But when they participate in the actual group choice process, it is with no reference whatsoever to the underlying criteria, all that counts is their resultant rankings.

Our approach differs from that of social choice theory in three significant ways.

First, although voting may be the best democratic procedure for making decisions in larger social systems - by providing well-defined and broadly accepted means of making decisions in face of disagreement as to ends and means - this will not usually be the case when "small" groups are involved, e.g. a group of managers who are to decide upon a production and sales plan. In such settings, turning to voting should be a last resort. Voting replaces active human involvement in decision making by the mechanical application of a rule. It thereby ignores the considerable value of the **communication process** in groups; in general, the sharing of views, evaluations, doubts and preference information will lead to modified preferences and hereby to quite different decisions than the blind application of a rule which can aggregate a series of votes into a decision. Group decisions resulting from a communication process which promotes consensus are better in the sense that they reflect a "collective rationality", and that they therefore have a greater chance of being successfully implemented.

Consider for example the case of three people who are to decide upon whether to choose alternative A, B or C. Assume that two of the three participants have a very slight preference for A over B and strong preferences for B over C. Assume too that it is vital for the third party that A is not chosen; he prefers B over C and both of these extremely strongly over A. Under many formal voting rules, A would be chosen, which would be disasterous for the third party. If the three individuals are to work together in the future, this could lead to serious problems. On the other hand, if the parties were able to communicate as to their preferences based upon their underlying values, their objectives and the criteria they choose to represent their objectives, it is not unlikely that B would be chosen leading to the establishment of a good working climate. More generally, we consider it to be a major drawback of social choice theory that all information on the individuals' intensities of preference and the reasons for their likes and dislikes is ignored.

This leads directly to the second major criticism of social choice theory from our multiple criteria planning perspective. Social Choice theory presumes that all the individuals participating in the voting have the same list of alternatives. In other words, the set of alternatives exist prior to the decision making and is given. In contrast, we have assumed throughout that there is a strong, dynamic interrelationship between our wishes and our possibilities, or, expressed in the terms of our modelling, between the alternatives and our preferences. Although the four taxonomical approaches do not directly focus upon the **creative design** of new alternatives, this concept permeates the presentation[2]. The idea that new alternatives can be identified during the planning process is fundamental to the concept of conflict dissolution, i.e. a new alternative is identified that all the involved parties can agree upon. Such an approach to conflict may be far more inspiring and synergetic than taking as given the existing set of alternatives and then attempting to solve the conflict by finding the group's best compromise solution as defined by some formal procedure.

While the above criticism of Social Choice theory was based on its treament of the alternatives, the third major criticism of Social Choice theory as seen from a multiple criteria perspective deals with the notion of criteria. When the members of a group are to jointly arrive at a decision, then a new criterion enters the scene. A criterion which is absent when each individual in splendid isolation simply ranks the alternatives. The new criterion is the desire to end up with a choice which is the product of **consensus**, and not just the results of an impersonal voting rule - or of a dictatorial assertion of power by a boss. The ability of the group members to say with conviction and pride "we have decided" can be of vital importance. It can be considered to be a new criterion, independent of the substantive criteria that the individual members may have reflected upon when making their rankings **before** they started participating in the group's planning process.[3]

[2] Even the prior articulation of alternatives assumes that the set of alternatives to be presented to the DM is based upon considerable knowledge as to his preferences; such knowledge is a precondition for the AN being able to employ the notion of efficiency as a filter when determining which of the alternatives should be presented.

[3] This criticism can be considered as an extension of our discussion in section 6.2 as to the possibility of experiencing opportunity costs if relevant criteria are not explicitly included in the determination of preferences.

This concludes our brief discussion of game theory and social choice theory. Although it would be exciting now to be able to describe an existing mathematical-theoretical and operational framework for multiple-person, multiple-criteria planning which included consideration of the ideas expressed above, we will desist from so doing. The reason is simple: although there is a huge analytically oriented literature dealing with decision making from the point of view of the individual, there is a dearth of such literature which formally deals with multiple-critieria, multiple-person contexts. This laconical statement implies that at present, planning in such contexts is mainly based on organization theory, soft systems methodologies, common sense, overly simplified, ad hoc tools and procedures, tradition and power. We will therefore lower our ambitions and discuss instead how a multiple criteria approach to interpersonal conflict can enrichen the process of planning in a group.

11.3. Multiple Criteria and The Structuring of Group Planning

Until now we have employed the term "group" in an intuitive manner. We will therefore briefly elaborate on this term before discussing how explicit consideration of multiple criteria can contribute to planning in a group context.

From the perspective of structuring planning, we will loosely define a group as any set of individuals all of whom jointly recognize and accept their responsibility for the planning process and for making a choice. Examples of a group could be the members of a family, a school board, a project team, a committee, a legislature, or the board of directors of a company. In each case however, the "groupness" is determined according to whether or not the individuals are oriented towards making a collective decision; even though the members of a project team may physically be together when they go to a bar after work, they are no longer a "group" from our planning perspective. On the other hand, note that membership of a group does not presume geographical proximity; with modern communications technology, group members can very well participate in solving or dissolving their interpersonnel conflicts without having face-to-face proximity.

The number of members is often used to characterize "groupness". In everyday language we generally think of a group in terms of anywhere from a few people to say upwards of a hundred members. This is really a communications parameter which is closely related to the willingness to accept responsibility for collective decisions. We will not attempt to delimit the membership of a group and to say that any collection of individuals greater than a given number may not be a group, while for a number less than such a threshold value, the members form a group. What will be decisive for our purposes is whether or not: **a) the members recognize and accept their joint membership and the planning responsibility which follows from membership, and b) are therefore able and willing to enter into active dialogue as to the decision to be made**. Clearly then, this communications condition leads to the conclusion that a board of directors interacting in the process of deciding who should be the next president of a company is functioning as a "group", while the members of a nation going to the polls to elect a new president are not a group.

Within this broad framework, we commence with a reservation; we are not suggesting that **formalized multiple criteria analyses** should in general be an integral part of the planning process in a group. In principle, in each case the expected benefits of implementing multiple criteria analyses would have to be compared with the "costs" involved. In other words, just as in the preceding chapter, where we considered choices between alternative approaches to multiple criteria planning, we now face a new, meta-level multiple criteria decision problem. Deciding whether a multiple criteria approach to group planning is to be recommended, and if so, how, is itself a new and complex group decision problem characterized by multiple criteria. However, it is quite unlikely that this meta-level multiple criteria problem is amenable to solution as such and will therefore in practice be solved based on intuition, experience etc.

We do suggest however that no matter whether or not formal multiple criteria analyses are performed within the context of interpersonal conflicts, even simple, institutionalized **multiple criteria thinking** can make considerable contributions to the investigative, communicative and choice aspects of the planning process. More specifically, let us imagine that the group has been formed, that a preliminary, loose problem formulation implicitly exists, and that this formulation includes a preliminary list of alternatives. Then, we suggest that the prescriptions summarized in figure 11.2 below should guide the planning process.

> 1. Each participant should determine for himself which values, objectives and criteria he feels are relevant to the planning process and the decision to be made.
>
> 2. The participants should openly discuss their objectives and then focus on the criteria which they choose to measure the quality of the group's proposed actions.
>
> 3. As a means of structuring the discussion, it may be helpful to generate a matrix of evaluations of the different alternatives with respect to the different criteria.
>
> 4. Based upon these discussions and analyses new alternatives should be identified (or created) and evaluated.
>
> 5. Based upon such discussions and analyses, a "collective" choi-ce should be arrived at.

Figure 11.2 Structuring of Group Planning

We consider now these five prescriptions in the order of their presentation.

We commence with the suggestion that each participant should **determine for himself** which values, objectives and criteria he feels are relevant to the process. It is our experience that this can best be done if the **organization** is value oriented. Although just how such a value orientation can be promoted lies outside the scope of the present text, we provide some hints later on. In any case, if this process is to be meaningful, it must be carried out in an atmosphere where the participants are used to considering and to discussing the interplay between their own personal values and those of the organization. We note at this point, that while many organizations use objectives as a steering tool, it is extremely seldom that organizations stimulate their members to consider this interplay between personal and organizational values.

It is quite difficult at times to distinguish between personal desires and aspirations and organizational goals. We therefore argue that each participant in the group planning process should first determine for himself which very personal objectives are at stake. Such objectives could e.g. include his prestige, power, dignity, income etc. He may not want to explicitly introduce such confidential matters into the group planning process for the very reason that by so doing he may adversely affect his aspirations, for example as to prestige, power, and dignity. His reflections here must balance his desires for privacy with the ensuing risks of contributing to a planning process which results in what he personally may regard as an unattractive choice. We postulate that it is the tension between an individual's unarticulated desires and the risk of having these desires thwarted via a rational planning process which often motivates dishonesty and the strategic use of information or attempts to close a discussion by appeals to experience, intutition or the use of hierarchical power. In other words, when a participant in the process does not explicitly introduce his important personal values and objectives via his choice of explicit criteria, he may resort to other means to avoid the potential opportunity losses which could result. As demonstrated earlier, efficient - and perhaps preferred - solutions can be ignored in the search process if criteria which affect the decision maker's preferences are omitted.

It is our contention that the leadership of an organization has a major responsibility for minimizing such possible inefficiencies. Management can strive to live up to this responsibility by actively contributing to the establishment of an environment which promotes the integration of personal and organizational values. Here too we find an expression of the concept "management by values".

Also, we should like to emphasize that the relevant criteria are not given once and for all. In fact the consideration of which criteria are relevant for one's preferences in a given context is one of the most vital elements of the planning process and can lead to the creative identification of new and more preferred alternatives as well as to insight on how to synthesize the criteria into an evaluation of the alternatives.

The criteria can include objective and quantitatively measurable attributes as well as more subjective and qualitative attributes. We note that in traditional approaches emphasizing simplicity and uni-criterion analysis, the more subjective and qualitative attributes are most often absent from explicit analyses. They are typically only employed to modify a decision which has been made based upon the more objective, quantitative criteria.

This leads to the second prescription presented in figure 11.2. dealing with the **group's** identification of relevant objectives and criteria. We suggest that in a concrete planning context, the participants should openly discuss which objectives are relevant and which criteria should be chosen to reflect these objectives and measure the quality of the alternatives. Note that in contrast to the first prescription which referred to an individual's consideration of values, objectives and criteria, we purposefully ignore the more fundamental value aspect here. Although the discussion of the relevant objectives, will directly or indirectly be based upon the participating individuals' underlying values, it could be disastorous to presume that each time a group was to make a decision, it should start by reflecting on basic values. Experience and tradition are valuable because they permit us to act without having to investigate and evaluate; requiring existential searches each time a decision is to be made could not only be time-prohibitive, it could lead to undue egoism and conflict. At the group level, the focus is usually on objectives and criteria. However, the more strategic and fundamental the decisions to be made, the more relevant it is that values become central to the discussion.

The open discussion as to objectives and criteria can help weed out misunderstandings including the possibility that apparently different words or measures are employed to cover the same underlying objectives. For example, in considering the possible location for a new major branch office of a firm, one member of the group may suggest proximity to schools and cultural facilities as a criterion to be included, another may suggest the availability of attractive housing while a third may suggest the rate of unemployment in the region. All three members of the group may in fact be suggesting these as surrogate measures for an overall objective: maximizing the ability to attract skilled labor and middle management (and their families) from the existing organization, as well as other qualified personnel to the localities being considered. A high level of unemployment can e.g. be of importance with respect to the ability to attract local workers. But it may also be an indication, that members of current employees' households may find it difficult to get a job, thus making the locality less attractive as seen from the point of view of the current employees. Discussion of the criteria may lead to a consensus as to what is important and what is not, and as to which measures are best suited to expressing the degree to which objectives are met.

In addition, such discussion of the objectives and criteria can lead to a recognition of certain factors which some members of the group had not considered. No matter whether the criteria are directly included in a formal evaluation procedure or not, these dialogues as to objectives and criteria contribute significantly to the investigative and communicative aspects of the planning process and to the achievement of consensus. It is just such consensus-promoting activities which are ignored in game theory and social choice theory.

Although just how such communication activities could be enhanced lies outside the scope of this text, we now very briefly relate some of our own experiences with middel- and top management in several Scandinavian concerns, unions and public service organizations.[4] In all cases, after some basic presentation of the notions of multiple criteria planning and of management by values, groups of from 7 to 10 people were formed. The members of the groups were first asked to identify and rank their 5 most important personal values in relation to family and friends, perhaps choosing them from the list of values presented below in figure 11.3. They were then asked to attempt to agree upon such a ranking for the group as a whole.

[4] The experiences referred to are the product of a close collaboration between one of the authors and his colleague, Thorbjörn Meyer, who, as project leader, also was actively involved in the development and implementation of the Ethical Accounting Statement described in section 11.6.

Value	Synonyms/Explanations
Unity	- sense of belonging, co-operation, team spirit
Comfortable life	
Pleasure	- enjoyable, leisurely life
Exciting life	- a challenging life
Peace	- non-violence, tranquility
Social recognition	
Love	- care for others, humaneness
Security	- safety, confidence
Freedom	- independence
True friendship	
Wisdom	- a mature understanding of life
Inner harmony	- stability, character
Self-respect	- self-esteem
Equality	- brotherhood
Meaningness	- a sense of purpose
Openness	- being frank in communication, open dialogue
Courage	- fearlessness
Monetary wealth	
Faith	
Compassion	
Truth	- honesty, integrity, true to oneself
Trust	
Happiness	
Salvation	
Spiritual insight	
Imagination	- creativity, innovation
Accomplishment	- a sense of achievement
Power	- authority
Attunement	- shared beliefs, values
Discipline	- self-discipline
Development	- growth, self-development
Commitment	- focus

Figure 11.3 List of Private Values

The participants were quite active, and in most cases the members of a group were able to arrive at a consensus as to their personal values. There were often similarities between the various groups as well. As a rule, the ensuing discussions as to definitions, motivations and the like were rather lively and the participants expressed satisfaction at being able to openly discuss their personal values without being considered egotistical and without any one feeling threatened. Then, several hours later, the same exercise was repeated, only this time the participants in each group were to attempt to arrive at consensus as to their actual perceptions of the organization's values. It was underlined that what was sought here were the organization's values as indirectly evidenced via its decisions, and not idealized expressions of what the organization's values should be. Here, too, the groups were very active and once again the members of a group were, as a rule, able to agree upon a group ranking.

What was startling on several occasisions were the gaps between the individuals' expressions of personal values and their perceptions of their organization's values. On several occasions this process eventually led to a major reorientation in the organization and to a far more explicit and energetic consideration of the importance of managing by values; the idea of "schizophrenic" employees having personal values out of tune with their organization's values was considered to be unfortunate and unhealthy for both parts.

The exercises referred to are but one way we have experimented in promoting individual insight as to personal values as well as the communication process regarding objectives and criteria at the group level. This theme will be greatly expanded in sections 11.4 and 11.5 which deal with multiple criteria planning within a framework of systemic conflict and ethics.

The third prescription in figure 11.2. emphasizes that when structuring the discussion in the group, it may be helpful to generate **a matrix of evaluations** of the different alternatives with respect to the different criteria. The matrix could for example have the alternatives listed as rows $i = 1, \ldots, m$ and the criteria listed as columns $j = 1, \ldots, n$. The individual elements of the matrix could then consist of some measure of how well the i'th alternative lives up to the j'th criterion. This may require staff members to carry out analyses in cases where the criterion is of a complex technical or economic nature. For more qualitative criteria it may simply suffice to have the participants make subjective evaluations, for example on a simple point scale from 1 to 10, and to then attempt to reach agreement upon these evaluations within the group. We note too, that if there are many alternatives, such a matrix of evaluations could be supplemented by the cross-effect matrix introduced in chapter 3.

The fourth recommendation in figure 11.2. is that based upon these discussions, the possibility of **generating new alternatives** should be considered. Quite often an open discussion of values, objectives and criteria can lead to the realization that either the existing problem formulation is inappropriate or that the alternatives being considered should be supplemented by new ones. In other words, the discussion can lead to a more creative design-oriented planning process where alternatives evolve via the consideration of our preferences - and vice versa. Conflicts of value are in fact a presupposition for the rational synthesis of what is desired with what is possible, which is said to be the very essence of the creative process.

While most attempts to introduce creativity into the planning process focus upon creativity enhancing techniques, e.g. brain storming, we have experienced that the open discussion of values and criteria - both personal and organizational - can make a significant contribution to a creative environment and to radically new approaches to the identification of alternatives - and therefore perhaps to the consensual dissolution of interpersonal conflicts.

Note the significant difference in this conceptual framework and those provided by game theory and social choice theory; these theories presume that the alternatives and values are given once and for all and thereby negate the possibility of dissolving group conflict via the group's own generation of new alternatives or its recognition of new criteria during the planning process.

Carrying out the recommendations of the first four steps in figure 11.2. is not identical to carrying out a multiple criteria analysis corresponding to one of the four approaches in our taxonomy. For example, the activities suggested do not directly include identifying efficient alternatives or a compromise solution. The point here is not that it is necessary to use formal means of evaluation to contribute to developing a collectively rational choice. Rather that a structuring of the planning problem as suggested can lead to much richer communication and insight than otherwise would be possible. And that this may pave the way for deciding on a common course of action which reflects the individual's as well as the group's preferences, c.f. our fifth and final "recommendation" in figure 11.2.

In addition, if the first two prescriptions lead to consensus as to objectives and criteria, this may provide the necessary background for carrying out more formal multiple criteria analyses in the context of group decision making, for example based on the taxonomical approach developed in chapters 5-9. In such a setting, characterized by open communication as to objectives and criteria - and perhaps as to personal and organizational values as well - the "group" may gradually come to function as an "individual" and the boundry between intra- and interpersonal conflict becomes amorphous. It is just such a setting which we will return to shortly in our discussion of what we refer to as "multiple criteria, group decision support systems".

It is clear that carrying out the steps in figure 11.2 can be very time consuming. Not only due to the fact that the activities involved may take time. But that they may make the planning process far more complex than otherwise would have been the case, where perhaps a participant with charismatic qualities is able to sell his intuitive arguments directly. Or where traditional uni-criterion investment analysis, performed by a staff member, may simply lead to accepting that alternative which appears to have the highest expected rate of return based on assumptions as to the time profile of costs and sales. Or where individual power is effectively employed to transform the group planning process aiming at efficiency and consensus into a dictatorial setting, where time is not wasted on the investigative and communicative processes. The active participation of the participants and the ensuing discussions of values, objectives, criteria and preferences can thus lead to procedures which are far more time consuming than those where charisma, financial analysis and power are the dominating characteristics of the planning process. And at times it may require someone at a higher level to stop the discussions and to expedite the generation of a decision.

On the other hand, it is postulated that for significant decision problems and strategic planning, the inclusion of such a multiple criteria framework will lead to far greater individual insight, to plans which receive broader support amongst those involved in the planning process, and to an improved experience of being part of an organization so that "the goals of the firm" acquire a new, more motivating and existential meaning. In this interactive manner, the gap between analysis and decision making and between analysts and decision makers can significantly be reduced. And the focus upon problems as givens, can be replaced by the awareness that problem formulations do not exist per se, they are the products of our cognition and action. Such insight can therefore lead to a greater emphasis upon creating new possibilities instead of only on solving given problems. Underlying the exposition is the postulate that insight into what we want (our values), and into our possibilities (our alternatives) is a far more valuable output of the planning process than the "solution" to a given problem.

We conclude this discussion of multiple criteria planning and the structuring of group planning with some perspectives as to developments in the 1990's. We do so by discussing the embryonic work which is being carried out in what we might call "**multiple criteria, group decision support systems**" (MCGDSS). This research builds upon the developments in the more established fields of MCDM and "decision support systems" (DSS).

Commencing in the late 1970's, research on DSS has provided a valuable conceptual framework for the design of computer oriented planning systems which attempt to harness the knowledge and preferences of a decision maker. This work has also provided a background for current developments in related fields such as "expert systems". A decision support system is often defined as any computer-based, interactive system that supports decision makers in solving problems with varying degrees of structure. Therefore, computer-based interactive systems designed to operationalize the progressive articulation of a decision maker's alternatives and/or preferences could be classified as decision support systems. Several such systems - mainly of rather questionable quality - have been commercially promoted in recent years and have been referred to as "multiple criteria decision support systems". The literature on DSS indicates a growing awareness of the need for integrating research and existing know-how as to MCDM and DSS. In fact, this may be considered one of the main motivations underlying the present text.

Of even greater relevance here however is the challenge of how to integrate multiple criteria analyses and what is now referred to as "group decision support systems" (GDSS), i.e. interactive computer models which extend the notion of DSS to what we have referred to as interpersonal conflict. The resulting multiple criteria group decision support systems could provide a broad framework for communication as to values, objectives, criteria, preferences, and alternatives, as well as for the search, evaluation and choice processes. The perspective here is far broader than just MCDM and interactive computer models. Physical and social settings will be integral components of such systems. Their design will not only include appropriate software but also appropriate environments, for example specially designed meeting rooms, communications technology and procedures, scenario techniques and the like. Furthermore, their implementation will require a new variety of analyst who will be knowledgeable with respect to multiple criteria analyses, group dynamics and management behavior and who will be a highly qualified mediator and communicator. Such an analyst will, in addition to more technical and analytical functions, be a catalyst for the identification of values and objectives and their expressions in terms of criteria as well as for the promotion of consensus and the solution of interpersonal conflicts of value.

11.4. Systemic Conflict and Ethics

In section 11.1 we briefly introduced the notion of systemic conflict. By this we meant the value conflicts that arise between those who make decisions, e.g. the top management in a firm, and those parties who are affected by the decisions, what we referred to as the **decision receivers**, e.g. the employees, the customers, the suppliers, and the local community. Virtually all literature on planning is oriented towards decision makers and decision making. The present section temporarily reorients this vantage point 180 degrees and then proceeds to integrate both perspectives within a framework of systemic conflict and ethics. This sets the stage for a vastly expanded vista for planning with multiple criteria. We conclude by demonstrating how it becomes "good" business to focus on both the economical and the ethical bottom lines.

We commence by expanding a bit on the concept of **stakeholders.** These are the more-or-less homogeneous groups of decision receivers who are affected by an organization's actions and whose reactions may affect the successful implementation and realization of the decisions. Of late the stakeholder concept has begun to win acceptance as a more meaningful and broader frame of reference than the traditional **shareholder** view of the firm. This later perspective focuses only on the economic situation of those who own a share of the enterprise, and hitherto has provided the implicit background for education in management and, in particular, in accounting and auditing.

The valuable insights which can be gained as to how an enterprise's actions affect others and how their reactions to these actions may affect the enterprise are virtually ignored in most of the literature on the economics of the firm and operations research. Due perhaps to the relative ease with which closed, power-oriented and profit-generating hierarchical systems can be formally modelled and analyzed, these disciplines continue to promote virtues and to refine techniques which are based upon a naive conception of planning. In so doing, they have not been able to transcend their own self-established boundries so as to be receptive to the developments in organization theory, systems science and applied philosopy. The "real world" of customers, employees, suppliers, financial institutions, unions, special interest groups, the community, the environment etc. has developed far more dynamically than the analytically oriented academic disciplines - which appear to have sought legitimacy, recognition and resources by specializing even more and seeking more detailed knowledge rather than systemic vision and understanding. Therefore, the naive analytical approaches of micro economics and operations research may not only be inappropriate in the context of social systems; we will also argue that they may be unethical.

The following are three postulates as to why a multiple criteria - multiple stakeholder perspective is highly relevant for planning in the modern organization:

First of all, **from an organizational perspective,** an appreciation of the stakeholders' multiple values, objectives and criteria is a prerequisite for organizational success.

By emphasizing stakeholders' interests we do not imply that the traditional economic measures of performance should no longer be of major interest. Rather that the uni-dimensional picture of efficiency provided by profits can lead to considerable inefficiencies seen from the point of view of the enterprise's long range viability and development. Both within and without the enterprise there are values which the enterprise must serve if it is to promote its own values. Employees are not simply value-less puppets filling certain roles and performing certain functions. Their talent, dedication and creativity are the enterprise's most valuable asset. Only via their development can the enterprise develop. Customers are not simply impersonal objects whose purchasing behavior can be calculated and manipulated. They are the enterprise's most important investors. Only through their needs and their sense of quality can the enterprise develop. And quality cannot be produced without their help. The stakeholders must in fact hold a stake in the enterprise. This leads to new ideas as to just what an enterprise is and what its goals are.

Secondly, **from the perspective of the individual**, the organization's appreciation of stakeholder interests is a prerequisite for his being able to integrate his own personal values with those of the organization.

It is our experience that employees, and in particular leaders, quite often are intellectually aware of - but most often sublimate - the fact that they behave in a schizophrenic manner. Like modern day Dr. Jekyls and Mr. Hydes they feel compelled to suppress the many broad values that shape their attitudes and behavior in private life and to replace them by a far more restricted bottom-line orientation when at work. Even if they would like to behave in accord with their personal convictions and feelings of social responsibility, the demands of the market, their peers and the shareholders only permit them very limited degrees of freedom for deviating from an orientation towards optimizing profits and shareholder equity. It requires a strong, charismatic and communicatively talented leader to be able to justify decisions which lead to poorer short term economic results than otherwise could have been obtained. A stakeholder orientation is a condition for a decision maker to be able to integrate his personal values with those of the organization - and for him to become a "whole" person.

But the integration of personal and organizational values is not just a matter of importance for management. The lack of such an orientation results in top-down organizations where the generation of the "organization's values" are not a result of an autopoietic (self-organizing) process, but rather are expressions of the owners' and/or top management's private aspirations. A result is a lack of sensitivity as to the needs of the members of the organization for experiencing a harmonious balance between **their** personal values and those of the organization. This was a major factor underlying the shocking discrepancy between these two sets of values which we referred to in connection with the discussion of figure 11.3 in the preceding section.

Thirdly **from an ethical perspective,** the supression of a multiple criteria - multiple stakeholder orientation leads to unethical behavior.

Ethics has appeared on the management scene as a response to the insight that traditional planning tools are not sufficient for coping with the challenges facing the modern enterprise. These tools are in the hands of specialists who feel little need for transcending their own narrow outlooks. They thrive when their methods and models become even more specialized and precise. It is easier to grow and to refine one's methods if one is able to ignore the "whole"; this is the real meaning of the economists' "ceteris paribus - everything else being equal" assumption, which again is an implicit expression of the focus of the "hard" sciences on controlled experiments. In their enthusiasm for developing their disciplinary values, experts tend to ignore - and to be inconsiderate of - other values. The increased dependence on specialists has therefore not only contributed to solving well-structured problems. It has contributed as well to creating new, more complex problems of integrating and coordinating different values and perspectives as well as different interest groups.

The development of the specialist society has been paralleled by the development of the pluarlistic society. Earlier, one could presume a reasonable degree of wide spread agreement as to rules of behavior, even amongst those who broke them. In a society which is fragmented into many subcultures, there is little agreement as to what is right or wrong. Behavioral norms are no longer a source of agreement and community but of conflict and fragmentation. When there are many opinions as to right and wrong, it is not sufficient to appeal to intuition or to any single group's norms. This underlies the modern appeal to ethics.

Philosophers usually consider morals to be concrete rules for how one should behave, while they consider ethics to be an attempt to justify these rules. We propose a new distinction such that ethics can be constructively employed and fill the vacuum created when morals lose their societal "we".

When many groups have their own morals, no group can prove that its view of right and wrong is right. Therefore, consensus cannot be based upon any one group's values. What is common for the many groups cannot be found **within** each group but must be sought **between** them. Ethics is therefore not just yet another set of moral rules. It contributes to a holistic perspective by focusing attention on agreement as to shared values. In this way it can integrate differences and create consensus out of conflict. Such an integration is vital for both the modern society and the modern enterprise. It can expand the narrow vistas which result from specialist and subcultural perspectives.

Idealistically speaking, we will call a decision **ethical** if it is accepted by the stakeholders affected by it, and we will call a planning process ethical if attempts are actively made to receive approval for a decision from the relevant decision receivers.

Ethics is a very special kind of planning tool. Normally, a tool can be employed without our getting personally involved; tool and person are ordinarily two different things. But this is not true in the case of ethics. Here the user as a person identifies himself with the tool. If he employs it instrumentally to manipulate others, i.e. if he considers himself to be above the ethical perspective, then ethics will rapidly degenerate to cynical power and profit maximization. Therefore it is a bit risky to introduce the notion of organizational ethics as though it were yet another tool in the manipulative toolbag of ice-cold management philosophy, where what counts is not if ethics is valid but if it is effective. Our theme is just the opposite: ethics is only effective if it is valid. And whether it is valid becomes manifest when ethical considerations collide with other considerations, in particular profits. It follows that multiple criteria planning is a prerequisite for the holistic perspective of organizational ethics.

It is not, however, sufficient to argue that planning behavior is ethical if it is "holistic" or "systemic". What matters here is **what** is meant by the "whole" or the "system" - and **who means** it. For example, if ethics is only unfolded within a group, while the relationships of the group to its external stakeholders are ruthless, as is the case for example within mafia families, then it will be difficult to use the word "ethics". There is in other words a demand that ethical considerations cannot be restricted to those whom we depend upon for economic success. To give another example, imagine that the top management of an enterprise decides that the time is ripe for it to introduce ethics as a steering tool and pronounces an ethical codex as "our organization's ethical guidelines". In that case it will be misguiding to use the word ethics. When the question is "who" is to determine what the whole is, there is once again a demand that this must be decided upon by the parties who may be affected by the decisions. If the members of an organization are not involved in identifying the organization's values, they will find it difficult to speak of "**our** organization's ethical guidelines".

Determining who are the stakeholders and who is to represent them must evolve from a dialogue. Just as the dialogue must determine which values are shared by the enterprise and its stakeholders and which criteria can be employed to represent these values, it must also determine its participants. There is no party **outside** the dialogue which can be appealed to as an authority and there is no single part **within** the dialogue that has the power to determine what is shared and preferred. What is considered to be the "whole" can not be determined by an elite, but must be determined by those parties that make and receive a decision.

In this way, notions of ethics and whole are intertwined; they combine the right to be different with the duty to respect others' differences. No one part can impose its values and preferences on others. Therefore, decision makers and decision receivers must participate in the ongoing dialogue which identifies and attunes their shared values. It follows, that what is ethical is contextually dependent and changes with time and place.

For all of the above reasons, it follows that there is a need for developing channels of communication as well as operational tools which can promote a multiple criteria - multiple stakeholder evaluation of an organization's activities. We will now discuss how that can be achieved, the difficulties to be encountered and the role to be played by multiple criteria analyses.

11.5. Multiple Criteria Planning, Management by Values, and Ethics

In order to integrate ethical considerations into the enterprise, management must initiate a process of inquiry which considers a series of existential questions; these deal with the enterprise's identity (who are "we"?), its values (what are our basic motivations?) and how the organization best can attune its values with those of its stakeholders. This goal of attunement presumes in turn that the enterprise identifies its stakeholders (whom do we affect by our decisions and who affects us?) as well as their values (what are their basic desires?). Considerable effort will be required here to determine who are the appropriate representatives for the stakeholders, to develop a common vocabulary as to shared values, and to establish appropriate lines of communication. The process will lead to demands on the organization's leadership which cannot be delegated to specialists or fulfilled by reliance on money, hierarchical power and charisma.

In comparison with the two types of conflict considered earlier (intra- and interpersonal conflicts), systemic conflict between decision makers and decision receivers is the most difficult to tackle. In the case of intra- and interpersonal conflicts, it is possible to carry out the required dialogues - with one's self and/or with the others. The individual can explore his own values and goals, define his own criteria and "converse" with himself as to his preferences. And a group of such individuals can meet and construct a frame of reference based on their relevant values, objectives and criteria. But as far as systemic conflicts are concerned, there exist several **barriers which inhibit dialogue** between decision makers and decision receivers.

Within the enterprise the hierarchical distribution of power and responsibility between organizational sub-units at different levels can impede the investigation of shared values; individuals speak with different weight, irregardless of their personal qualities. Between the enterprise and its external stakeholders, different opinions as to what the relevant "whole" is can impede communication as to common values. It can be difficult to agree as to who the stakeholders are and who represents them. One cannot e.g. attempt to obtain the approval of all the customers of an enterprise - and who is the correct representative for the environment or coming generations?

Such difficulties will be inherent in a large and complex organization. If it has many types of employees, operates in geographically and culturally heterogeneous settings, and has many and diversified customers, then the shear size and complexity present great challenges to the communication process underlying our notion of organizational ethics. It is impossible in such a setting to have a dialogue with all the stakeholders - and even communicating with broadly representative groups may be a very time and resource consuming process.

Furthermore, many of the stakeholders will not be used to - or be motivated for - taking responsibility for a whole, they may not feel that they belong to. They can be suspicious of words such as "ethics" and consider it to be a new management PR number which in some clever new way is aimed at getting them to contribute more to the firm's profits or to swallow a bitter pill without protest. If, for example, the relationship between the enterprise on the one hand and society, the employees and the local community on the other hand, has been characterized by mutual distrust, it will not be easy to establish the necessary dialogue. The parties involved are afraid to get into a clinch. And the dialogue cannot be carried out on an "objective" basis; emotions, politics and culture enter the picture. A common language does not exist apriori; it must be constructed. But that it can be constructed is a condition for, e.g. management, shop stewards, environmentalists and members of the local community to be able to carry out dialogues which are not just infighting based on prejuidice and mistrust, but which promote the identification and attunement of shared values and the attainment of consensus.

It is primarily here that multiple criteria analysis enters the scene. Without a common frame of reference in the form of values, objectives and their expression in terms of operational criteria, it will not be possible for management and the stakeholders to evaluate the ethical quality of the organization's operations and plans.

Thus, the integration of ethical considerations into the enterprise places new, idealistic demands on management as to openness and communication. It must formulate principles for identifying and balancing the many stakeholders' interests, for organizing the enterprise as to be ethically oriented and for establishing an ongoing process of communication between the enterprise and its stakeholders - and above all, it must live up to its own precepts. This requires in turn that the enterprise is self-organizing and thereby "knows" who it is and what its values are.

Clearly, all these idealistic demands as to a multiple criteria - multiple stakeholder orientation cannot in general be met. And certainly, due to competitive pressures and the resources of the parties involved, the communication and consensus-seeking process cannot in general be permitted to continue until such time as complete agreement is reached. Just as the enterprise must establish ethical principles to guide its relationships with its stakeholders, it must also establish - and communicate to the many stakeholders - principles for decision making when consensus cannot be obtained within the time limits imposed by e.g. the market. At a minimum, agreement must be reached upon how to proceed in the face of disagreement. For example, when to employ a voting procedure, when a disagreement should be handled by hierarchical referral, or when reference should be made to an ombudsmand. And once again, this decision as to procedure must ideally be a product of dialogue and consensus if the ethical perspective is to prevail.

There are considerable potential benefits associated with such a multiple criteria - multiple stakeholder approach to planning. These include:

* It will lead to more **broadly accepted strategic planning**, when the relevant stakeholder groups have left their fingerprints on the plans.

* It will also contribute to the development of an **"early warning system"**; the ongoing dialogues between decision makers and decision receivers will lead to an increased organizational awareness as to potential systemic conflicts before they arise.

* It may also gradually lead to the **internalization of external stakeholders** as these become more involved in - and feel greater responsibility for - the operations and well-being of the organization. Seen from this perspective, the deliniation between "system" and "non-system" becomes amorphous when decision receivers begin to participate in decision making.

Let us end this discussion of systemic conflict, multiple criteria planning and organizational ethics by emphasizing that the planning concept presented requires radical shifts in orientation: From shareholders to stakeholders, from decision makers to decision receivers, from decisions to consensus, from the bottom line to values, from analysis to synthesis, and from concrete results to ethical process.

11.6. The Ethical Accounting Statement: A Case Study in Multiple Criteria Planning and Ethics

We have presented a multiple criteria - multiple stakeholder approach to ethics that deals with conflict dissolution via the active promotion of consensus. It unfolds in a process where parties each with their own values must jointly determine which of these values are strong enough to be shared and to serve as the basis for a collective evaluation of decisions and results. In this way, values become attuned and new, more general values evolve. The Ethical Accounting Statement to be described below is both a product of, and contributes to the development of, such a dialogue-culture.

In 1989-90, one of the authors partipcated in a teamwork between a major Danish bank (Sparekassen Nordjylland), the Copenhagen Business School and the Danish Academy for Applied Philosophy. The major goal of the project was to develop the multiple criteria vocabulary and methods necessary for establishing a consensus-forwarding dialogue between an enterprise and its stakeholders.

The bank had for several years attempted to define what it refered to as its basic values. All the employees were involved in defining these values, which are expressed as a set of "rules of the game". They describe how the management and employees obligate themselves to behave in relation to the customers and to each other. The statement of values was approved by the employees in 1988 together with a plan as to how, during the next three years, the values would be operationalized in the form of norms, rules and procedures. This effort to identify the organization's values and to integrate them into the bank's strategic planning and operations was considered to be a major step on the way to developing the bank's culture. There was concern however as to how to update the values and integrate them into the firm's ongoing planning. Furthermore, the bank realized that it would be of considerable value to involve other stakeholder groups in its development.

At the same time, researchers at the Institute of Computer and Systems Sciences at the Copenhagen Business School were considering how to integrate fundamental concepts from multiple criteria planning and ethics so as to develop a broader, operational concept of planning. A teamwork was therefore established between the bank and the researchers with the goal of designing and implementing what the researchers called The Ethical Accounting Statement. The Ethical Accounting statement was intended to contribute to the development of a dialogue-culture which can identify and attune values shared by the organization and its stakeholders.

The bank's team consisted of the top management, with the CEO as the most active and commited participant, as well as a group of employees representing various functional and geographical groupings. The team from the Copenhagen Business School consisted of 2 professors (of systems science and philosophy) as well as three researchers with primary interests in psychology, communications and human values. At the later stages of the development, the team was supplemented by representatives for the stakeholder groups. For the first Ethical Accounting Statement covering the operating year 1989, these stakeholders were chosen to be the bank's employees, its customers and the region of Denmark where the bank has its major operations. Spokesmen were selected for the employees and customers based upon pertinent demographic and economic data from the bank's database while the region was represented by spokesmen for the environment, culture, education and research, sports and social welfare as well as for six categories of economic activity, namely industry, agriculture, fishing, turism, commerce and services.

The shared values which are illuminated by the ethical accounting statement are the result of extensive dialogues between the bank's management and representatives for the stakeholders. Three panels, with representatives of the customers, employees and the local region, were established. These stakeholder panels and the management actively participated in meetings with the researchers where all parties contributed to the definition of the most important shared values as well as the criteria to employ when measuring the quality of the bank's contributions to these shared values. Based upon the information provided by these panels, questionnaires were designed so as to extend the "dialogue" to much larger groups than the panels. These questionnaires were sent to a) all the bank's employees, b) statistically representative groups of customers, and c) inhabitants of the region, both customers and non-customers.

The ethical accounting statement consists of an "operating statement" and a "balance sheet".

The **operating statement** presents the "costs" and "benefits" of the bank's activities which are specifically intended to further the values shared by the bank and its stakeholders. Examples are the allocation of more than a million dollars to a regional "science park" (a contribution to education and research in the region), the gift of a large, attractive property to the region under the provision that it be open to the public as a recreational area (contribution to nature and the envrionment), extensive managerial support to a local shipyard so as to secure a major source of employment (contribution to social welfare), and offers of free education to mates of the bank's employees corresponding to the educational offers to the employees themselves (contribution to the integration of family, leisure time and work). Such "costs" are subsummed under various headings in the traditional accounting statement. But here, they will also be expressed as "benefits" to those stakeholders whose values are promoted. An example of an activity which results in income on the traditional accounting statement, but which appears both as a "cost" and "benefit" in the Ethical Accounting Statement is the bank's promotion of investment schemes to reduce the tax burdens of high-income customers. The marketing activity resulted in income for the bank and reduced tax burdens for a small group of customers, but it adversely affected the region's tax base.

Although many of these activities could also have been expressed in monetary terms, many other quantitative and qualitative measures were employed. These were supplemented by an extensive set of notes and explanations.

The **balance sheet** is by far the most informative part of the Ethical Accounting Statement. It measures the "status" as to the shared values. That is, it expresses the attitudes and opinions of the stakeholder groups with respect to how the bank's activities supported their values. As mentioned earlier, for 1989 the stakeholder groups included the employees, customers and the region; this list may be expanded in future years to include suppliers, competitors and the Danish society.

Figure 11.5 lists the shared values which were treated for 1989. Corresponding to each value is a number in parantheses. This is the number of criteria which were determined by the stakeholders to operationalize the values.[5]

SHARED VALUES WITH RESPECT TO

EMPLOYEES		CUSTOMERS		REGION	
Independence	(5)	Mutual trust	(5)	Commitment	(5)
Appreciation	(7)	Human respect	(4)	Trust and credibility	(3)
Personal development	(8)	Competence	(2)		
Commitment	(5)	Quality	(6)		
Integration of family, leisure time and work	(8)				
Security	(9)				
Communication	(9)				
Well-being	(5)				
Total: 56 criteria		Total: 17 criteria		Total: 8 criteria	

Figure 11.5 Shared Values

The following are examples of criteria which operationalize the shared values so that the stakeholders can evaluate the bank's activities:

(a) Independence - an employee value:
"I exert considerable influence on my work situation and do not only do work ordered by others"

(b) Quality of work life - an employee value:
"My daily job situation is not so demanding that I feel overwhelmed by the amount of information I receive"

(c) Quality - a customer value:
"I am served by a qualified staff that knows their business"

(d) Mutual trust and interdependence - a customer value:
"The bank informs why it is necessary to charge fees for services"

[5] The number of values shared with customers and the regional society will be increased in the future; in the first year, major emphasis was placed on the employees.

(e) Commitment and solidarity in the local community - a regional value: "The bank is actively involved in the development of the communities in our region"

Summary statistics of the stakeholders' evaluations of these criteria are provided in figures 11.6(a) - (e). Such summaries are the basic entities of the balance sheet in The Ethical Accounting Statement. The complete ethical accounting statement itself is roughly 30 pages and provides a wealth of information on stakeholder values and on their evaluation of the bank's contribution to these values.

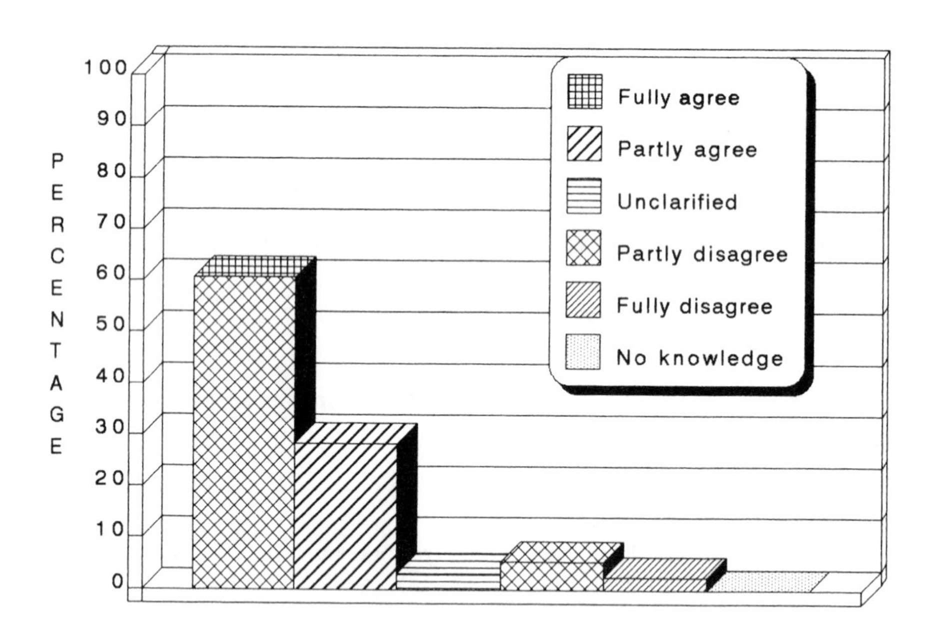

Figure 11.6a "I exert considerable influence on my work situation"

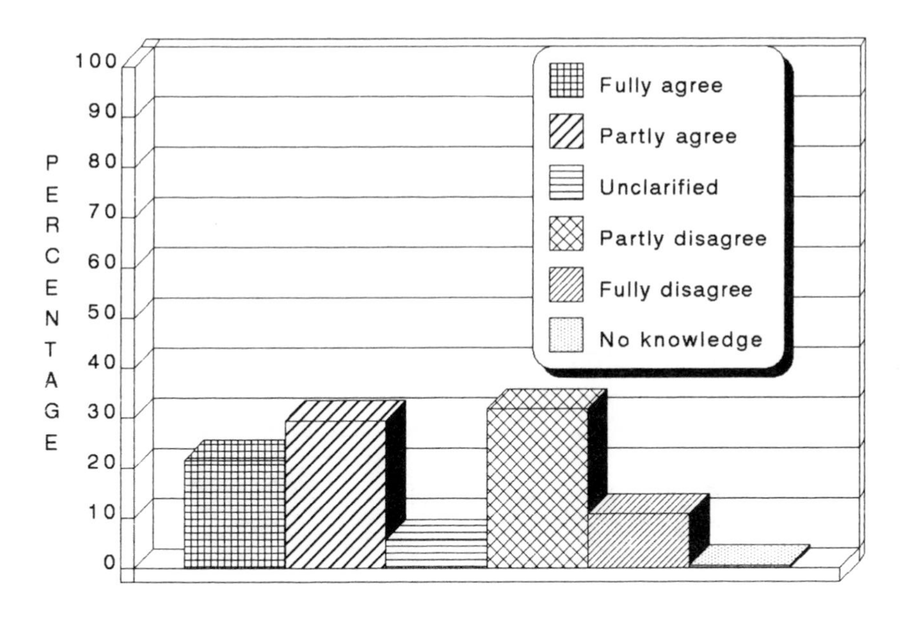

Figure 11.6b "I am not overwhelmed by the amount of information I receive"

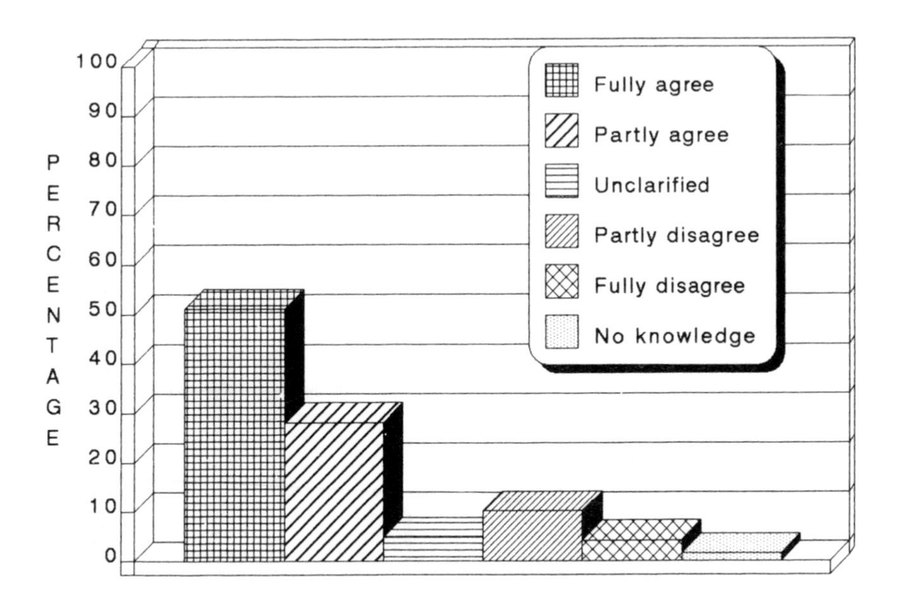

Figure 11.6c "I am served by a qualified staff that knows their business"

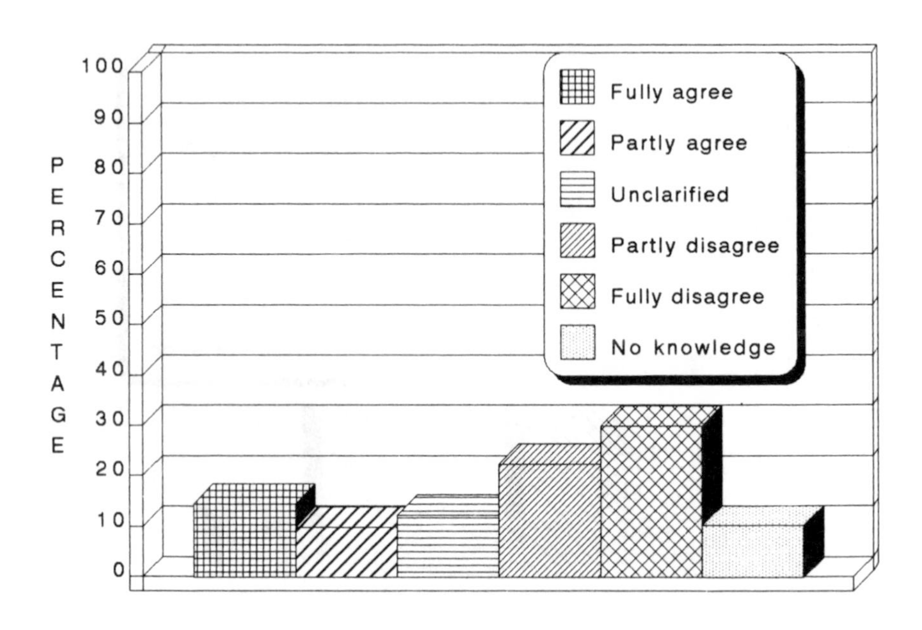

Figure 11.6d "The bank informs why it is necessary to charge fees for services"

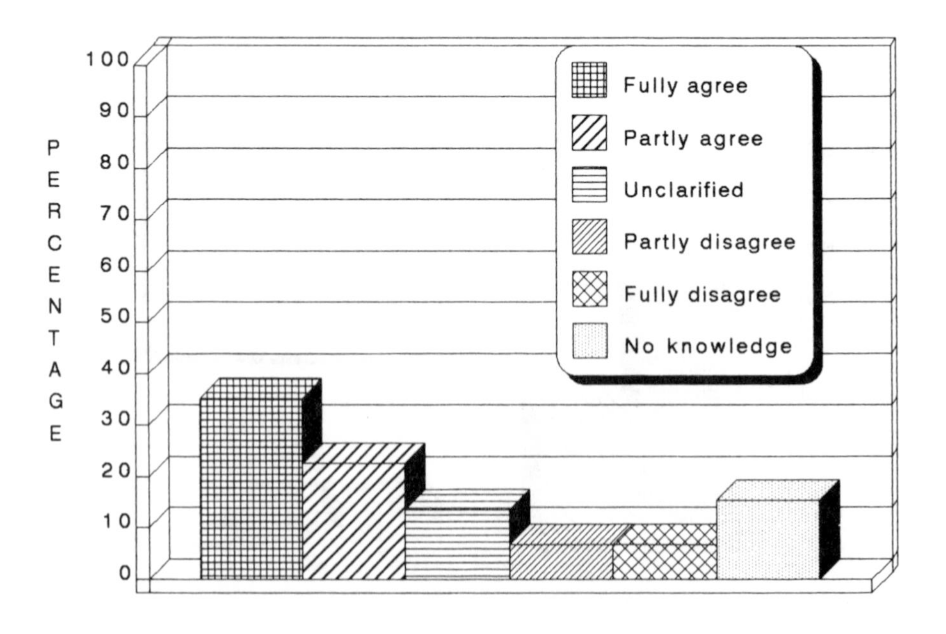

Figure 11.6e "The bank is active in the development of my local community"

It is noteworthy that the values that were identified and operationalized as well as the procedures employed for carrying out the evaluations were not simply dictated by management. Although the researchers and the bank's top management took the initiative as to the design of The Ethical Accounting Statement, its final form was a result of consensus between the management and the stakeholder representatives. This reflects the philosophy underlying The Ethical Accounting Statement; its main purpose is to contribute to an ongoing, consensus-promoting dialogue between the enterprise and its stakeholders.

There are three important factors which distinguish The Ethical Accounting Statement from traditional accounting statements:

1. The Ethical Accounting Statement is based upon a multiple of values and a multiple of criteria which operationally express these values. In contrast, the traditional accounting statement operates with only one unit of measure, money.

2. The target audience for the Ethical Accounting Statement is the stakeholders while the traditional accounting statement is oriented towards the shareholders (and financial institutions). Therefore, while the traditional accounting statement is essentially Greek for most people, the Ethical Accounting Statement can be read and understood by stakeholders in general.

3. The traditional accounting statement is developed by accountants and financial experts. The Ethical Accounting Statement is, for the main, designed and developed by the stakeholders themselves.

We can also elaborate on the notion of the shared values employed in the Ethical Accounting Statement. These values have four salient characteristics:

1. They are not simply instrumental tools to increase the enterprise's profits. They have meaning in their own right, corresponding to the notion of values introduced in chapter 1, and there is no simple connection between these values and profits.

2. They must be expressable in terms of criteria. These criteria permit measurement of the degree to which the enterprise promotes the values.

3. The values should not express all the enterprise's or all the stakeholders' values, but only those which are shared by both parties. Both parties have many more values than those which appear on the interface between them.

4. Just which values and criteria are relevant cannot be determined in advance. This depends on the context and evolves from the dialogue. However, once they have been chosen, it will be important to continue with them for some time, since otherwise it will be difficult to develop comparative analyses over time.

We note in conclusion that the Ethical Aaccounting Statement has provided the starting point for the development of an **internal ethical accounting statement** and an **ethical budget.** The internal ethical accounting statement utilizes the wealth of detailed information available. For example, although all replies are anonymous, data is available describing the evaluations provided by various groupings, e.g. for customers by age, income, sex, location, type and size of accounts. Such information may for example be of importance for evaluating individual branches, the needs of particular customer groups or the opinions of particular groups of employees. Based upon the results provided by the balance sheet and the internal accounting statement, the top management is preparing a budget in the form of plans for improving its results, i.e. the evaluations by the stakeholders in comming years. This will be in the form of commitments and will, together with the balance sheet, provide the basis for future evaluations of the bank's contributions towards its stakeholders' values. Finally, we note that the major contribution of The Ethical Accounting Statement is not its measurements but its contribution to the organization's ethical process. Since committing itself to the ongoing development of The Ethical Accounting Statement has also actively begun to promote the integration of an ethical perspective in the bank's identity, self-organization, strategic planning and leadership - what we have referred to as "Management by values".

11.7. Summary

The introduction of a multiple criteria of decision makers and receivers leads to a broader and more complex framework for planning with multiple criteria. While the previous chapters were oriented towards intrapersonal conflict, i.e. conflicts within an individual, the present chapter 11 has extended the notion of conflict to both interpersonal conflict, i.e. conflicts within a group, and systemic conflict, i.e. conflicts between decision makers and decision receivers.

The two major analytical disciplines dealing with **interpersonal conflict** are game theory and social choice theory. The theoretical frameworks they provide for analyzing conflict within a group neglect the investigative and communicative aspects of planning. In addition, they ignore the multiple criteria nature of planning. And they ignore the social nature of groups whereby an individual member may be motivated by a desire not only to maximize the degree to which he fulfills his own objectives but also to be part of the group and to make decisions which are the product of a consensus-seeking process. Thus, they omit crucial characteristics of practical planning situations. In contrast, we argued that multiple criteria thinking provides a useful framework for the resolution of interpersonal conflicts and we developed a series of recommendations as to the design of a multiple criteria approach to planning in a group.

The lack of a multiple criteria framework is even more blatant when we consider the notion of **systemic conflict** and introduce a stakeholder perspective based on the notion of shared values. This multiple criteria - multiple stakeholder perspective denies the relevance of the simple minded uni-dimensional, bottom line view of the enterprise so prevalent in much of the literature. The concept of **management by values** was then introduced. It was postulated that for an organization to have success, it must orient itself towards its stakeholders, identify their values, and contribute to their ability to promote these values.

This leads to radically new ways of considering the planning process and its organization. In particular, it leads to **an operational approach to ethics**. Idealistically speaking, an ethical decision is one which is approved of by its decision receivers speaking, an ethical decision is one which is approved of by its decision receivers and an ethical planning process is one which promotes consensus amongst the stakeholders. As with the case of interpersonal conflict, we do not recommend formal multiple criteria analysis here. Rather our starting point is a conceptual framework of self-organizing systems developing their own values. We propose a setting characterized by a dialogue culture where the stakeholders are invited to contribute to the planning process. This leads to the notion of the **Ethical Accounting Statement** as a means of promoting the dialogue between the organization and its stakeholders. The statement measures how well the decision receivers feel that the decision makers have contributed to the shared organizational-stakeholder values.

11.8. Bibliographic Notes

Interpersonal conflicts and group decisons are of longstanding interest to researchers from a wide spectrum of disciplines ranging from psychology over organizational theory and economics to management science and operational research. We cannot possibly make proper references to the extensive literature which could be relevant; the reader may therefore wish to consult some of the many textbooks available. Rather, we simply provide some references directly relevant to the approach advocated in this chapter. Initially, we should note that a substantial part of the MCDM literature is more or less implicitly concerned with the support of decision making in multiple person environments. In fact, many MCDM-texts are loose in their interpretation of "the decision maker", and in many applications "the decision maker" has actually been a group of persons. Also, some of the traditional methods have explicitly been extended in an attempt to handle group decision making. This includes the Zionts-Wallenius method, c.f. Korhonen, Wallenius & Zionts(1980), the Surrogate-Worth Trade-off method, c.f. Hall & Haimes(1976), the Displaced Ideal method, c.f. Hafkamp(1984), the Reference-Point method, c.f. Grauer, Bisschoof & Wierzbicki(1983), and the Pairwise-Comparisons method, c.f. Kok(1986) and Kok & Lootsma(1985). The ideas of these extensions generally conforms with those expressed in this chapter, namely that structural discussions of the multiple criteria involved may promote the attainment of consensual choice. On the other hand, they focus on specific techniques rather than multiple criteria planning and some of them come close to suggesting formal, ad-hoc aggregations of different interests. Formal extensions of game theory to multiple criteria environments are presented in Bergstresser and Yu(1977), Shapley(1959), and Zeleny(1976b), c.f. also Zeleny(1982, ch. 10.2). Moulin(1983) provides a formal presentation of social choice theory. Basic references to the issue of designing group decision support systems are DeSanctis and Gallupe(1987), Huber(1984), and Jarke(1986). The interaction of creativity and conflict is treated in Areti(1976).

Systemic conflicts are also of interest to researchers from many disciplines although the literature on the resolution of such conflicts is considerably more scarce. A stakeholder view of organizations can be found in Ackoff(1974), Freeman(1984) and Freeman and Gilbert(1988). Autopoiesis in social systems is the subject of Morgan(1985) and Zeleny(1985). The role of ethics to cope with systemic conflicts is the subject of Pruzan and Thyssen(1990) and Jensen, Pruzan and Thyssen(1990). Finally, we should mention that, with the exception of Pruzan(1990) and Hansen, Meyer and Pruzan(1990), publications on the Ethical Accounting Statement, including the first such statement, Sparekassen Nordjylland(1990), are so far only available in Danish.

Appendix 1

EFFICIENT ALTERNATIVES

In this appendix we give a somewhat more formal treatment of efficiency, the generation of efficient alternatives, and the nature and role of trade-off information.

1. Preliminaries

Let the set of **alternatives** or feasible decisions be represented by an arbitrary set

$$X = \text{set of alternatives in decision space}$$

and let the **criteria** of possible relevance to the decision maker be represented by real functions

$$f_i: X \rightarrow \mathfrak{R},\ i=1, \ldots, n$$

Then, in **criteria space**, the set of alternatives is represented by

$$Y = \{(y_1, \ldots, y_n) \mid x \in X\} = \{(f_1(x), \ldots, f_n(x)) \mid x \in X\}$$

i.e. as a subset of $\mathfrak{R}^n$. Let us assume that Y is non-empty, and closed, and that there exists an M such that $y_i \leq M$, $i=1, \ldots, n$, for all y in Y, i.e. Y is bounded from above.

To ease the exposition some shorthand notation is convenient. In particular, let us use $<<$, $<$, and $\leq$ to denote the following **partial orderings** of vectors $y=(y_1, \ldots, y_n)$ and $y'=(y_1', \ldots, y_n')$ in $\mathfrak{R}^n$:

$$y << y' \Leftrightarrow \forall i: y_i < y_i'$$
$$y < y' \Leftrightarrow \forall i: y_i \leq y_i' \quad \wedge \quad \exists j : y_j < y_j'$$
$$y \leq y' \Leftrightarrow \forall i: y_i \leq y_i'$$

We note that $y << y' \Rightarrow y < y' \Rightarrow y \leq y'$. Also, let us say that a real function F: $\Re^n \rightarrow \Re$ is **weakly increasing** if and only if

$$y < y' \Rightarrow F(y) \leq F(y')$$

and **strongly increasing** if and only if

$$y < y' \Rightarrow F(y) < F(y')$$

Note that these conventions regarding F conform with the usual meaning when applied to real numbers instead of vectors.

2. Efficiency

Definition 1

A vector $y \in \Re^n$ is said to be **dominated** by a vector $y' \in \Re^n$ if and only if $y < y'$. It is said to be weakly (strongly) dominated if $y \leq y'$($y << y'$) ○

Definition 2

An attainable vector $y \in Y$ is said to be **efficient** (with respect to Y) if and only if it is not dominated by another feasible vector $y' \in Y$. An alternative $x \in X$ is called efficient if $(f_1(x), \ldots, f_n(x))$ is efficient. ○

Let Y_E denote the set of efficient alternatives in criteria space. Then we might express the above definition as follows:

$$\begin{aligned} Y_E &= \{y \in Y \mid y \text{ nondominated}\} \\ &= \{y \in Y \mid \neg(\exists y' \in Y: y' > y)\} \\ &= \{y \in Y \mid \forall y' \in Y: y' \geq y \Rightarrow y' = y\} \end{aligned}$$

Corresponding expressions apply for X_E, the set of efficient alternatives in decision space. We see that the efficient alternatives are those that we cannot improve upon in any dimension without having to pay for such an improvement in at least one other dimension.

Lemma 1

Under the assumed regularity of Y we have $Y_E \neq \emptyset$, and for any $y \in Y$

$$y \notin Y_E \Rightarrow \exists\, y' \in Y_E: y' > y \qquad \bigcirc$$

<u>Proof</u>

Consider initially the second part of the lemma. If $y \notin Y_E$, then $Z = \{y'' \in Y \mid y'' > y\} \neq \emptyset$ and

$$\{y'' \in Y \mid y'' \geq y\} = Z \cup \{y\}$$

is a non-empty, bounded and closed subset of $\mathfrak{R}^n$. Hence, the continuous function g: $\mathfrak{R}^n \rightarrow \mathfrak{R}$ defined by $g(y'') = \Sigma_i y''_i$ attains its maximum on $Z \cup \{y\}$ in some point y'. This point is clearly efficient, since otherwise $\exists$ y'': $y'' > y'$ and we would have $g(y'') > g(y')$ by g strictly increasing. Also, by g strictly increasing we have $y' \in Z$. Hence, y' dominates y as desired. It follows immediately that $Y_E \neq \emptyset$ since $y \in Y_E$ or $y' \in Y_E$. $\bigcirc$

We emphasize that the assumed regularities on Y are convenient for the mathematical treatment, but in no way restrictive from a practical point of view.

In the literature, alternative notions of efficiency have been suggested. A restricted type of efficiency is that of "proper efficiency" introduced by Geoffrion(1968), the idea of which is to exclude efficient decisions with unbounded trade-offs between the criteria, see also Soland(1979) and Benson and Morin(1977). A related concept is introduced by White(1985). Burkard, Krarup and Pruzan(1982,1984) also introduce a restricted type of efficiency, "strict efficiency", which only includes solutions that simultaneously are efficient with respect to two, related sets of criteria. A relaxed type of efficiency is "weak" or "quasi" efficiency meaning that the alternative cannot be strongly dominated by another one, see e.g. Lowe, Thisse, Ward, and Wendel(1984).

In some expositions, the problem of determining all efficient alternatives is expressed as a **vector optimization program**

$$\max_{y} \ [y_1, y_2, \ldots, y_n] \quad \text{s.t.} \quad y \in Y$$

So, by definition, the solution to this problem is Y_E. Although we will not use this notation here, it is a useful reminder of what is going on. At first, the program appears somewhat peculiar, since optimizing with respect to the different objectives may point towards different alternatives. However, this is the essence of MCDM. We face conflicting intentions.

Much of the relevance of the efficiency concept in multiple criteria decision making rests on the following result:

Theorem 1

Consider the basic decision problem

$$(P) \qquad \max_{y} \ F(y) \quad \text{s.t.} \quad y \in Y$$

where F is weakly increasing. Now

(i) For any y optimal in P:
$\exists$ y' efficient: $F(y')=F(y)$

(ii) For any y' efficient:
$\exists$ F weakly increasing: y' unique solution to P ○

<u>Proof</u>

To prove (i), let y be optimal in P. If $y \in Y_E$, let $y' = y$ and we are done. If $y \notin Y_E$, it is by lemma 1 dominated by some $y' \in Y_E$, i.e. $\exists y' \in Y_E$: $y' > y$. By F weakly increasing then, $F(y') \geq F(y)$, and by y optimal, $F(y') \leq F(y)$, i.e. we have $F(y') = F(y)$.

To prove (ii), let $y' \in Y_E$ and define F: $\Re^n \rightarrow \Re$ by

$$F(y) := \max\{t \in \Re \mid y - t(1, \ldots, 1) \geq y'\}$$

Then, F is weakly increasing since $y^* > y^{**}$ implies

$$\{t \in \Re \mid y^* - t(1, \ldots, 1) \geq y'\} \supseteq \{t \in \Re \mid y^{**} - t(1, \ldots, 1) \geq y'\}$$

such that the maximum of the first set is no less than the maximum of the last set, i.e. $F(y^*) \geq F(y^{**})$. Also, it is clear that $F(y')=0$. It suffices therefore to show that

$$F(y^*) < 0 \quad \forall\, y^* \in Y \setminus \{y'\}.$$

To do so, let us assume that this is not the case, i.e. $\exists\, y^* \in Y \setminus \{y'\}$ such that $F(y^*) \geq 0$. It follows that

$$\exists\, t \geq 0: y^* - t(1, \ldots, 1) \geq y'$$

However, this implies $y^* \geq y'$ and by $y^* \neq y'$ we get $y^* > y'$. This contradicts y' being efficient and we are done. We might add that a similar result holds even if F is restricted to be strictly increasing. This has been demonstrated by - among others - Soland(1979). ○

According to theorem 1, we do not loose anything by focusing on efficient alternatives. By (i) an optimal alternative can always be found among the set of efficient alternatives. On the other hand, the set to be considered to find the optimal alternative cannot a priori be confined to a smaller set than Y_E if all we know about the decision maker's preference function F is that it is weakly increasing. By (ii), any efficient alternative may turn out to be the unique optimal choice for a decision maker with a weakly increasing F. Thus, Y_E is the smallest sufficient set of alternatives to consider.

3. Generating Efficient Alternatives

Next, let us turn to the characterization and generation of efficient alternatives by use of ordinary, scalar optimization problems.

First, consider **the constraint approach.**

Theorem 2

Consider the scalar-maximization problem

$$(P_\epsilon) \quad \begin{aligned} \max_{y} \quad & y_1 \\ \text{s.t.} \quad & y_2 \geq \epsilon_2 \\ & \vdots \\ & y_n \geq \epsilon_n \\ & y \in Y \end{aligned}$$

Now,

$$y^* \in Y_E \Leftrightarrow \exists\, \epsilon \in \Re^{n-1}: y^* \text{ is a unique optimal solution to } P_\epsilon \qquad \bigcirc$$

<u>Proof</u>

This result may be attributed to Haimes(1970), Yu(1974) or Haimes, Hall, and Freedman(1975).

To prove the ($\Leftarrow$) part, let y^* be a unique optimal solution to P_ϵ. Now, if y^* is not efficient, there exists a $y' \in Y$ such that $y' > y^*$. Therefore y' is feasible in P_ϵ. Also, it is a better ($y'_1 > y^*_1$) or at least an alternative ($y'_1 = y^*_1 \wedge y' \neq y$) solution to P_ϵ, hence contradicting our assumption.

To prove the ($\Rightarrow$) part, let $y^* \in Y_E$ and $\epsilon = (y^*_2, \ldots, y^*_n)$. Then, y^* is the unique optimal solution to P_ϵ. To see this, observe first that y^* is feasible. Also, it must be optimal since otherwise a better solution would dominate y^* and hence y^* would not be efficient. Similarly, it must be a unique optimal solution since otherwise it would again be dominated by an alternative optimal solution. ○

According to theorem 2, all efficient alternatives may be traced out by imposing varying minimum requirements on the last n-1 criteria. Of course, the choice of the first criterion as the one to be maximized is arbitrary. When we solve P_ϵ for varying values of ϵ, we might in some instances generate inefficient alternatives. Often, we do not care since our main concern is to generate at least the set of efficient alternatives. However, inefficiency may be avoided by restricting attention to those generated as unique solutions. Alternatively, we could assign positive but infinitely small weights to the last n-1 criteria and introduce these in the objective function in addition to y_1. Also, observe that the generation of efficient alternatives by varying the constraints is completely general. No special assumptions about Y are required.

Next, let us turn to **the weighting approach** or the parametric approach. This approach to generating efficient alternatives is not generally applicable. Still, it works in the important class of convex settings and it may be useful in other settings as well.

Theorem 3

Consider the scalar maximization problem

$$(P_\alpha) \quad \max_y \sum_{i=1}^{n} \alpha_i y_i$$
$$\text{s.t.} \quad y \in Y$$

Now,

(i) $y^* \in Y_E \Rightarrow \exists\ \alpha=(\alpha_1, \ldots, \alpha_n)>0$: y^* is an optimal solution to P_α

if (a) Y is convex, or (b) X is convex and $f_1, \ldots, f_n$ are concave, and

(ii) $y^* \in Y_E \Leftarrow \exists\ \alpha=(\alpha_1, \ldots, \alpha_n)>0$: y^* is an optimal solution to P_α

if (a) y^* is the unique optimal solution, or (b) $\alpha>>0$, or (c) Y is strictly convex, or (d) X is convex, $f_1, \ldots, f_n$ are concave, and $\exists j$: $\alpha_j>0 \wedge f_j$ strictly concave. ○

Proof

Results along these lines are well known within applied mathematics and have a long tradition among economists who interpret α as a price vector. It may be attributed to names like Arrow, Barankin and Blackwell(1953), Da Cunha and Polak(1967), Geoffrion(1968), and Kuhn and Tucker(1951), c.f. Chankong and Haimes(1983a) and Zeleny(1974). A stronger result also applicable to non-convex settings and to 0-1 problems is obtained by replacing P_α by a scaled convex combination of the n criteria, c.f. Burkard, Keiding, Krarup and Pruzan (1981). A proof may proceed as follows.

To show (i), and to treat subcases (a) and (b) simultaneously, we introduce the perturbation function Φ: $\Re^{n-1} \rightarrow \Re$ defined as the value of P_ϵ as a function of ϵ:

$$\Phi(\epsilon):= \max\{y_1 \mid y\in Y,\ y_2 \geq \epsilon_2, \ldots, y_n \geq \epsilon_n\}$$

If, for some ϵ, the set is empty, we define Φ to be $-\infty$. Now, independent of whether we are in case (a) or (b), Φ is concave. This is an elementary result in convex analysis. It is proved by simply recalling the definitions of convex sets and concave functions and is left as a useful exercise here. Now, by Φ concave,

$$Y^\circ = \{y^\circ \in \Re^n \mid y^\circ_1 \leq \Phi(y^\circ_2, \ldots, y^\circ_n)\}$$

is convex. Note that this set is relaxed with respect to the original set Y, i.e. $Y \subseteq Y^{\circ}$. Also, by theorem 2, all $y^* \in Y_E$ are located at the boundary of Y° since $y^*_1 = \Phi(y^*_2, \ldots, y^*_n)$. It follows that y* may be weakly separated from Y° by a hyperplane, i.e.

$$\exists\ \alpha \neq 0:\ \Sigma_i\ \alpha_i y^*_i\ \geq\ \Sigma_i\ \alpha_i y^{\circ}_i\quad \forall\ y^{\circ} \in Y^{\circ}$$

Consequently, y* solves P_{α} since it even solves a relaxed version where Y° has been substituted for Y. Now, it remains only to be shown that $\alpha > 0$. We know that $\alpha \neq 0$. So, it suffices to show that $\alpha_j < 0$ is not possible. Assume $\exists j$: $\alpha_j < 0$. Then the right hand side in the inequality above tends to infinity when y°_j tends to minus infinity and the separation cannot hold, i.e. we get a contradiction.

Next, consider (ii). Let $\alpha > 0$ and y* an optimal solution to P_{α}. Now, (a), if y* is unique it must be efficient, since any y' dominating y* would give a higher value of αy or an alternative optimal solution to P_{α}. Similarly, (b), if $\alpha >> 0$, y* must be efficient since otherwise any y' dominating y* would give a strictly larger value of P_{α}, hence contradicting our assumption. In case (c), α defines a hyperplane supporting Y at y* and by strict convexity at y* only. If y* were not efficient, any y' dominating y* would have at least the same value of $\alpha y'$ as αy^* and by the optimality of y* in P_{α} they must in fact be equal, i.e. we have $\alpha y' = \alpha y^*$ for two different points in Y which contradicts the strict convexity. Finally, (d) implies that

$$f(x)\ =\ \Sigma_i\ \alpha_i f_i(x)$$

is strictly concave. In this case, y* must be the unique optimal solution to P_{α}. For if not and if y' is an optimal solution distinct from y* with x* and x' the corresponding basic decisions, then f strictly concave implies

$$f(\lambda x^* + (1\text{-}\lambda x'))\ >\ \lambda f(x^*) + (1\text{-}\lambda) f(x')\ =\ f(x^*)\quad \forall\ \lambda \in (0,1)$$

in which case y* could not be an optimal solution. Again, by y* a unique optimal solution to P_{α}, it follows that y* is efficient since any dominating solution would give a better or an alternative solution to P_{α}. ○

According to theorem 3, in settings endowed with reasonable convexity assumptions, all efficient solutions may be generated by imposing varying importance parameters $\alpha_1, \ldots, \alpha_n$ on the n different criteria. Again, to avoid generating inefficient alternatives, we must have unique optimality or optimality under a strictly increasing objective function. Extensions of this approach to non-convex settings using more general notions of prices or weights are given in Bogetoft(1985a,b,86) and in Bogetoft and Tind(1990).

Even in less regular cases, the parametric approach may often be useful. In some cases, it is simply felt that the set of efficient alternatives generated by P_α for varying α constitutes a representative subset of Y_E. Any efficient alternative y^* that may be generated this way is sometimes called **convex non-dominated** since it may alternatively be characterized by

$$\neg\ (\exists\ y^1 \in Y, \ldots, y^k \in Y,\ \lambda^1 \geq 0, \ldots, \lambda^k \geq 0:\ \Sigma_j \lambda^j y^j > y^*)$$

i.e. y^* belongs to $(\mathrm{conv}(Y))_E$, the set of efficient alternatives in the convex hull of Y.

In other cases, it may be argued or even tested that the overall preference function is linear

$$F(y) = \Sigma_i\ \beta_i y_i$$

but that we just do not know what value $\beta > 0$ takes. In this case, the set of alternatives generated by P_α for varying $\alpha > 0$ is clearly the smallest sufficient set of alternatives to consider, just like Y_E is when F is only known to be increasing.

By combining the results and ways of establishing proofs presented above, it is easy to develop similar theorems for **mixed approaches**, where some criteria are governed by importance weights while others are controlled by constraints. This type of approach has been used in the related problem of multilevel planning, c.f. Atkins(1979), Meijboom(1986), and Obel(1978) for linear programming cases and Van Roy(1983) and Burkard, Hamacher and Tind(1985) for mixed integer and general algebraic settings. In MCDM, the use of **hybrid approaches** where all criteria are governed both by importance weights and constraints has been suggested by Corley(1980) and by Wendel and Lee(1977). A generalization is given in Soland(1979).

Finally, consider **the target approach**; reference is made to the results in Chankong and Haimes(1983a) or Yu(1973). For the present purposes, it suffices to establish the following:

Theorem 4

Consider the scalar minimization problem

$$(P_{p,\beta,y^\circ}) \quad \min_y \ (\Sigma \beta_i |y_i - y^\circ_i|^p)^{1/p} \quad \text{s.t.} \quad y \in Y$$

with $\beta > 0$ and $1 \le p \le \infty$. Now,

(i) $y^* \in Y_E \Rightarrow \exists\, y^\circ$: y^* is an optimal solution to P_{p,β,y°, and

(ii) $y^* \in Y_E \Leftarrow \exists\, \beta > 0,\ 1 \le p < \infty$: y^* is an optimal solution to $P_{p,\beta,yI}$

if (a) $\beta >> 0$ or (b) y^* is the unique optimal solution, where $y^I = (\max_y y_1, \ldots, \max_y y_n)$ is the ideal vector. ○

<u>Proof</u>

The first part (i) is trivial by choosing $y^\circ = y^*$. The second part (ii) follows immediately by arguments similar to those used previously since the conditions in this part insure that the objective is either strictly decreasing in the relevant part of $\Re^n$, in which case a dominating alternative would be better if it existed, or that the optimal solution is unique, and a dominating alternative which is not strictly better would be an alternative solution. ○

There is a vast literature on different methods for generating solutions using various versions of the target approach, c.f. for example the references provided in Chankong and Haimes(1983a,83b) and Steuer(1986). Also, let us note that although it may not be possible to generate all efficient solutions if we restrict the possible variations in y°, β, and p, the set of solutions generated under such restrictions may still be considered to be representative or in another sense the relevant subset. Indeed, if we believe that the DM thinks in terms of targets, the set of alternatives generated this way may be the relevant set to consider much like the set of non-convex dominated alternatives is the relevant set when his overall preference function is assumed to be linear. While it is often believed that the target and the weights can be meaningfully supplied by the DM, the proper choice of the deviation measure p is not at all obvious. In goal-programming, initiated by Charnes and Cooper(1961) and subsequently expanded upon by many others, c.f. the surveys and texts by Charnes and Cooper(1977), Ignizio(1976), Kornbluth(1973), and Lee(1972), the choice of $p=1$ is used merely as a convenience. Yu(1974) and Zeleny(1973) introduced the idea of **the compromise set** composed of all those alternatives that can be generated by fixing the weights β, using the ideal as the target, $y^{\circ}=y^{I}$, and varying p in $[1,\infty]$. If the DM finds it difficult to select his best compromise solution from the set so generated, the set should be reduced further. Zeleny(1973,74, 76a,77,82) suggests several ways to do so and in particular he develops an interactive strategy using his notion of the displaced ideal for reducing the compromise set until the best compromise solution can be conveniently selected.

4. Trade-off Information

Finally, let us turn to the **dual relationship** between the constraint and the weighting approaches to generating efficient alternatives. This relationship is analytically convenient in several instances and it is useful when we seek more conceptual and economic interpretaions of the different approaches.

Theorem 5

Consider a convex setting. Now, if y^* is an optimal solution to

$$(P_\epsilon)\quad \max_{y}\ y_1 \quad \text{s.t.}\quad \begin{array}{ll} y_2 \geq \epsilon_2 & \gamma_2 \\ \vdots & \\ y_n \geq \epsilon_n & \gamma_n \\ y \in Y & \end{array}$$

with associated Lagrange multipliers $\gamma^*_2, \ldots, \gamma^*_n$, then y is an optimal solution to

$$(P_\alpha)\quad \max_{y} \sum_{i=1}^{n} \alpha_i y_i \quad \text{s.t.}\quad y \in Y$$

with $\alpha_1 = 1$, $\alpha_i = \gamma^*_i$, $i = 2, \ldots, n$ ○

Proof

Consider the Lagrangean of P_ϵ

$$L(y,\gamma) := y_1 + \sum_{i=2}^{n} \gamma_i (y_i - \epsilon_i) \text{ for } y \in Y,\ \gamma_i \geq 0\ i = 2, \ldots, n$$

Now, by y^* being optimal with associated Lagrange multipliers $\gamma^*_2, \ldots, \gamma^*_n$, we have by the saddlepoint theorem that

$$L(y,\gamma^*) \leq L(y^*,\gamma^*) \leq L(y^*,\gamma) \quad \forall\ y \in Y,\ \gamma \geq 0$$

The left inequality reads

$$y_1 + \Sigma\, \gamma^*_i y_i - \Sigma\, \gamma^*_i \epsilon_i \leq y^*_1 + \Sigma\, \gamma^*_i y^*_i - \Sigma\, \gamma^*_i \epsilon_i \quad \forall\ y \in Y$$

which gives us that y^* is an optimal solution to P_α with $\alpha = (1,\gamma^*_2, \ldots, \gamma^*_n)$ ○

Theorem 5 shows us how the alternative characterizations of efficient alternatives in terms of P_ϵ and P_α are related. The change from P_α to P_ϵ was not included since it is trivial - simply let $\epsilon = (y^*_2, \ldots, y^*_n)$, c.f. the proof of Theorem 2.

In economic contexts, P_ϵ and P_α represent rationing and price mechanisms respectively, i.e. resource (or budget) directive and price directive planning methods.

The existence of a similar relationship between the target approach P_{p,β,y°, or more generally P_{d,y° as in chapter 6, and the weighting approach P_α is developed in Bogetoft, Hallefjord, and Kok(1987) and in Nakayama and Sawaragi(1984).

Presently, theorem 5 is also important as a reminder that additional information is generally available when we generate an alternative. Whether we generate y^* by solving P_ϵ or P_α, we learn in addition about a hyperplane supporting Y in y^*. This information is available directly when solving P_α by simply remembering α. Also, if we solve P_ϵ, it is available as the Lagrange multipliers $(\gamma_2, \ldots, \gamma_n)$. In particular, if P_ϵ is a linear programming problem, any standard code will provide us with $\gamma_2, \ldots, \gamma_n$ immediately. This additional information provides insight into the substitution possibilities between the performance in the different criteria. The hyperplane gives a locally precise and globally exaggerated (optimistic) picture of the possibilities for substituting around y^*. Thus, e.g., by giving up one unit of y_2 we can at the most hope to gain γ_2 units of y_1.

Such insight may not only be useful in a prior articulation of alternatives approach. It may also be used in, for example, progressive articulation of alternatives approach since the DM may use it to guide the search for new and better alternatives, c.f. Bogetoft(1985a,b,86), Bogetoft, Hallefjord and Kok(1987), and Bogetoft and Tind(1990). An extensive discussion of the types of trade-off information available in different methods is given by Haimes and Chankong(1979) and Kok(1984).

Appendix 2

PREFERENCE MODELLING

In this appendix we give a somewhat more formal treatment of the fundamental assumptions, concepts and results used in preference modelling. Some useful general references to the mathematical study of preferences, i.e. to **utility theory** and more broadly **measurement theory**, are Fishburn(1964,70), Krantz, Luce, Suppes and Tversky(1971), Roberts(1979), and Roubens and Vincke(1985). The outstanding application oriented reference is Keeney and Raiffa(1976).

1. Preliminaries

Let X be set of objects or alternatives. A **binary relation** R on X is then simply a subset R of the cartesian product XxX. i.e. $R \subseteq X^2$. To denote that an ordered pair (x',x") belongs to R we might equivalently write

$$(x',x") \in R, \quad x'Rx", \quad \text{or} \quad \text{" x' is in relation R to x" "}$$

Similarly, one may define r'th order relations as subsets of X^r, $r=1,2, \ldots$, but in the models below we are primarily going to work with binary relations.

The starting point - or primitive - of preference theory is usually taken to be an **empirical relation system**

$$(X, R_1, \ldots, R_p)$$

i.e. a set of alternatives endowed with certain relations $R_1, \ldots, R_p$. These relations represent the DM's basic evaluations or comparisons of alternatives.

When only binary relations are considered and the set of alternatives is finite, it is often convenient to think of relations in terms of (directed) graphs. A **graph representation** of the relation R is defined by the graph with nodes X and arcs R, i.e. there exists an arc from x' to x" if and only if x'Rx".

Naturally, we must assume some degree of regularity in the empirical relation system if we want to use expressed evaluations to guide choices or, more ambitiously, to guarantee the existence of criteria and preference functions. The building blocks of these regularities are usually taken to be the **basic properties of binary relations** defined in figure A2.1 below. These properties are related in various ways. Some properties - alone or as a group - may imply or exclude others. Now, in order to get enough structure, we must typically assume a certain combination of the basic properties. The most commonly encountered properties in preference modelling are the **order relations** defined in figure A2.2. Only the defining properties are indicated. Thus, for example, a strict weak order which is asymmetric and negative transitive by definition, is easily proved to be transitive and antisymmetric as well.

An important theme in measurement theory, is how to represent the basic, empirical relation system $(X, R_1, \ldots, R_p)$ in terms of a more handy symbolic or **numerical relation system** $(Z, R_1', \ldots, R_p')$. A value function or **measurement**

$$v: X \rightarrow Z$$

represents $(X, R_1, \ldots, R_p)$ in $(Z, R_1', \ldots, R_p')$ if it is a **homomorphism,** i.e.

$$x' R_i x'' \Leftrightarrow v(x') R_i' v(x'') \quad \forall\ i=1, \ldots, p,\ x' \in X,\ x'' \in X$$

If we choose Z as for example the real numbers $\Re$ and $R_1', \ldots, R_p'$ as wellknown comparisons like "equals" (=) and "is larger than" (>), we get an **operational representation** of the DM's basic evaluations and comparisons $R_1, \ldots, R_p$ of the alternatives in X.

Property of R		Definition ($\forall\, x_1, \ldots, x^n \in X$)
P1:	Reflexive	x^1Rx^1
P2:	Irreflexive	$\neg x^1Rx^1$
P3:	Symmetric	$x^1Rx^2 \Rightarrow x^2Rx^1$
P4:	Antisymmetric	$x^1Rx^2 \wedge x^2Rx^1 \Rightarrow x^1 = x^2$
P5:	Asymmetric	$x^1Rx^2 \Rightarrow \neg x^2Rx^1$
P6:	Complete/Weakly Connected	$x^1Rx^2 \vee x^2Rx^1$ for $x^1 \neq x^2$
P7:	Strongly Complete/ Connected	$x^1Rx^2 \vee x^2Rx^1$
P8:	Transitive	$x^1Rx^2 \wedge x^2Rx^3 \Rightarrow x^1Rx^3$
P9:	Negatively Transitive	$\neg x^1Rx^2 \wedge \neg x^2Rx^3 \Rightarrow \neg x^1Rx^3$
P10:	Semi-Transitive	$x^1Rx^2 \wedge x^2Rx^3 \Rightarrow x^1Rx^4 \vee x^4Rx^3$
P11:	Ferrers Relation	$x^1Rx^2 \wedge x^3Rx^4 \Rightarrow x^1Rx^4 \vee x^3Rx^2$
P12:	Acyclic	$x^1Rx^2 \wedge \ldots \wedge x^{n-1}Rx^n \Rightarrow x^1 \neq x^n$

Figure A2.1 Basic Properties of Binary Relations

Relation	Defining Properties										
	P1	P2	P3	P4	P5	P6	P7	P8	P9	P10	P11
Equivalence	x		x					x			
Quasi	x							x			
Weak							x	x			
Total (Simple)				x			x	x			
Strict Total (Simple)					x	x		x			
Strict Weak					x				x		
Partial	x			x				x			
Strict Partial					x			x			
Total Interval		x									x
Total Semi		x								x	x

Figure A2.2 Some Order Relations

The core of measurement theory is composed of **representation theorems** linking properties of the basic, empirical relation system, the value function and the operational, numerical relation system. A standard representation theorem specifies axioms or properties of $(X,R_1, \ldots, R_p)$ that are necessary or sufficient to allow a representation in a certain numerical relation system $(Z,R_1', \ldots, R_p')$ by a value function v - possibly with some additional requirements like additivity or concavity on v. Furthermore, uniqueness results are typically given. They characterize the extent to which two similarly structured representations of a given preference relation can differ. Note that sufficient axioms are interesting by guaranteeing a representation. Necessity is relevant to avoid too excessive assumptions. Additionally, necessary axioms are fundamental when we want to illuminate the implicit assumptions in some presumed, but not really argued, representation of underlying preferences by for example a linear preference function.

The relevance of different **axioms** depend on the context. If we take a normative approach, and regard the axioms as expressions of the regularity or "rationality" which the DM wants to structure and guide the evaluations, we would like them to be "basic", "primitive", or "intuitive", so that the DM can accept them directly. If instead we take more of a descriptive approach, and seek a model imitating the DM's implicit evaluation we would probably be more concerned that they are testable, so that we can check their validity by questioning the DM.

2. Measurement Theory And Planning with Multiple Criteria

Based on the short outline above it is clear that measurement theory is relevant to the study of the choice activities in multiple criteria planning.

First, imagine that the choice set X is the set of basic decisions available to the DM. Now, if R is some (order) relation, we may want to identify conditions which R must fulfill such that (X,R) may be represented in $(\mathfrak{R},>)$, i.e. conditions guaranteeing the existence of a value function $v: X \rightarrow \mathfrak{R}$ such that

$$x'Rx'' \Leftrightarrow v(x') > v(x'')$$

If R represents the DM's evaluation from one perspective, e.g. the safety of cars, this concerns the existence and construction of a criterion such that more is preferred to less. If R represents the DM's comprehensive "better than" evaluation, this concerns the existence and construction of a preference function.

Secondly, imagine that the choice set is the set of alternatives in criteria space $Y=\{(f_1(x), \ldots, f_n(x)) \mid x \in X\} \subseteq \mathbb{R}^n$. We may now seek conditions on the DM's aggregate evaluation R^* of points in Y such that

$$y' R^* y'' \Leftrightarrow F(y') > F(y'')$$

Perhaps we even want the representation to hold with a special structure on F, e.g. a linear structure $F(y)=\Sigma_i \lambda_i v_i(y_i)$. This concerns the existence and construction of a particular type of aggregation of the n different criteria.

In summary, therefore, measurement theory is both directly and indirectly relevant to planning with multiple criteria. It is directly relevant when we seek to construct a complex model of the DM's preferences in parts and the DM is willing to accept certain axioms as part of the rationality he wants his behavior to conform with. It is indirectly relevant by illuminating the assumptions implicitly introduced when we claim that the DM's preferences may be represented in a given way, e.g. by a linear preference function. Furthermore, measurement theory relates to multiple criteria planning at two levels - it concerns both the existence and nature of criteria and the existence and nature of preference functions.

3. Strict Weak Orders

The classical preference model involves a binary relation $>^* \subseteq X^2$ interpreted as "strictly preferred to" and assumed to be a strict, weak order. From $>^*$ we may define a relation $\geq^*$ interpreted as "weakly preferred to" by

$$x' \geq^* x'' \Leftrightarrow \neg\, x'' >^* x'$$

and a relation $\approx^*$ interpreted as "indifferent to" may be defined by

$$x' \approx^* x'' \Leftrightarrow x' \geq^* x'' \wedge x'' \geq^* x'$$

When $>^*$ is a strict, weak order, $\geq^*$ becomes a weak order and $\approx^*$ an equivalence relation. Alternatively, we could start with $\geq^*$ being a "weak" order and derive $>^*$ as a strict weak order and $\approx^*$ as an equivalence relation by the definitions above.

A fundamental representation result for strict weak orders is the following. Recall that a set X is countable if there exists a function of $\{1,2,3, . . \}$ onto X, i.e. the elements of X may be enumerated.

Theorem 1
Let X be countable and $>^*$ a binary relation on X. Then $>^*$ is a strict weak order if and only if there exists a value function v: $X \rightarrow \Re$ exists such that

$$(1) \qquad x' >^* x'' \Leftrightarrow v(x') > v(x'') \quad \forall\ x',x'' \in X$$

Furthermore, the value function v is unique up to strictly increasing transformations, i.e. an alternative value function $v^\circ(.)$ gives the representation (1) if and only if $v^\circ(x) = g(v(x))$ for some $g: v(X) \rightarrow \Re$ strictly increasing. ○

Proof
We first prove that if a function such as v exists, $>^*$ must be a strict weak order, i.e. asymmetric and negative transitive. This is simple. By

$$x' >^* x'' \Leftrightarrow v(x') > v(x'') \Rightarrow \neg\ v(x'') > v(x') \Leftrightarrow \neg\ x'' >^* x'$$

we have asymmetry, and by

$$\neg\, x' >^* x'' \wedge \neg\, x'' >^* x''' \;\Leftrightarrow\; v(x') \leq v(x'') \wedge v(x'') \leq v(x''')$$
$$\Rightarrow\; v(x') \leq v(x''')$$
$$\Leftrightarrow\; \neg\, x' >^* x'''$$

we get negative transitivity.

Next, let us show that when $>^*$ ia a strict weak order it can be represented as in (1). Numerous constructive proofs are available. However, the following idea of D. Radford, used in Roberts(1979), seems especially simple. Let us list X as $x^1, x^2, x^3, \ldots$ . . . , and define r_{ij} as 1 if $x^i >^* x^j$ and as 0 otherwise. Now, consider

$$v(x_i) = \sum_{j=1}^{\infty} 2^{-j} r_{ij}$$

(If X is finite, we could simply use $v(x^i) = \Sigma_j r_{ij}$, i.e. the number of alternatives worse than x^i). Since $\Sigma_j 2^{-j}$ converges, so does $v(x^i)$, i.e. our definition of v(.) is valid. To prove the ($\Rightarrow$) part of (1), let $x' = x^i$ and $x'' = x^k$. Then $x^i >^* x^k$ gives us $\neg\, x^k >^* x^i$ by asymmetry and $\forall x''' \in X$: $x^k >^* x''' \Rightarrow x^i >^* x'''$ by transitivity, which is an implied consequence of the defining properties of a strict weak order, as mentioned earlier. Thus, $r_{kj} = 1 \Rightarrow r_{ij} = 1\ \forall j$, and since we have $r_{ik} = 1$ and $r_{ki} = 0$, we get

$$v(x^i) \geq v(x^k) + 2^{-k} > v(x^k)$$

The ($\Leftarrow$) part of (1) follows by a contradiction. Assume that $v(x_i) > v(x_k)$ but $\neg\, x^i >^*$ x^k. Then $x^i >^* x''' \Rightarrow x^k >^* x'''\ \forall x''' \in X$ by negative transitivity (and a contradiction), and hence $r_{ij} = 1 \Rightarrow r_{kj} = 1\ \forall j$, i.e. $v(x^i) \leq v(x^k)$ and we have the contradiction to $v(x^i) > v(x^k)$.

Finally, consider the uniqueness result. If v satisfies (1) and g is strictly increasing we have

$$x' >^* x'' \;\Leftrightarrow\; v(x') > v(x'') \;\Leftrightarrow\; g(v(x')) > g(v(x''))$$

and hence $v^\circ = g \circ v$ gives an equivalent representation. If on the other hand v° is an equivalent representation we have

$$(1^\circ) \qquad x' >^* x'' \Leftrightarrow v^\circ(x') > v^\circ(x'')$$

Together, (1) and (1°) give us $v(x') = v(x'') \Rightarrow v^\circ(x') = v^\circ(x'')$ and hence g defined by

$$g(v(x)) := v^\circ(x) \quad \forall\, x \in X$$

is well defined. Moreover g is strictly increasing on $v(X)$ since

$$v(x') > (x'') \Leftrightarrow v^\circ(x') > v^\circ(x'') \Leftrightarrow g(v(x')) > g(v(x''))$$

by (1) and (1°) and the definition of g. o

When X is not finite or countable, the existence of a representation like (1) - and hence the existence of criteria and preference functions - is not generally true. The key to noncountable cases is the notion of **relation order dense** subsets. A subset $X^\circ \subseteq X$ is $>^*$-order dense if and only if $\forall\, x',x'' \in X : x' >^* x'' \Rightarrow \exists\, x^\circ \in X^\circ : x' \geq^* x^\circ \geq^* x''$. Now, the general version of theorem 1, the Birkhoof-Milgram theorem, says that the representation (1) is possible if and only if $>^*$ is a strict weak order and has a countable order dense subset, c.f. fx. theorem 3.1 in Fishburn (1970). The proof of this result builds on the countable case by first constructing a representation on a certain countable order dense subset and next extending this "measurement" rod to the whole set in an obvious manner.

Next, let us turn to the case where the alternative or object set has **product structure**, say $Y = \Pi^n_{i=1} Y_i$ with $Y_i = [a_i, b_i]$, and $a_i, b_i \in \Re \cup \{-\infty, \infty\}$. When, for example, y represents a commodity bundle, vector addition and scalar multiplication make good sense. Therefore, we might substitute plain order denseness by other conditions, dominance and continuity, that seem more natural or economically intuitive. In fact, however, they accomplish the same.

Theorem 2

If $Y = \Pi^n_{i=1} [a_i,b_i] \subseteq \Re^n$, there exists a representation v: $Y \rightarrow \Re$ such that

$$(1') \qquad y' >^* y'' \Leftrightarrow v(y') > v(y'')$$

whenever

(i) $>^*$ is a strict weak order on Y,

(ii) $>^*$ satisfies the **dominance**/nonsaturation condition

$\forall\, y',y'' : [\forall i{:}y'_i \geq y''_i \wedge \exists j{:}y'_j > y''_j] \Rightarrow y' >^* y''$, and

(iii) $>^*$ satisfies the **continuity**/Archimedean condition

$\forall\, y' >^* y^o >^* y'' \;\; \exists\, \lambda \in [0,1] : y^o \approx^* \lambda y' + (1-\lambda)y''$ ○

Proof

We prove the theorem for the case $Y=[a,b]^n$. Other cases may be handled by transforming the variables or by "similar reasoning". A general proof is given in Fishburn (1970), Ch. 3. The proof involves two steps.

First, observe that

$$\forall\, y \in Y \; \exists!\, \alpha \in \Re: y \approx^* \alpha(1, . . ,1)$$

i.e. each vector is indifferent to precisely one diagonal vector. To see this, let

$$y^{max} = (\max_i y_i)(1, . . . ,1), \; y^{min} = (\min_i y_i)(1, . . . ,1).$$

If $y=y^{max}=y^{min}$, y is a diagonal vector directly. If not, dominance gives us

$$y^{max} \geq y \geq y^{min} \Rightarrow \exists \lambda: y \approx^* \lambda y^{max} + (1-\lambda)y^{min}$$

Now, let $\alpha = \lambda \max_i y_i + (1-\lambda)\min_i y_i$, and again we have a diagonal vector indifferent to y. The equivalent diagonal vector is unique since

$$y \approx^* (\alpha, . . . ,\alpha) \wedge y \approx^* (\alpha', . . . ,\alpha') \Rightarrow (\alpha, . . . ,\alpha) \approx^* (\alpha', . . . ,\alpha') \Rightarrow \alpha = \alpha'$$

by transitivity of $\approx^*$ and dominance of $>^*$.

Next, let

$$v(y) = \alpha(y)$$

where $\alpha(y)$ is determined uniquely as above. Then we have

$$\begin{aligned} y' >^* y'' &\Leftrightarrow \alpha(y')(1, \ldots, 1) >^* \alpha(y'')(1, \ldots, 1) \\ &\Leftrightarrow \alpha(y') > \alpha(y'') \\ &\Leftrightarrow v(y') > v(y'') \end{aligned}$$

where the first bi-implication follows from the definition of α and the rule $y^1 \approx^* y^2 >^* y^3 \Rightarrow y^1 >^* y^3$, which is easily proved, the second follows from dominance and the fact that the vectors compared are diagonal, and the last is by definition of v. ○

The proof of theorem 2 is instructive. We essentially transform the multiple dimensional problem to a one dimensional problem by extensive use of the indifference relation. Any point in Y is equally good as precisely one diagonal vector. In other words, all indifference surfaces intersect the line composed of diagonal vectors. Hereby, the problem is reduced to one of developing a representation over this line and the dominance assumption makes this a trivial task.

Usually, we do not only want a representation, we also want it to be convenient. The simplicity looked for has typically been additivity. A value function v representing $>^*$ as in (1) is said to give an **additive, representation** if functions $v_i : Y_i \rightarrow \Re$ exist such that

$$(2) \qquad v(y_1, \ldots, y_n) = \sum_{i=1}^{n} v_i(y_i) \quad \forall\, y \in Y$$

There is of course nothing magic about addition as opposed to other specifications like for example multiplication. Indeed, if $v_i(y_i) \geq 0$, we might by the uniqueness part of theorem 1 equivalently represent the preferences by the multiplicative model $v^o(y) = \Pi^n_{i=1} v^o_i(y_i)$ where $v^o_i(y_i) = \exp(v_i(y_i))$, since exp(.) and log(.) are strictly increasing transformations. What is essential, however, is the high degree of **decomposability, separability** or **independence** embedded in (2).

When Y is finite, it is possible to describe necessary and sufficient conditions for the existence of an additive representation, c.f. for example Fishburn(1970), chapter 4, or Krantz et al.(1971), chapter 9. The idea is "simple". The ability to produce an additive representation comes down to whether or not one can find a solution to a given set of linear equalities and inequalities. Next, using Faka's Lemma, these conditions are transformed into the requirements that, loosely speaking, all conceivable cancellation axioms hold. These include the independence assumptions below. Also, Thomsen's condition below gives a (mild) taste of what this amounts to. The problem with this approach is that many of the derived condisions are completely unintuitive.

Without the assumption of finiteness, necessary and sufficient conditions are - to the best of our knowledge - still an open question. However, sufficient conditions including some important necessary ones are known. Below, we present some of the relevant theory as developed by Luce and Tukey(1969) and subsequently refined by Krantz et al.(1971), chapter 6.

Let us start by the **necessary** conditions. The first axiom, A1, is obvious in view of theorem 1

A1: $>^*$ is a strict weak order

This hypothesis is maintained throughout this section but it will be loosened later.

To formulate the next axiom, let us for any $M \subseteq \{1, \ldots, n\}$, use $(y'_{i\in M}, y''_{i\notin M})$ to denote the vector y with coordinates $y_i = y'_i$ when $i \in M$ and $y_i = y''_i$ when $i \in \{1, \ldots, n\} \setminus M$. Now, the second necessary condition is the essential decomposition, separability or independence assumption

A2: $>^*$ is (strongly) independent, i.e.

$$\forall \ M \subseteq \{1, \ldots, n\}:$$

$$(y'_{i \in M}, y_{i \notin M}) >^* (y''_{i \in M}, y_{i \notin M}) \text{ for some } y, y', y'' \in Y$$

$$\Downarrow \ (y'_{i \in M}, y^{\circ}_{i \notin M}) >^* (y''_{i \in M}, y^{\circ}_{i \notin M}) \text{ for all } y^{\circ} \in Y$$

This assumption is often expressed by saying that the n attributes are **mutually preferentially independent** (MPI). Also, any set M fulfilling the implication is called **preferentially independent** (PI) of its complement. To show the necessity of A2, simply use (1) and (2) to write the above preference inequalities in value terms and prove the implication by cancelling identical terms.

Consider the induced preferences $>^*_M$ on the M attributes defined by

$$(y'_{i \in M}) >^*_M (y''_{i \in M}) \Leftrightarrow (y'_{i \in M}, y_{i \notin M}) >^* (y''_{i \in M}, y_{i \notin M})$$

for some fixed value of $(y_{i \notin M})$. It is easy to see that the binary relation $>^*_M$ on $\Pi_{i \in M} Y_i$ defined this way is a strict weak order. Now, independence means that this conditional preference model given $(y_{i \notin M})$ is independent of the values of these other attributes.

When $n=2$, the independence assumption simply says that the value of y_2 cannot change the ranking of y_1 values and vice versa. Thus, it is basically the general "more is preferred to less" assumption made throughout the main text. When $n>2$, the independence assumption has substantially more implications. If, for example, $n=3$, it implies that the trade-offs between y_1 and y_2 must be independent of the level of y_3.

Control of the (strong) independence assumption is of course very difficult, since it involves considering the conditional preferences on all possible M for all possible values of $(y_{i \notin M})$. The first of these multiplicities may be partly avoided by building up MPI from a set of more limited PI results. A fundamental result by Gorman(1968a,b) demonstrates this.

Lemma 1
Let $M_1 \subseteq \{1, \ldots, n\}$, $M_2 \subseteq \{1, \ldots, n\}$ such that $M_1 \cap M_2 \neq \emptyset$, $M_1 \cup M_2 \neq \{1, \ldots, n\}$. Then if M_1 and M_2 are preferentially independent of their respective complements, so is $M_1 \cup M_2$, $M_1 \cap M_2$, $M_1 \setminus M_2$, $M_2 \setminus M_1$, and $(M_1 \setminus M_2) \cup (M_2 \setminus M_1)$. ○

We will not prove this result, but simply note an obvious implication. If (y_i, y_{i+1}) is PI of its complement, $i=1, \ldots, n-1$ or if (y_1, y_i) is PI of its complement, $i=2, \ldots, n$, then $y_1, \ldots, y_n$ are MPI. So, to build up the rather demanding MPI condition, it actually suffices to guarantee n-1 pairwise preferential independencies.

The next condition is somewhat harder to understand. It concerns the case $n=2$, where the independence assumption above has more limited implications.

<u>A3:</u> The Thomsen Condition/Double Cancellation with Indifferences:
When $n=2$, $\forall\ y, y', y'' \in Y$:

$$(y_1, y_2) \approx^* (y'_1, y'_2) \wedge (y'_1, y''_2) \approx^* (y''_1, y_2)$$
$$\Downarrow$$
$$(y_1, y''_2) \approx^* (y''_1, y'_2)$$

Again the proof of necessity is simple. By (1), $y \approx^* y^\circ \Leftrightarrow v(y) = v(y^\circ)$, so we can rewrite the above indifference equations as value equations. Now, using (2) and adding the first two equations and cancelling identical terms, we get the implication. To understand the intuition, one may think as follows. If we are just willing to pay for the increase $y_1 \uparrow y'_1$ by the decrease $y_2 \downarrow y'_2$ and we are just willing to pay for the increase $y'_1 \uparrow y''_1$ by the decrease $y''_2 \downarrow y_2$, we must also be just willing to pay for the whole increase $y_1 \uparrow y''_1$ by the whole decrease $y''_2 \downarrow y'_2$. Of course, this ability to independently add increases and decreases in the two dimensions lies at the heart of an additive representation.

The last necessary condition requires a new concept. Let $(y_i^k)_{k=1,2..}$ be a sequence of values of the i'th attribute. Such a sequence is called a **standard sequence** if and only if (a) $\neg(y_i^1 \approx^*_i y_i^2)$ and (b) $\exists\ y_{-i}, y'_{-i} \in \Pi_{j\neq i} Y_j : (y'_{-i}, y_i^k) \approx^* (y_{-i}, y_i^{k-1})\ \forall k$. So, loosely speaking, a standard sequence is a sequence of attribute values with constant value change. The change in attributes $y_i^{k-1} \rightarrow y_i^k$ is constantly offset by the same change $y_{-i} \rightarrow y'_{-i}$, in the other attributes. Now, the necessary condition may be stated as

<u>A4:</u> The Archimedean Condition:

$$\forall i \in \{1, \ldots, n\}\ \forall\ (y_i^k)_{k=1,2,\ldots}\ \text{standard sequence:}$$
$$\neg\ [\ \exists\ y_i^U, y_i^L \in Y_i : y^U_i \geq^*_i y_i^k \geq^*_i y_i^L\ \ \forall k\ ]$$

i.e. every (infinite) standard sequence must be unbounded. The proof of necessity is again simple. If $(y_i^k)_{k=1,2,\ldots}$ is a standard sequence, (1),(2) and (b) imply

$$v_i(y_i^k)-v_i(y_i^{k-1}) = \sum_{j\neq i} v'_j(y_j) - \sum_{j\neq i} v_j(y'_j)$$

Now, the right hand side is a constant value change independent of k. It cannot be 0 since this would contradict (a). Also, if it is positive (negative), we get $v_i(y_i^k) \rightarrow \infty(-\infty)$ for $k \rightarrow \infty$. Hence, we cannot have an upper (lower) bound y_i^U (y_i^L) on y_i^k $\forall k$. An alternative formulation of The Archimedean Condition says that every bounded standard sequence must be finite. But either way the result is that constant preference difference between y_i^k and y_i^{k-1} cannot be so small that it is possible to pack infinitely many between two "prizes" y_i^U and y_i^L. It helps rule out order denseness difficulties. Also, let us note that socalled Archimedean Axioms are part of most representation results. They generally state that nothing can be infinitely good nor bad.

The next assumption is not necessary, but it works together with the above assumptions to give a set of sufficient axioms. It says that

<u>A5:</u> Restricted Solvability:

$$\forall i \in \{1, \ldots, n\},\ y, y' \in Y,\ y_i^U, y_i^L \in Y_i:$$
$$(y_{-i}, y_i^U) >^* y' >^* (y_{-i}, y_i^L)\ \Rightarrow\ \exists\ y^\circ_i \in Y_i: (y_{-i}, y^\circ_i) \approx^* y'$$

This is clearly a continuity axiom. When changing from y_i^U to y_i^L gives a jump in preference levels, it must also be possible to trace out all intermediate levels. The axiom substantially strengthens the other axioms by saying that these hold for a lot of points.

Also, let us define the notation of an **essential component**. We say that the i'the attribute $i \in \{1, \ldots, n\}$ is essential if and only if

$$\exists\, y_i^U, y_i^L \in Y_i: (y_{-i}, y_i^U) > (y_{-i}, y_i^L)$$

for some value of y_{-i}. So an attribute is essential if its value ever matters to the DM.

Now, the main theorem on additive measurement may be formulated as follows.

Theorem 3

Let $>^*$ be a binary relation on $Y = \Pi^n_{i=1} Y_i$. Then sufficient sets of conditions for there to be an additive conjoint representation

$$y' >^* y'' \Leftrightarrow \sum_{i=1}^{n} v_i(y'_i) > \sum_{i=1}^{n} v_i(y''_i)$$

are

(i) For three or more essential components: A1, A2, A4, A5

(ii) For two essential components: A1, A2, A3, A4, A5

Also, in either case, $v^\circ_1, \ldots, v^\circ_n$ gives an alternative additive representation if and only if

$$v^\circ_i(.) = \alpha_i + \beta v_i(.) \qquad i=1, \ldots, n$$

for some $\beta>0$, $\alpha_1, \ldots, \alpha_n \in \Re$. ○

The proof of this theorem is given in Krantz et al.(1971), chapters 2 and 6.

Finally, let us note that although additive representations are the classical ones, numerous other less demanding and consequently less simple representations have been studied. Thus, for example, there is an extensive literature on **quasi-additive representations** which for the case n=2 looks

$$v(y_1,y_2) = v_1(y_1) + v_2(y_2) + \lambda_1(y_1)\lambda_2(y_2)$$

where $\lambda_1(y_1)\lambda_2(y_2)$ allows for some degree of interaction. Introductions and references to this and other related representations may be found in Krantz et al.(1971) and Roberts(1971).

4. Semi Orders, Interval Orders and Pseudo Orders

To capture the possibility that indifferences may not be transitive, we can model criteria or preferences as **semi-orders**. Thus, let us assume that the "strictly preferred to" relation $>^* \subseteq X^2$ is a total semi-order, c.f. figure A2.2, and let us define indifferences in the usual way

$$x \approx^* x' \Leftrightarrow \neg\, x >^* x' \;\wedge\; \neg\, x' >^* x$$

In this model, the indifference relation need not be transitive. This can be seen most clearly from the following representation theorem for semi-orders due to Scott and Suppes(1958).

Theorem 4
Let X be finite, $>^*$ a binary relation on X and $\delta>0$ a threshold. Then $>^*$ is a total semi-order if and only if there exists a value function v: $X \rightarrow \Re$ such that

$$(3) \qquad x >^* x' \Leftrightarrow v(x) > v(x') + \delta \qquad \bigcirc$$

Different proofs of this theorem may be found in the general references to this appendix. Let us just note that the necessity of $>^*$ being a semi-order is easily proved. Also, the choice of δ is arbitrary. Thus, if v represents $>^*$ as in (3), $v^\circ(.)=[\delta'/\delta]v(.)$ also represents $>^*$, with threshold value equal to δ'

When v represents $>^*$ as in (3), the indifference condition becomes

$$x \approx^* x' \Leftrightarrow |v(x)-v(x')| \leq \delta$$

This is clearly not a transitive relation. If, e.g. $v(x_1) = 0$, $v(x^2) = 0.75\delta$, and $v(x^3) = 1.5\delta$, we have $x^1 \approx^* x^2 \wedge x^2 \approx^* x^3$ but $x^3 >^* x^1$.

Sometimes the assumption of an indifference-preference threshold q, which is fixed independently of the values x and x' being compared, may be too demanding. Equivalently, the semi-transitivity assumption P10 in figure A2.1 may seem unrealistic. In such cases, one may consider modelling criteria or preferences as **interval orders.** The fundamental representation theorem for interval orders is given in our next theorem.

Theorem 5

Let X be countable and $>^*$ a binary relation on x. Then $>^*$ is a total interval order if and only if there exist v(.) and q(.): $X \rightarrow \Re_+$ such that

$$(4) \qquad x >^* x' \Leftrightarrow v(x) > v(x') + q(x') \qquad \circ$$

The sufficiency of $>^*$ being a total interval order is proved in Fishburn(1970) p. 21-22, and the necessity is trivial to prove.

To interprete the interval order, let

$$I(x) = [v(x), v(x)+q(x)] \quad \forall x \in X$$

This interval may be thought of as the set of potential performances attached to x. So we are somewhat vague or fuzzy about how well x is going to perform, or about what we really mean by performing. Now, the representation (4) reads

$$x >^* x' \Leftrightarrow \forall\, z \in I(x),\, z' \in I(x'): z > z'$$
$$\Leftrightarrow I(x) \text{ is all to the right of } I(x')$$

Also, the condition for indifference may be written

$$x \approx^* x' \Leftrightarrow \neg\, x > x' \;\wedge\; \neg\, x' > x$$
$$\Leftrightarrow I(x) \cap I(x') \neq \emptyset$$

Thus we strictly prefer x to x' if and only if all conceivable outcomes from x, I(x), is better than those possibly resulting from x', I(x'). If, on the other hand, the two intervals intersect, we cannot precisely say whether we will be better off choosing x or x' and we regard them as indifferent, i.e. not ranked. Also, let us note that a semi-order corresponds to the special case of an interval order where $q(x) = \delta$, i.e. the same level of vagueness holds throughout, and that the strict weak ordering of the last section is the special case where $q(x) \equiv 0$, i.e. no vagueness at all.

The above models take into account that small differences in performance may not matter while larger ones may. Still, in some sense, this just pushes the problem to the next level. In the semi-order model, for example, how can we feel that a difference of δ does not matter, while a difference ever so slightly above δ does? It seems more natural simply to let increasing differences represent increasing degrees of preferences. The generalized criteria of the Promethee method, cf. Brans and Vincke(1985,86), is a good illustration of this idea. Unfortunately, to formalize the measurement basis of this kind of criteria, i.e. give axiomatic relation system descriptions, we probably have to turn to the fuzzy literature, and this goes beyond our intentions. Also the idea of complete valued preference structures where a whole family of orders is defined corresponding to different preference intensities, seems important here. See Roubens and Vincke(1985), chapter 5, for an introduction.

Still, one step in this direction may be introduced by simply having two thresholds. In the **pseudo-order** preference model by Vincke(1980), see also Roubens and Vincke(1985), chapter 6, and Roy and Vincke(1984), there are two exclusive preferences, a "strict preference" S and a "weak preference" W, $S \cap W = \emptyset$. Then indifference I is given by the complement

$$xIx' \Leftrightarrow \neg\, xSx' \wedge \neg\, xWx' \wedge \neg\, x'Wx \wedge \neg\, x'Sx$$

If we assume both S and $S \cup W$ to be semi-orders, and naturally connected as specified below, we get a representation with both an indifference threshold q(.) and a preference threshold p(.), cf. Vincke(1980).

Theorem 6

Let X be countable and S and W be binary, exclusive relations on X. Then S is a semi-order, $S \cup W$ is a semi-order and $SIW \subseteq S$, $WIS \subseteq S$, $SWI \subseteq S$, $IWS \subseteq S$, if and only if there exist $v(.): X \rightarrow \mathfrak{R}$, $q(.): \mathfrak{R} \rightarrow \mathfrak{R}_+$, $p(.): \mathfrak{R} \rightarrow \mathfrak{R}_+$ such that

$$xSx' \Leftrightarrow v(x) > v(x') + p(v(x'))$$
$$xWx' \Leftrightarrow v(x') + q(v(x')) < v(x) \leq v(x') + p(v(x')) \qquad \bigcirc$$

In this theorem, we have used socalled relative products of relations. If R and P are two binary relations, RP simply means $\{(x,x') \in X^2 \mid \exists\, x'' \in X: xRx'' \wedge x''Px'\}$. Thus, for example, $SIW \subseteq S$ is just a short way of writing $x^1Sx^2 \wedge x^2Ix^3 \wedge x^3Wx^4 \Rightarrow x^1Sx^4$. The pseudo-order preference model in the case of level-independent thresholds is illustrated in figure A2.3 below.

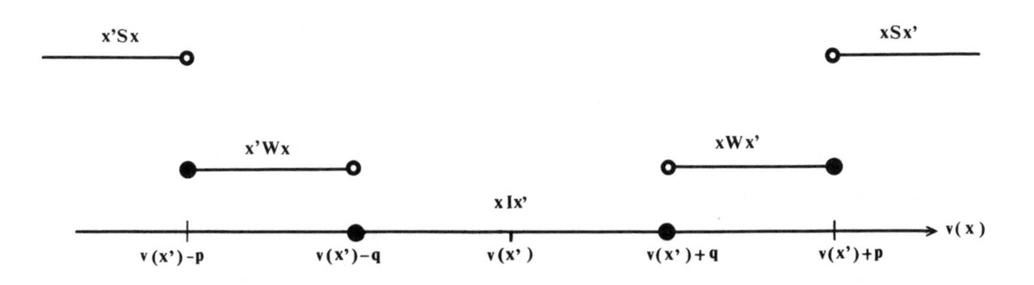

Figure A2.3 A Pseudo-Order Preference Model

In this section we have allowed for intransitive indifferences of criteria or preferences defined directly on X. Unfortunately, there are to the best of our knowledge - no simple results on these less demanding models applied to a product structure $Y = \Pi^n_{i=1} Y_i$. Interested readers may find it useful to consult the rather general theory of conjoint measurement by Tversky(1967). Also, an interesting starting point could be the additive difference model in Tversky(1969), where functions v_i: $Y_i \rightarrow \Re$ and continous, increasing Φ_i: $\Re \rightarrow \Re$ are sought so as to represent

$$y >^* y' \Leftrightarrow \sum_{i=1}^{n} \Phi_i\,[v_i(y_i)-v_i(y_i')] > 0$$

Note that the additive measurement model of the last section corresponds to the special case $\Phi_i(\delta)=\delta$.

In the semi-order, interval-order and pseudo-order models we have assumed that preferences are semi-transitive

P10: $x^1 \;{}^*\!> x^2 \wedge x^2 \;{}^*\!> x^3 \Rightarrow x^1 >^* x^4 \vee x^4 >^* x^3$

or at least a Ferrers relation

P11: $x^1 >^* x^2 \wedge x^3 >^* x^4 \Rightarrow x^1 >^* x^4 \vee x^3 >^* x^2$

As demonstrated above, these assumptions allow for intransitive indifferences. Still, they may not be satisfied if several factors influence preferences or if there is only one basic factor along which preferences increase up to a point and thereafter decrease. Thus, for example, if x measures the amount of sugar in a cup of coffee and you are most happy with 10 units of sugar, you might well feel that $3 >^* 2 \wedge 17 >^* 18$ but $3 \approx^* 18 \wedge 17 \approx^* 2$ in contradiction with P11. Also you might feel that $16 >^* 17 >^* 18$ but $16 \approx^* 3 \wedge 3 \approx^* 18$ in contradiction with P10. These "inconsistencies" may be thought of as a result of the single peaked preference and a lack of discriminating power. Or they may be explained by multiple factors. The amount of sugar may not only determine the sweetness, but also influence the temperature. When comparing 3 and 2, 17 and 18 or 16, 17 and 18, respectively, the temperature may be relatively constant, and you may simply focus on sweetness. However, when comparing across levels, like 3 vs. 18, temperature suddenly may become important, and you might find it hard to state a ranking.

5. Partial Orders

Even more flexibility is offered by modelling criteria and preferences as **partial orders**. Thus, assuming $>^*$ to be a strict partial order, includes as special cases the strict weak, the total semi and the total interval orders as one may easily check. Apart from allowing for intransitive indifferences, the general partial order model allows for more incomparabilities than the semi and interval order models. Thus, for example, it is easy to see that $>^* = \{(x_1,x_2),(x_3,x_4)\}$ defined on $X=\{x^1,x^2,x^3,x^4\}$ is a strict partial order, but neither a strict weak, a semi or an interval order. These latter models do not allow $>^*$ to have two or more completely unrelated sets of internally ranked alternatives, cf. the Ferrers property.

The basic representation theorem for partial orders is not very useful in practice. However, it does indicate some of the basic problems of working with partial rankings in decision making contexts. Following Fishburn(1970) it runs as follows. Let $\approx^*$ denote the usual indifference relation, i.e. a lack of expressed preference

$$x \approx^* x' \Leftrightarrow \neg\, x >^* x' \wedge \neg\, x' >^* x$$

Also, let $\simeq^*$ be the special part of $\approx^*$ defined by

$$x \simeq^* x' \Leftrightarrow x \approx^* x' \wedge (x \approx^* x'' \Leftrightarrow x' \approx^* x'' \;\forall x''\in X)$$

It is easy to check that $\simeq^*$ is an equivalence relation when $>^*$ is a strict partial order.

Theorem 7

Let X be countable and $>^*$ a strict partial order on X. Then there exists a $v: X \rightarrow \Re$ such that

$$x >^* x' \Rightarrow v(x) > v(x')$$
$$x \simeq^* x' \Rightarrow v(x) = v(x')$$

○

The problem with this representation is that although it faithfully represents $>^*$ and $\simeq^*$, it does not guarantee $v(x)=v(x')$ when $(x \approx^* x' \wedge \neg\, x \simeq^* x')$. In this case we may have $v(x) < v(x')$, $v(x) = v(x')$, or $v(x) > v(x')$. Clearly, with such a representation, it is not justified to pick as the "best" plan an x with maximal value of $v(x)$.

Appendix 3

SYMBOLS AND ABBREVIATION

The following is an overview of the major notation and abbreviations employed in the text. Omitted are more elementary symbols such as "=", "+", "-", ">", and "≥".

$y=(y_1, \ldots, y_n)$ The vector y is an ordered collection of n numbers, sometimes referred to as n coordinates. E.g. $x=(1.3, 6)$ is a 2-dimensional vector with coordinates 1.3 and 6. The coordinates of a vector are typically indicated in the text by the same symbol as the vector together with a subscript. E.g. y_i is the i'th coordinate of the vector y.

$X=\{x^1, \ldots, x^n\}$ The set X represents the collection of n elements $x^1, \ldots, x^n$. In the context of the book, an element x^i will typically either represent a single number or a vector of numbers. Elements of a set are often indicated in the text by lower case letters possibly with superscripts. E.g. x is any element of X and x^i is the specific "i'th" element of X.

$\emptyset$ The empty set

$\Re$ The set of all real numbers

$\Re^n$ The set of all points, each of which is defined by an n-dimensional vector of real numbers.

$\in$ "Belongs to" or "is a member of". E.g. $x \in X$ means that x is a member of X.

$\notin$	"Does not belong to"
$\subseteq$	"Is a subset of". E.g. $\{(5, -18)\}\subseteq C$ means that the vector (5, -18) belongs to C and that C possibly contains additional elements.
$\subset$	"Is a proper subset of". E.g. $\{(5, -18)\}\subset C$ means that the set composed of the vector (5, -18) is a subset of the set C which also contains additional elements, i.e. $C \neq \{(5, -18)\}$.
$\cup$	"The union of". E.g. if $A=\{1,2\}$ and $B=\{3,4\}$ then $A\cup B$ is the set formed by uniting the elements of A and B, i.e. $\{1,2,3,4\}$.
$\cap$	"The intersection of". E.g. if $A=\{0,1,6\}$ and $B=\{4,7,1\}$, then $A\cap B$ is the set composed of those elements which belong to both A and B, i.e. $\{1\}$.
X x Y	"The Cartesian product of the sets X and Y". I.e. the set of vectors (x,y) where $x\in X$ and $y\in Y$.
$\mid$	"Given that" or "for which". E.g. $Y = \{(f_1(x), \ldots, f_n(x)) \mid x\in X\}$ refers to the set of all points $(f_1(x), \ldots, f_n(x))$ for which x is a member of the set X.
$\exists$	"There exists"
$\forall$	"For all"
:	"Such that"
g: X→Y	A function g, i.e. a procedure which to each element x in a set X assigns an element g(x) in the set Y.
→	"Assigns" or "maps".

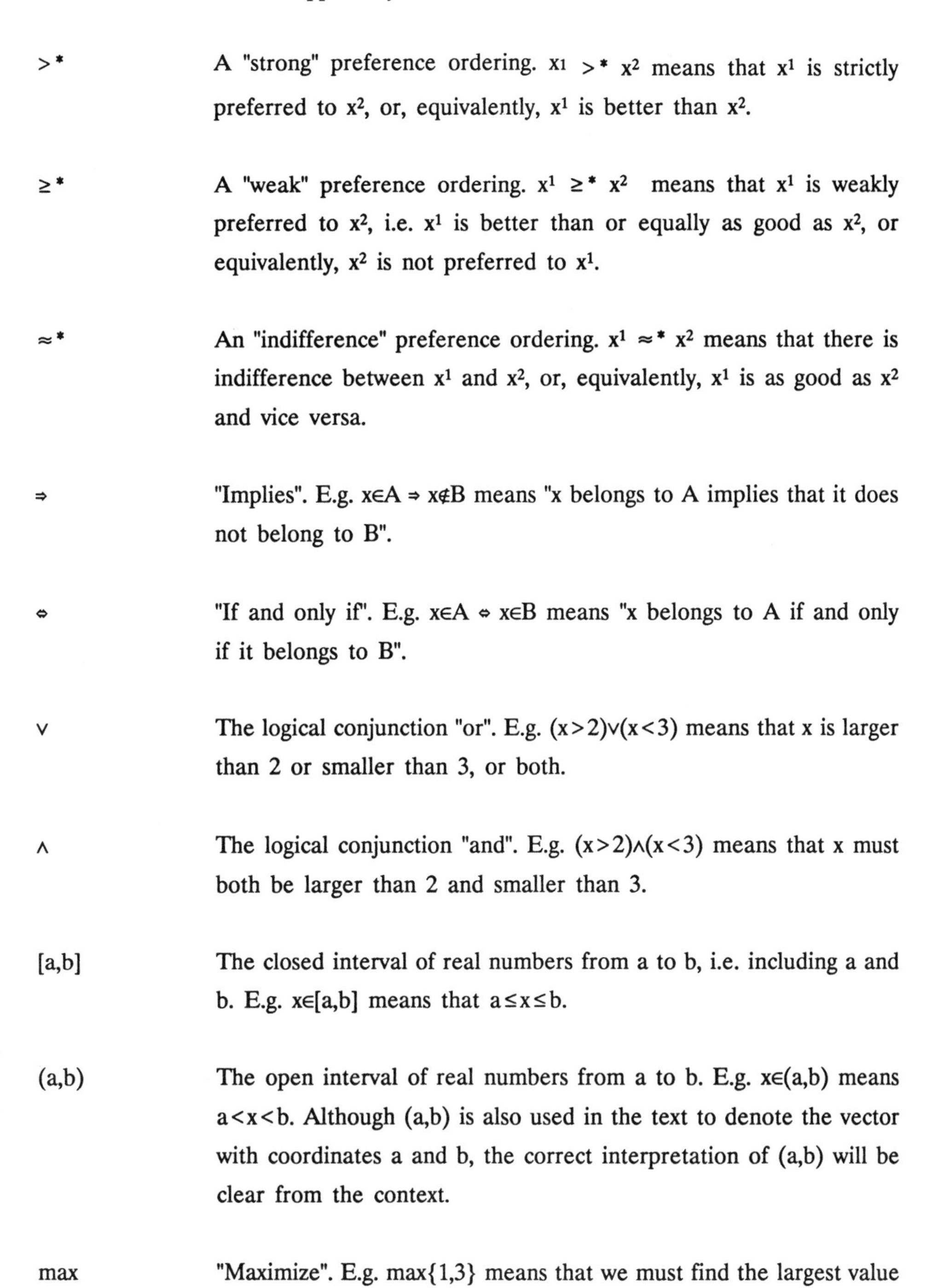

$>^*$ — A "strong" preference ordering. $x_1 >^* x^2$ means that x^1 is strictly preferred to x^2, or, equivalently, x^1 is better than x^2.

$\geq^*$ — A "weak" preference ordering. $x^1 \geq^* x^2$ means that x^1 is weakly preferred to x^2, i.e. x^1 is better than or equally as good as x^2, or equivalently, x^2 is not preferred to x^1.

$\approx^*$ — An "indifference" preference ordering. $x^1 \approx^* x^2$ means that there is indifference between x^1 and x^2, or, equivalently, x^1 is as good as x^2 and vice versa.

$\Rightarrow$ — "Implies". E.g. $x \in A \Rightarrow x \notin B$ means "x belongs to A implies that it does not belong to B".

$\Leftrightarrow$ — "If and only if". E.g. $x \in A \Leftrightarrow x \in B$ means "x belongs to A if and only if it belongs to B".

$\vee$ — The logical conjunction "or". E.g. $(x>2) \vee (x<3)$ means that x is larger than 2 or smaller than 3, or both.

$\wedge$ — The logical conjunction "and". E.g. $(x>2) \wedge (x<3)$ means that x must both be larger than 2 and smaller than 3.

[a,b] — The closed interval of real numbers from a to b, i.e. including a and b. E.g. $x \in [a,b]$ means that $a \leq x \leq b$.

(a,b) — The open interval of real numbers from a to b. E.g. $x \in (a,b)$ means $a<x<b$. Although (a,b) is also used in the text to denote the vector with coordinates a and b, the correct interpretation of (a,b) will be clear from the context.

max — "Maximize". E.g. max{1,3} means that we must find the largest value in the set {1,3}, i.e. 3.

s.t. "Subject to". E.g. max g(x) s.t. $x \in X$ means that we must find the largest value of g(x) subject to the condition that x belongs to X, i.e. it is equivalent to $\max\{g(x) \mid x \in X\}$.

REFERENCES[1]

Ackoff, R.L., A Concept of Corporate Planning, Wiley, 1970.

Ackoff, R.A., Redesigning the Future - A Systems Approach to Societal Problems, Wiley, 1974.

Arieti, S., Creativity - the Magic Synthesis, Basic Books, 1976.

Arrow, K.J., The Limits of Organization, W.W. Norton, 1974.

Arrow, K.J., E.W. Barankin and D. Blackwell, *Admissible Points of Convex Sets*, in: H.W. Kohn and A.W. Tucker (eds.), Contribution to the Theory of Games, Princeton University Press, 1953, pp 87-91.

Atkins, D.R., *Decentralization by Joint Price and Budget Controls: The Problem and An Important Special Case*, Working Paper, University of British Columbia, 1979.

Banathy, B.H. and B.A. Banathy (eds.), Toward a Just Society for Future Generations, Proceedings of the Annual Conference of the International Society for the Systems Sciences, 1990.

Bell, D., R. Keeney and H. Raiffa (eds.), Conflicting Objectives in Decisions, Wiley, 1977.

Benayoun, R., J. de Montgolfier, J. Tergny and O. Laritcher, *Linear Programming with Multi Objective Functions, Step Method (STEM)*, **Mathematical Programming**, 1971, 1, 366-371.

Benson, H.P. and T.L. Morin, *The Vector Maximization Problem: Proper Efficiency and Stability*, **SIAM Journal on Applied mathematics**, 1977, 32, 64-72.

Bergstresser, K. and P.L. Yu, *Domination Structures and Multiple Criteria Problems in N-Person Games*, **Theory and Decision**, 1977, 8, 5-48.

Bogetoft, P., *Characterizing and Selecting Efficient Decisions*, Publications from Department of Management, 1985a, 1/85, Odense University (in Danish).

[1] Books are underlined, articles are in italics and journals are in bold-face.

Bogetoft, P., *On General Duality in Multicriteria Optimization*, Publications from Department of Management, 1985b, 2/85, Odense University.

Bogetoft, P., *General Communication Schemes for Multiobjective Decision Making*, **European Journal of Operational Research**, 1986, 26, 108-122.

Bogetoft, P., *Choosing Between Models of Choice: On the Selection of MCDM Planning Modes*, Proceedings, IXth International Conference on MCDM, 1990, pp 1-15, to appear.

Bogetoft, P., Å. Hallefjord and M. Kok, *On the Convergence of Reference Point Methods in Multiobjective Programming*, **European Journal of Operational Research**, 1988, 34, 56-68.

Bogetoft, P. and P. Pruzan, *Towards a Contextual Theory of MCDM*, working paper, DASY, Copenhagen Business School, 1990.

Bogetoft, P. and J. Tind, *Dual Decomposition Schemes for Multicriteria Decision Making*, **IMA Journal of Mathematics Applied in Business and Industry**, 1990, to appear.

Brans, J.P. and Ph. Vincke, *A Preference Ranking Organization Method*, **Management Science**, 1985, 31, 647-656.

Brans, J.P. and Ph. Vincke, *How to Select and How to Rank Projects: The Promethee Method*, **European Journal of Operational Research**, 1986, 24, 228-238.

Burkard, R.E., H.W. Hamacher and J. Tind, *On General Decomposition Schemes in Mathematical Programming*", **Mathematical Programming Study**, 1985, 24, 238-252.

Burkard, R.E., H. Keiding, J. Krarup and P. Pruzan, *A Relationship between Optimality and Efficiency*, **Computers and Operations Research**, 1981, 8, 241-247.

Burkard, R.E., J. Krarup and P. Pruzan, *Efficiency and Optimality in Minisum, Minimax 0-1 Programming Problems*, **Journal of the Operational Research Society**, 1982, 33, 137-150.

Burkard, R.E., J. Krarup and P. Pruzan, *Some Relationships between Multicriteria and Parametric Discrete Optimization Problems with Bottleneck Objectives*, **Deutsche Zeitschrift für Operationsforschung und Statistik**, 1989, 5, 389-396.

Burton, R.M. and B. Obel, Designing Efficient Organizations, Modelling and Experimentation, North-Holland, 1984.

Chankong, V. and Y.Y. Haimes, Multiobjective Decision Making: Theory and Methodology, North-Holland, 1983a.

Chankong, V. and Y.Y. Haimes, *Optimization-Based Methods for Multiobjective Decision-Making: An Overview*, **Large Scale Systems**, 1983b, 5, 1-33.

Charnes, A. and W.W. Cooper, Management Models and Industrial Applications of Linear Programming, Vol. I., Wiley, 1961.

Charnes, A. and W.W. Cooper, *Goal Programming and Multiple Objective Optimization*, **European Journal of Operational Research**, 1977, 1, 39-54.

Cochrane, J.L. and M. Zeleny (eds.), Multiple Criteria Decision Making, University of South Carolina Press, 1973.

Corley, N.W., *A New Scalar Equivalent for Pareto Optimization*, **IEEE Trans. on Automatic Control**, 1980, AC-25, 829-830.

DaCunha, N.O. and E. Polak, *Constrained Minimization under Vector Valued Criteria in Finite Dimensional Spaces*, **Journal of Mathematical Analysis and Applications**, 1967, 19, 103-124.

DeGroot, M., Optimal Statistical Decisions, McGraw-Hill, 1970.

DeSanctis, G. and R.B. Gallupe, *A Foundation for the Study of Group Decision Support Systems*, **Management Science**, 1987, 33, 589-609.

Dirickx, Y.M.I. and L.P. Jennergren, System Analysis by Multilevel Methods, Wiley, 1979.

Evans, G.W., *An Overview of Techniques for Solving Multi-Objective Mathematical Programs*, **Management Science**, 1984, 30, 1268-1282.

Faludi, A., Planning Theory, Pergamon Press, 1973.

Fandel, G. and T. Gal (eds.), Multiple Criteria Decision Making: Theory and Applications, Lecture Notes in Economics and Mathematical Systems, 177, Springer-Verlag, 1980.

Fandel, G. and J. Spronk (eds.), Multiple Criteria Decision Methods and Applications, Springer-Verlag, 1985.

Fishburn, P.C., Decision and Value Theory, Wiley, 1964.

Fishburn, P.C., Utility Theory for Decision Making, Wiley, 1970.

Freeman, R.E., Strategic Management - A Stakeholder Approach, Pitman, 1984.

Freeman, R.E. and D.R. Gilbert, Corporate Strategy and the Search for Ethics, Prentice Hall, 1988.

French, S., R. Hartley, I.C. Thomas and D.J. White (eds.), Multi-Objective Decision Making, Academic Press, 1983.

Geoffrion, A.M., *Solving Bicriterion Mathematical Programs*, **Operations Research**, 1967, 15, 39-54.

Geoffrion, A.M., *Proper Efficiency and the Theory of Vector Maximization*, **Journal of Mathematical Analysis and Applications**, 1968, 22, 618-630.

Geoffrion, A.M., *Elements of Large-Scale Mathematical Programming, Parts I and II*, **Management Science**, 1970, 16, 652-691.

Geoffrion, A.M., J.S. Dyer and A. Feinberg, *An Interactive Approach for Multicriterion Optimization*, **Management Science**, 1972, 19, 357-368.

Gorman, W.M., *The Structure of Utility Functions*, **Review of Economic Studies**, 1968a, 35, 367-390.

Gorman, W.M., *Conditions for Additive Separability*, **Econometrica**, 1968b, 36, 605-609.

Grauer, M., E. Bisschoof and A.P. Wierzbicki, *Mediation in Long-Term Planning*, in: Proceedings of the SWISS Conference, 1983, pp 162-166.

Grauer, M. and A.P. Wierzbicki (eds.), Interactive Decision Analysis, Lecture Notes in Economics and Mathematical Systems, 229, Springer-Verlag, 1984.

Hafkamp, W.A., *Economic-Environmental Modelling in a National-Regional System*, in: Studies in Regional Science and Urban Economics, North-Holland, 1984.

Haimes, Y.Y., The Integration of System Identification and System Optimization, Ph.D. dissertation, Eng. Syst. Dep., School of Eng. and Appl. Sci., Univ. of California, Los Angeles, 1970.

Haimes, Y.Y. and V. Chankong (eds.), Decision Making with Multiple Objectives, Lecture Notes in Economics and Mathematical Systems, 242, Springer-Verlag, 1985.

Haimes, Y.Y. and V. Chankong, *Kuhn-Tucker Multipliers as Trade-offs in Multiobjective Decision-Making Analysis*, **Automatica**, 1979, 15, 59-72.

Haimes, Y.Y., W.A. Hall and H.T. Freedman, Multiobjective Optimization in Water Resource Systems: The Surrogate Worth Trade-off Method, Elsevier, 1975.

Hall, W.A. and Y.Y. Haimes, *The Surrogate Worth Trade-Off Method with Multiple Decision Makers*, in: M. Zeleny (ed.), 1976, pp 207-233.

Hansen, F., T. Meyer and P. Pruzan, *The Ethical Process and the Ethical Accounting Statement*, in: New Ways in Marketing and Marketing Research, Esomar, 1990, pp217-234.

Hansen, P. (ed.), Essays and Surveys on Multiple Criteria Decision Making, Lecture Notes in Economics and Mathematical Systems, 209, Springer-Verlag, 1983.

Huber, G.P., *Issues in the Design of Group Decision Support Systems*, **MIS Quarterly**, 1984, 8, 195-204.

Hwang, C.-L. and A.S.M. Masud, *Multiple Objective Decision Making - Methods and Applications*, Lecture notes in Economics and Mathematical Systems, 164, Springer-Verlag, 1979.

Ignizio, J.P., Goal Programming and Extensions, Lexington Books, 1976.

Jarke, M., *Group Decision Support through Office Systems: Developments in Distributed DSS Technology*, in: Decision Support Systems: A Decade in Perspective, Elsevier, 1986.

Jensen, H.S., P. Pruzan and O. Thyssen, The Ethical Challenge, Copenhagen Business School Publishing, 1990, (in Danish).

Johansen, L., Lectures on Macroeconomic Planning, Part I: General Aspects, North-Holland, 1977.

Johansen, L., Lectures on Macroeconomic Planning, Part II: Centralization, Decentralization, Planning under Uncertainty, North-Holland, 1978.

Johnsen, E. Studies in Multiobjective Decision Models, Studenterlitteratur, 1968.

Keeney, R.L. and H. Raiffa, Decisions with Multiple Objectives: Preferences and Value Tradeoffs, Wiley, 1976.

Kickert, W.J.N., Organization of Decisionmaking - A Systemtheoretical Approach, North-Holland, 1980.

Kohn, M. and S. Shavell, *The Theory of Search*, **Journal of Economic Theory**, 1974, 9, 93-123.

Kok, M., *Tradeoff Information in Interactive Multi-Objective Linear Programming Methods*, WP-84-35. IIASA, Austria, 1984.

Kok, M. and F.A. Lootsma, *Pairwise-Comparison Methods in Multi-Objective Programming with Applications in a Long-Term Energy-Planning Model*, **European Journal of Operational Research**, 1985, 22, 44-55.

Kok, M., Conflict Analysis via Multiple Objective Programming, Ph.D. thesis from Department of Mathematics and Informatics, Delft University of Technology, Delft, 1986.

Korhonen, P.J. and J. Laakso, *A Visual Interactive Method for Solving the Multiple Criteria Problem*, **European Journal of Operational Research**, 1986, 24, 277-287.

Korhonen, P., J. Wallenius and S. Zionts, *A Bargaining Model for Solving the Multiple Criteria Problem*, in: G. Fandel and T. Gal (eds.), 1980, pp 178-188.

Korhonen, P., J. Wallenius and S. Zionts, *Solving the Discrete Multiple Criteria Problem Using Convex Cones*, **Management Science**, 1984, 30, 1336-1345.

Kornbluth, J.S.M., *A Survey of Goal Programming*, **OMEGA**, 1973, 1, 193-205.

Kornbluth, J.S.H., *Duality, Indifference and Sensitivity Analysis in Multiple Objective Linear Programming*, **Operational Research Quarterly**, 1974, 25, 599-614.

Krantz, D.H., R.D. Luce, P. Suppes and A. Tversky, Foundations of Measurement, Vol. I, Academics Press, 1971.

Kuhn, H.W. and A.W. Tucker, *Nonlinear Programming*, in: J. Neyman (ed.), 1951, pp 481-492.

Lawrence, J.R. (ed.), Operational Research and the Social Sciences, Tavistock Publications, 1966.

Lasdon, L.S., Optimization Theory for Large Systems, Mac Millan, 1970.

Latsis, S.J. (ed.), Methods and Appraisal in Economics, Cambridge University Press, 1976.

Lee, S.M., Goal Programming for Decision Analysis, Auerbach, 1972.

Lewandowski, A. and M. Grauer, *The Reference Point Optimization Approach - Methods of Efficient Implementation*, in: A.P. Wierzbicki (ed.), 1982, pp 353-376.

Linstone. H.A., Multiple Perspectives for Decision Making, North-Holland, 1984.

Linstone, H.A., *Multiple Perspectives: Concept, Applications, and User Guidelines*, **Systems Practice**, 1989, 2, No. 3, 307-331.

Lowe, T.J., J.F. Thisse, J.E. Ward and R.E. Wendel, *On Efficient Solutions to Multiple Objective Mathematical Programs*, **Management Science**, 1984, 30, 1346-1349.

Luce, R.D., *Semiorders and a Theory of Utility Discrimination*, **Econometrica**, 1956, 24, 178-191.

Luce, R.D. and J.W. Tukey, *Simultaneous Conjoint Measurement: A New Type of Fundamental Measurement*, **Journal of Mathematical Psychology**, 1969, 1, 1-27.

March, J.G., *Bounded Rationality, Ambiguity, and the Engineering of Choice*, **Bell Journal of Economics**, 1978, 9, 587-608.

MacQueen, J.B., *Optimal Policies for a Class of Search and Evaluation Problems*, **Management Science**, 1964, 10, 746-759.

Marchuk, G.I. (ed.), Optimization Techniques, Lecture notes in Computer Science, 1975, 27, Springer Verlag.

Matsuda, T. and M. Hirano, *A Study on the Structure of Planning Behavior*, **European Journal of Operational Research**, 1982, 9, 122-132.

Matsuda, T. and M. Hirano, *A Perspective of Planning Literature*, **European Journal of Operational Research**, 1983, 12, 138-145.

McGuire, C.B. and R. Radmer (eds.), Decision and Organization, North-Holland, 1972.

Meijboom, B.R., *Horizontal Mixed Decompositions*, **European Journal of Operational Research**, 1986, 27, 25-33.

Mintzberg, H., Power in and Around Organizations, Prentice Hall, 1983.

Morse, J.N. (ed.), Organizations: Multiple Agents with Multiple Criteria, Lecture Notes in Economics and Mathematical Systems, 190, Springer-Verlag, 1981.

Morgan, G., Images of Organizations, Sage, 1985.

Morgan, P. and R. Manning, *Optimal Search*, **Econometrica**, 1985, 53, 923-944.

Moulin, H., The Strategy of Social Choice, North-Holland, 1983.

Musselman, K. and Talavage, *A Tradeoff Cut Approach to Multiple Objective Optimization*, **Operations Research**, 1980, 28, 1424-1435.

Nakayama, H. and Y. Sawaragi, Satisficing Tradeoff Method for Multiobjective Programming and its Applications, paper presented at the 9th IFAC World Congress, July 2-4, Budapest, Hungary, 1984.

Neyman, J. (ed.), Proceedings of the Second Berkely Symposium on Mathematical Statistics and Probability, Univ. of California Press, 1951.

Nijkamp, P. and J. Spronk, *Interactive Multiple Goal Programming: An Evaluation and Some Results*, in: G. Fandel and T. Gal (eds.), 1980, pp 278-293.

Obel, B., *A Note om Mixed Procedures for Decomposing Linear Programming Problems*, **Mathematische Operationsforschung und Statistik, Series Optimization**, 1978, 9, 537-544.

Obel, B., Issues of Organizational Design: A Mathematical Programming View of Organizations, Pergamon Press, 1981.

Oppenheimer, K.R., *A Proxy Approach to Multi-Attribute Decision Making*, **Management Science**, 1978, 24, 675-689.

Ostanello, A., *Outranking Methods*, in: G. Fandel and J. Spronk (eds.), 1985, pp 41-60.

Pruzan, P., *Adaptive Planning for Significant Decision Problems*, in: Problems in Connection with Traffic Planning, Proceedings of NATO Advanced Study Institute, Copenhagen, 1966.

Pruzan, P., *Measures of Performance for Significant Planning Problems*, **Erhvervsøkonomisk Tidsskrift**, 1966a, 30, 91-100.

Pruzan, P., *Is Cost-Benefit Analysis Consistent with the Maximization of Expected Utility?*, in: J.R. Lawrence (ed.), 1966b, pp 319-336.

Pruzan, P., *Towards a Systems Theory of Planning*, Lecture notes, University of Copenhagen, 1984.

Pruzan, P., *Systemic OR and Operational Systems Science*, **European Journal of Operational Research**, 1988, 37, 34-41.

Pruzan, P., *The Ethical Accounting Statement: Theory and Practice*, in: B.H. Banathy and B.A. Banathy (eds.), 1990, pp 984-990.

Pruzan P. and R. Jackson, *On the Development of Utility Spaces for Multi-Goal Systems*, **Erhvervsøkonomisk Tidsskrift**, 1963, 27, 257-275.

Pruzan, P. and O. Thyssen, *Conflict and Consensus: Organiational Ethics as a Shared Value Horizon for Strategic Planning*, forthcoming in **Human Systems Management**, 1990.

Radmer, R., *Satisficing*, in: G.I. Marchuk (ed.), 1975, pp 252-263.

Rietveld, P., Multiple Objective Decision Methods and Regional Planning, North-Holland, 1980.

Roberts, F.S., Measurement Theory - with Applications to Decision Making, Utility, and the Social Sciences, Encyclopedia of Mathematics and its Applications, Vol. 7, Addison-Wesley, 1979.

Ross, M. (ed.), OR'72, North-Holland, 1973.

Rotschild, M., *Searching for the Lowest Price when the Distribution of Prices is Unknown*, **Journal of Political Economy**, 1974, 82, 689-712.

Roubens, M. and P. Vincke, Preference Modelling, Lecture Notes in Economics and Mathematical Systems, 250, Springer-Verlag, 1985.

Roy, B., *Classement et Choix en Présence de Points de Vue Multiples, (le Methode ELECTRE)*, **RIRO**, 1968, 2, 57-75.

Roy, B., *La Méthode ELECTRE II*, **METRA**, Direction Scientifique, Note de Travail, 1971, No. 142.

Roy, B., *How Outranking Relation Helps Multiple Criteria Decision Making*, in: J.L. Cochrane and M. Zeleny (eds.), 1973, pp 179-201.

Roy, B., *Partial Preference Analysis and Decision-Aid: The Fuzzy Outranking Concept*, in: D. Bell, R. Keeney and H. Raiffa (eds.), 1977, pp 40-74.

Roy, B., *ELECTRE III: Un Algorithme de Classement Fondé sur une Représentation Floue des Préférences en Présence de Critères Multiples*, **Cahiers Centre Etudes Recherche Opérationelle**, 1978, 20, 3-24.

Roy, B., Méthodologie Multicritère d'Aide à la Décision, Economica, 1985.

Roy, B. and P. Bertier, *La Méthode ELECTRE II, une Application au Media-Planninf*, in: M. Ross (ed.), 1973, pp 291-302.

Roy B. and J.C. Hugonnaard, *Ranking of Suburban Line Extension Projects on the Paris Metro System by a Multicriteria Method*, **Transport Research**, 1982, 16A, 301-312.

Roy B. and Ph. Vincke, *Multicriteria Analysis: Survey and New Directions*, **European Journal of Operational Research**, 1981 8, 207-218.

Roy, B. and Ph. Vincke, *Relational Systems of Preference with One or More Pseudo-Criteria: Some New Concepts and Results*, **Management Science**, 1984, 30, 1323-1335.

Saaty, T.L., The Analytical Hierarchy Process, McGraw-Hill, 1980.

Saaty, T.L., Multicriteria Decision Making: The Analytic Hierarchy Process, RWS Publications, 1988a.

Saaty, T.L., Decision Making for Leaders, RWS Publications, 1988b.

Saaty, T.L. and J.M. Alexander, Conflict Resolution: The Analytic Hierarchy Approach, Praeger, 1989.

Sawaragi, Y., K. Inoue and H. Nakayama (eds.), Towards Interactive and Intelligent Decision Support Systems, Lecture Notes in Economics and Mathematical Systems, Springer-Verlag, 1987.

Scott, D. and P. Suppes, *Foundational Aspects of Theories of Measurement*, **Journal of Symbolic Logic**, 1958, 23, 113-128.

Serafini, P. (ed.), Mathematics of Multi Objective Optimization, CISM Courses and Lectures, 238, Springer-Verlag, 1985.

Shapley, L.S., *Equilibrium Points in Games with Vector Payoffs*, **Naval Research Logistic Quarterly**, 1959, 6, 57-61.

Simon, H.A., *Theories of Decision-Making in Economics and Behavioral Science*, **American Economic Review**, 1959, 49, 253-283.

Simon, H.A., *Theories of Bounded Rationality*, in: C.B. McGuire and R. Radmer (eds.), 1972, Ch. 8.

Simon, H.A., *From Substantive to Procedural Rationality*, in: S.J. Latsis (ed.), 1976, pp 129-148.

Simon, H.A., *Rationality as Process and as Product of Thought*, **American Economic Review**, 1978, 68, 1-16.

Soland, R.M., *Multicirteria Optimization: A General Characterization of Efficient Solutions*, **Decision Science**, 1979, 10, 26-38.

Sparekassen Nordjylland, The Ethical Accounting Statement, 1990, (in Danish).

Starr, M.K. and M. Zeleny (eds.), *Multiple Criteria Decision Making*, **TIMS Studies in Management Sciences**, 6, North-Holland, 1977.

Steuer, R.E., Multiple Criteria Optimization: Theory, Computation and Application, Wiley, 1986.

Steuer, R.E. and E.U. Choo, *An Interactive Weighted Tchebycheff Procedure for Multiple Objective Programming*, **Mathematical Programming**, 1983, 26, 326-344.

Steuer, R.R. and A.T. Schuler, *An Interactive Multiple-Objective Linear Programming Approach to a Problem in Forest Management*, **Operations Research**, 1978, 26, 254-269.

Thieriez, H. and S. Zionts (eds.), Multiple Criteria Decision Making, Springer, 1976.

Tversky, A., *A General Theory of Polynomial Conjoint Measurement*, **Journal of Mathematical Psychology**, 1967, 4, 1-20.

Tversky, A., *Intransitivity of Preferences*, **Psychology Review**, 1969, 76, 31-48.

Van Roy, T.J., *Cross Decomposition for Mixed Integer Programming*, **Mathematical Programming**, 1983, 25, 46-63.

Vincke, Ph., Vrais, Quasi, Pseudo et Précritères dans un Ensemble Fini: Propriétés et Algorithmes, Université de Paris-Dauphine, Cahier du LAMSADE, 27, 1980.

Wendel, R.E. and D.N. Lee, *Efficiency in Multiobjective Optimization Problems*, **Mathematical Programming**, 1977, 12, 406-515.

White, D.J., *Multiple-Objective Interactive Programming*, **Journal of Operational Research Society**, 1980, 31, 517-523.

White, D.J., *Concepts of Proper Efficiency*, **European Journal of Operational Research**, 1985, 13, 180-188.

Wierzbicki, A.P., *The Use of Reference Objectives in Multi-Objective Optimization - Theoretical Implications and Practical Experience*, IIASA WP-79-66, Laxenburg, Austria, 1979.

Wierzbicki, A.P. (ed.), Multiobjective and Stochastic Optimization, IIASA CP-82-S12, Laxenburg, Austria, 1982.

Yu, P.L., *A Class of Solutions for Group Decision Problems*, **Management Science**, 1973, 19, 936-946.

Yu, P.L., *Cone Convexity, Cone Extreme Points and Nondominated Solutions in Decision Problems with Multiobjectives*, **Journal of Optimization Theory and Applications**, 1974, 14, 319-377.

Zeleny, M., *Compromise Programming*, in: J.L. Cochrane and M. Zeleny (eds.), 1973, pp 373-391.

Zeleny, M., Linear Multiobjective Programming, Lecture Notes in Economics and Mathematical Systems, 95, Springer-Verlag, 1974.

Zeleny, M. (ed.), Multiple Criteria Decision Making, Lecture Notes in Economics and Mathematical Systems, Springer-Verlag, 1976a.

Zeleny, M., *The Theory of the Displaced Ideal*, in: M. Zeleny (ed.), 1976a, pp 153-206.

Zeleny, M., *Games with Multiple Payoffs*, **Int. Journal of Game Theory**, 1976b, 4, 179-191.

Zeleny, M., *Adaptive Displacement of Preferences in Decision Making*, in: M.K. Starr and M. Zeleny (eds.), 1977, pp 147-158.

Zeleny, M., Multiple Criteria Decision Making, McGraw-Hill, 1982.

Zeleny, M., *Spontaneous Social Orders*, in: The Science and Praxis of Complexity, The United Nations University, 1985, pp 312-329.

Zionts, S. (ed.), *Multiple Criteria Problem Solving*, Lecture Notes in Economics and Mathematical Systems, 155, Springer-Verlag, 1978.

Zionts, S., *A Multiple Criteria Method for Choosing among Discrete Alternatives*, **European Journal of Operational Research**, 1981, 7, 143-147.

Zionts, S. and J. Wallenius, *An Interactive Programming Method for Solving the Multiple Criteria Problem*, **Management Science**, 1976, 22, 652-663.

Zionts, S. and J. Wallenius, *An Interactive Multiple Objective Linear Programming Method for a Class of Underlying Nonlinear Utility Functions*, **Management Science**, 1983, 29, 519-529.

SUBJECT INDEX